D1505124

General Crystallography
A BRIEF COMPENDIUM

General Crystallography

A BRIEF COMPENDIUM

by W. F. de Jong

Lecturer at the Technical University of Delft

with the collaboration of

J. Bouman

W. H. Freeman and Company

SAN FRANCISCO, 1959

Preface

Until a few decades ago crystallography was usually considered a subdivision of mineralogy. Although theorists speculated on the inner structure of crystals or studied such of their physical properties as conductivity and elasticity, crystallography was, in general, confined to descriptive work on the outer form and habit of crystals, and to the study of crystal optics.

The subject became highly interesting to physicists and other non-mineralogists after Laue's discovery of the interference effects shown by X-rays on their passage through crystals, and this interest was markedly increased when electrotechnics and infrared optics, during World War II, began to make extensive use of monocrystalline materials. Nowadays crystallography is an important part of physics, equal in importance, for example, to thermodynamics.

In 1947 it seemed to my Dutch publisher that the right moment had come for a review of the whole domain of crystallography. He therefore asked me to write a brief compendium of the subject, and this appeared, in the Dutch language, in 1951. The book owed a great deal to the collaboration of Dr. J. Bouman, who criticized the text in all its stages and made many valuable suggestions. Without his help, indeed, Parts II and IV would have had a rather different aspect.

The translation into English was entrusted, in its first stage, to Miss J. Pouwelsen; Mr. Theodore McClintock then undertook to make the language idiomatic; and Dr. N. F. M. Henry supervised the translation of technical terms. To those named, and to Mr. C. van Werkhoven, who provided the excellent illustrations, I offer my best thanks.

This American edition is more, however, than a translation of the Dutch edition. A few sections have been enlarged; the last section of Part IV has been rewritten; new illustrations have been added; and the classification of symmetry now follows the International Tables for X-ray Crystallography, second edition (1952).

Though this compendium is not primarily a textbook, the literature cited in it has been chosen in such a way that it may be used as a guide in private study. In its present form, with its emphasis on the role of symmetry (demonstrated most simply in the longest part, that on geometric crystallography), the book will serve undergraduate students as a summary of the modern view of crystallography.

April 1959   W. F. DE JONG

Contents

Introduction

The name *crystallography* is derived from the Greek word "krystallos," indicating, in old times, rock-crystal. This rock-crystal was found in magnificent specimens in the high regions of the Alps, and in those times it was considered to be ice that had been cooled to such a degree that it could not melt again.[1]

A crystal is usually defined as a solid body, homogeneous and anisotropic (p. 187), bounded by natural flat faces. Since the discovery in 1912 of the diffraction of X-rays by crystals, it can better be said that a crystal is a body in which the centers of gravity of the atoms (ions) form a structure (p. 98). This definition covers (1) crystals hampered in their growth — that is, not bounded by flat faces; (2) very small particles, whose nature is recognized by the X-ray diffraction patterns they produce (p. 104). Objections to this definition arise mainly from the fact that the mathematical conception of structure has to be understood in a physical sense (pp. 98 and 226).

Crystallography can be divided into four parts:

1. *Geometric:* Deals with the external shape of crystals.
2. *Structural:* Description and determination of the internal geometry of the structure.
3. *Chemical:* Description and study of the structural arrangement of the atoms (ions) and of the bonds between these particles.
4. *Physical:* Description and explanation of the physical properties.

---

[1] Historical works: C. M. Marx, *Geschichte der Kristallkunde* (1825); F. von Kobell, *Geschichte der Mineralogie und Krystallographie* (1866); P. Groth, *Entwicklungsgeschichte der mineralogischen Wissenschaften* (1926); W. F. de Jong and E. Stradner, "Zeittafel," Tschermaks Mitt. 5 (1956), 362–379.

Part

I | Geometric Crystallography [1]

Geometric crystallography deals with the description, calculation, projection, and drawing of the external shape of freely developed crystals, which, according to experience, are convex polyhedra (with flat faces and straight edges). In an appendix we shall study twins and repeated twin crystals.

A. Crystal Description

This part is governed by three laws: (1) Stensen's law, (2) Haüy's law (the principal law of geometric crystallography), and (3) the law of symmetry.

Stensen's Law

This law, which is also called the *law of constancy of the angles*, was discovered in 1669 by Stensen (Latin, Steno), but was finally confirmed only in 1772, after many measurements, by Romé de Lisle. The law indicates: (1) that the angle between two faces of an individual is constant, does not change when the faces are displaced owing to the growth of the crystal; (2) that the angle is equal to the corresponding angle of another individual of the same species of crystals. From this it follows also that the angles between the *edges* are constant.

Bernhardi's Principle (1809)

It follows from Stensen's law that what is characteristic is direction. Directions are of two kinds: edges and normals to faces. The shapes of crystals and the sizes of the faces are not important; in geometric crystallography we call the two individuals in Fig. 1 equal (octahedra).

Henceforth crystals are considered either (1) normalized by the placing of equivalent faces (p. 22) at the same distance from an arbitrary point, the center O, or (2) reduced to a sheaf (Bernhardi).

---

[1] Literature survey: *Encyklopädie der mathematischen Wissenschaften*, Vol. V, Part 1, p. 391; P. Niggli, "Krystallographische und strukturtheoretische Grundbegriffe" in *Handbuch der Experimentalphysik*, VII, 1 (1928).

If we imagine that all faces and edges pass through a point, we have what we shall call the *direct sheaf*. If we imagine that all planes normal

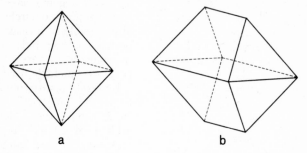

FIG. 1. Development of two octahedral crystals: (*a*) unhampered; (*b*) elongated parallel to one edge direction.

to the edges and the normals to the faces pass through a point, we have what we shall call the *indirect sheaf*.

Measuring the Angles [1]

Angles are usually measured between faces because measurements of the directions of edges are generally less accurate.

The angles between faces can be measured with an accuracy of about 1° with the *contact goniometer* (Carangeot, 1770). The two arms (Fig. 2) are placed along two faces, their plane normal to the edge.

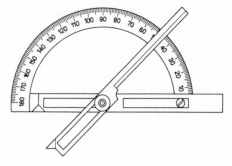

FIG. 2. Contact goniometer; the angle between the arms is read along the semi-circle.

More accurate measurements can be executed with the *reflection goniometer* (Wollaston, 1809) and a single-circle instrument with one graduated circle is widely used (Fig. 3). Because the incident light is a parallel beam, it is possible to measure, in one setting of the crystal, the angles between all the faces that are parallel to one edge — that is, faces situated in one *zone* (bundle) with the edge as *zone axis*.

The *theodolite goniometer*, which has two graduated circles, mutually

[1] P. Terpstra, *Kristallometrie* (1946), Ch. 9; V. Goldschmidt, *Kursus der Kristallometrie* (1933); F. C. Phillips, *An Introduction to Crystallography* (1956), p. 93.

perpendicular, gives the position of each face (p. 60) without the necessity of resetting for each zone (Fig. 4). With a goniometer having three graduated circles [1] it is also possible to measure angles between edges; but, as these instruments are very expensive, they are but little used.

It must be pointed out that the angles are not strictly constant (p. 2), but their deviations seldom exceed 5'.[2] So it is not necessary to use goniometers with the highest possible accuracy; the construction of most instruments allows measurements accurate to about 1'.

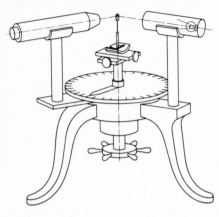

FIG. 3.   Single-circle goniometer, with one graduated circle.

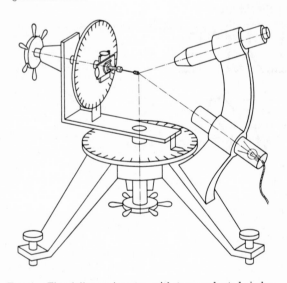

FIG. 4.   Theodolite goniometer, with two graduated circles.

[1] G. F. Herbert Smith, Min. Mag. 12 (1899), 175, and 14 (1904), 1; A. E. H. Tutton, *Crystallography and Practical Crystal Measurement* (1922), p. 459.

[2] P. Niggli, *Lehrbuch der Mineralogie und Kristallchemie* (1941), p. 581; M. H. Hey, "On the Accuracy of Mineralogical Measurements," Min. Mag. 23 (1933), 495.

Crystallographic Axes, Parameters, Indices, Symbols

In order to indicate the directions of the faces and edges of a crystal, we take a set of three coordinate axes (crystallographic axes). The simplest calculations would be obtained by our taking a Cartesian set; this is sometimes done (p. 187), but usually a set fitted to the crystal is chosen.

We choose three crystal faces as coordinate planes;[1] hence their intersections define the axes. A fourth crystal face (*unit face*, parametral face) is placed at some distance from the center, and the intercepts of the axes by this face are taken as units a, b, and c (called *axial lengths*); or, more correctly, the ratio of these lengths, $a : b : c$, is taken, but it is often simpler to take absolute values — for example, $b = 1$ cm. For the true absolute axial lengths, see p. 99.

The four faces mentioned above are called the *fundamental* faces. The positive axial directions form a right-handed set, ABC;[2] the interaxial angles are α, β, and γ (Weiss, 1815); a, b, c, α, β, and γ are called the (direct) *crystal elements*. The C axis is placed vertically, the A axis is in the sagittal plane (back-front direction), sloping towards the spectator, and the B axis slopes towards the right, except in the four-axial set (p. 7).

The axes in the indirect sheaf are fixed by those of the direct one. The *indirect axes* are the normals to the three direct coordinate planes, and the normal to the unit face is the indirect unit line (J. G. Grassmann, 1829). Indirect axes and crystal elements are indicated as A^*, B^*, C^*, a^*, b^*, c^*, α^*, β^*, γ^*; for the positive axial directions we take $A^* \wedge A < 90°$; $B^* \wedge B < 90°$; $C^* \wedge C < 90°$ (p. 50).

The direction of any crystal face can be described in the direct set by its equation or by three parameters. These parameters may be the

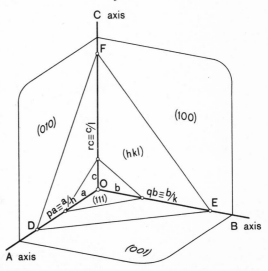

FIG. 5. The three axial planes, the parametral (unit) plane, and a general face, with symbols.

ratios of the intercepts on the axes, each expressed in its own axial length (Weiss, 1817). Fig. 5 shows the parameters

$$p = \frac{OD}{a}; \quad q = \frac{OE}{b}; \quad r = \frac{OF}{c}$$

As a rule, the ratios of the inverses [1] of these parameters are used, and these are called *indices* (Miller, 1839):

$$h = \frac{1}{p} = \frac{a}{OD}; \quad k = \frac{1}{q} = \frac{b}{OE}; \quad l = \frac{1}{r} = \frac{c}{OF}$$

The direction of the face is indicated by the *symbol* (*hkl*), in which

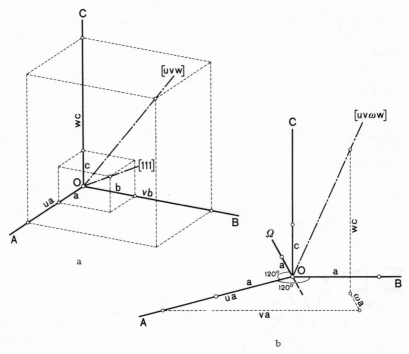

Fig. 6. (a) The directions [111] and [*uvw*] in a three-axial set. (b) The direction [*uvωw*] in a four-axial (Bravais) set. A condition can be imposed here on $u + v + \omega$: by analogy with $h + k + \varkappa = 0$ (p. 24) we take $u + v + \omega$ to equal 0. In the drawing this condition has not yet been imposed.

[1] J. J. Bernhardi (1808), W. Whewell (1825), J. G. Grassmann (1829), M. L. Frankenheim (1829).

$h : k : l$ is significant; multiplication or division by any number does not change the meaning of the symbol.

If a face is parallel to an axis, the index in question is zero; the coordinate planes have as symbols (100), (010), and (001), the unit plane (111). If the index is negative, the sign is placed above it.

The direction of a line (edge, zone axis) is indicated in the direct set by a symbol comprising the three coordinates of an arbitrary point on the edge, expressed in axial lengths; these coordinates also are often called indices. Fig. 6-a gives the symbols of the unit edge and of an arbitrary edge; the symbols of the axes are [100], [010], and [001].

In the hexagonal system (p. 19) a four-axial set is often used ($AB\Omega C$, Fig. 10), and then there are four indices. We may change to symbols with three indices, referring to the A, B, and C axes by omitting the third index in the symbol of a face $(hk\varkappa l)$ [1] and reading $[u-\omega \ v-\omega \ w]$ for the symbol of an edge $[uv\omega w]$ (Fig. 6-b). In order to change from symbols with three indices (hkl) and $[uvw]$ to symbols with four indices, one reads for the symbol of a face $(h \ k \ -h-k \ l)$ and for that of an edge $[2u-v \ \ 2v-u \ \ -u-v \ \ 3w]$.[2]

Haüy's Law (Principal Law of Geometric Crystallography)

There are two formulations, the first from Haüy (1783) and the second from Weiss (1804); their equivalence (p. 46) was pointed out by Neumann (1823).

First formulation: If three faces of a crystal are chosen as coordinate planes and a fourth as unit face, the indices of all faces and edges are whole numbers, usually small ones (*arithmetical derivation* of the faces).

If the indices are not given as whole numbers, they are still *rational numbers*; so, by multiplying them with an appropriate factor, we can reduce them to whole numbers. If the indices contain a greatest common divisor, they are usually divided by it.

Second formulation: All possible faces and edges of the crystal are obtained as follows (*geometrical derivation*). Let us take four faces, forming a tetrahedron. These determine six edges, which, taken in pairs, determine seven faces,[3] of which four are already present and three are new. These seven faces, taken in pairs, again determine a number of edges, some of which are new, etc. In this form the law is called the *zone law*.

---

[1] We use $\varkappa$ instead of i or a point because it corresponds better with Ω for the fourth axis and ω for the fourth edge index.

[2] L. Weber, *Zeitschrift für Kristallographie* 57 (1922), 200; J. D. H. Donnay, *Am. Min.* 32 (1947) 52, 477.

[3] A face is determined by two edges if it is parallel to these edges.

Since only faces with integral indices are possible (are *crystallonomic*), and since indices are seldom larger than 6, the sheaf consists of a relatively small number of planes.

Nothing is said about the ratios of the axial lengths, $a : b : c$, which can be irrational (Neumann, 1823). (Cf. p. 195.)

The explanation of the principal law is simple as soon as one assumes Bravais' hypothesis (p. 103).

The importance of the law lies in the restriction of the number of possible faces and especially in the restriction of the possible cases of symmetry (p. 9).

It is not possible to give the evidence in an experimental way. Owing to the limited accuracy of the measurements, we cannot distinguish between irrational indices and very great ones. Mostly, however, we find a set of indices in the neighborhood of a set of small indices. But the result of the law -- the non-appearance of fivefold symmetry axes (p. 10), for example — appears to hold good; the law therefore has to be considered absolutely correct, and the occurrence of very large indices has to be explained as being of minor importance (vicinal faces, p. 259).

Symmetry

Symmetry Elements

It is a plausible assumption that, when crystallization takes place undisturbed, all equal atoms will create the same environment; and examination by X-rays shows the assumption to be correct. Environment is understood to be the structure except the atom in question; taken strictly, the assumption can hold good only for an infinitely extended crystal (but cf. p. 98).

Thus, in the crystal, repetition (symmetry) occurs; this appears internally as a repetition of the properties in various directions, externally as a repetition of the bounding faces and their angles, hence of the whole body.

In order to ascertain this repetition, one has to start from an arbitrary position and to note for each point the three coordinates, x, y, z, in a fixed Cartesian axial set. If, after a "change in position" (*symmetry operation*), a repetition has been achieved, there is again a point on each of the points denoted x, y, z, and no new coordinates are noted; it is then said that *coincidence* has been achieved.

A change in position can, in the first place, be a shifting (translation) or a rotation. With a *finite* body, however, the first phenomenon cannot result in coincidence (cf. p. 96). In order to ascertain whether a body can be made to coincide with itself by symmetry operations, we remark that not only the three coordinates but also all distances between all points are the same in the two positions. These distances are of the form

$$\sqrt{(x_1 - x_2)^2 + (y_1 - y_2)^2 + (z_1 - z_2)^2}$$

It is possible to obtain the same distances by giving an opposite sign to (a) all x's (or y's or z's), (b) all x's and y's (or another pair), (c) all x's, y's, and z's. Operation a is called *reflection* about a plane; b is a *rotation* of 180°; c is called reflection about a point (*inversion*).

Possible symmetry operations for a finite body are therefore rotation, reflection, and inversion and their combinations, rotation + reflection, rotation + inversion (gives the same result as rotation + reflection), reflection + inversion (gives the same result as rotation), and rotation + reflection + inversion (gives the same result as rotation).

These operations can be described with the aid of *symmetry elements:* symmetry axis (rotation axis), symmetry plane (reflection plane), inversion point (sometimes called center), rotatory reflection axis, and rotatory inversion axis.

When, for the first time after a rotation of $\dfrac{360°}{n}$ round a symmetry axis, an equal position has been reached, the axis is called an *n-fold axis*. An n-fold axis denotes the presence of the initial position and of $n - 1$ symmetry operations, each of which produces a repeated position. An axis is uniterminal, or *polar*, if the two directions of the axis are not brought into coincidence by any of the other symmetry operations; generally, in this case, the crystal faces develop in such a way that a distinction can be made between the one and the other direction of the axis. When an n-fold rotatory inversion axis is present, equality is reached after $2\dfrac{360°}{n}$, $4\dfrac{360°}{n}$ ..., and after $1\dfrac{360°}{n}$, $3\dfrac{360°}{n}$ ... the inverse position is reached.

Two kinds of symmetry operations can be distinguished; the rotations belong to the first kind and the others to the second kind.

Crystallonomic symmetry axes can be only 2-, 3-, 4-, or 6-fold. This follows from the lattice structure of a crystal,[1] but we may also demonstrate this fact by using the principal law.[2] In Fig. 7 let OM be an n-fold axis perpendicular to the drawing plane T; $\dfrac{360°}{n} = \alpha°$. Then any given edge (direction) OA is multiplied to n edges; the intersections with T form the corners of a regular n-polygon. In pairs the edges determine faces; we choose OAB, OBC, and OCD as coordinate planes and

---

[1] P. Niggli, *Geometrische Kristallographie des Diskontinuums* (1919), p. 33.

[2] A. Gadolin (1867) in Ostwalds Klassiker der exakten Wissenschaften, No. 75 (1896), pp. 7 and 78; H. Hilton, *Mathematical Crystallography* (1903), p. 43.

therefore OB, OC, and OP as crystallographic axes and OAD as unit face. If this face is moved to pass through BC, the axial lengths on the axes OB and OC appear to be equal; the axial length on OP is different,

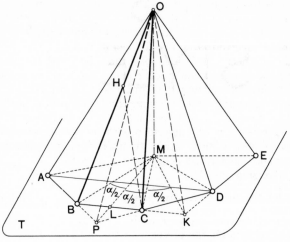

FIG. 7.

but this is of no importance here. If the face ODE is also moved to pass through C, it intersects the first two axes in H and C, so that CH is $// OK$, and the intersection with the third axis is again of no importance.

According to the principal law, therefore, the following ratio must be rational:

$$\frac{OB}{OH} : \frac{OC}{OC}$$

Now

$$\frac{OB}{OH} = \frac{BK}{CK} = 1 + 2\cos\alpha$$

From examination it appears that rational values of $2\cos\alpha$ here can only be 0, ± 1, and ± 2; hence $\alpha = 0°$, 60°, 90°, 120°, 180°, 240°, 270°, or 300°, and $n = 1, 2, 3, 4,$ or 6. The axes, therefore, can be 1-, 2-, 3-, 4-, or 6-fold; we indicate the last four as 2, 3, 4, and 6 respectively.

In an analogous way it can be demonstrated that rotatory inversion axes can be $\bar{1}$, $\bar{2}$, $\bar{3}$, $\bar{4}$, and $\bar{6}$; but the effect of $\bar{1}$ is equal to that of an inversion point J, that of $\bar{2}$ to that of reflection plane m, that of $\bar{6}$ to that of a combination of 3 and a reflection plane m normal to 3.

Sometimes, in literature and for instruction purposes, rotatory reflection axes I^m, II^m, III^m, IV^m, and VI^m are used instead of rotatory inversion axes; it can be shown that

$$I^m \equiv \bar{2} \equiv m$$
$$II^m \equiv \bar{1} \equiv J$$
$$III^m \equiv \bar{6}$$
$$IV^m \equiv \bar{4}$$
$$VI^m \equiv \bar{3}$$

In Fig. 8 some symmetry elements are shown.

Stereographic Projection Method

Apply a construction sphere (Fig. 9) round the crystal (round the direct sheaf) with center at O and radius R. Erect on each crystal face at O a normal and on each edge a normal plane; these lines and planes intersect the sphere in points and circles respectively. We connect the points and all points of the circles with the nadir (projection point) of the sphere. The intersections of these connecting lines with the horizontal projection plane T form the stereographic projections of the crystal faces and edges respectively. A crystal face is therefore projected as a point, an edge as a circle or arc of a circle (p. 68).

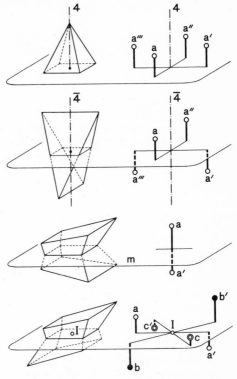

FIG. 8.   Polyhedra and collections of points, with the symmetry elements 4, $\bar{4}$, m, and J.

The principal properties of the stereographic projections are that figures on the sphere appear angle-true and that circles on the sphere are projected as circles.[1]

The intersection of the projection plane with the sphere is the *primitive circle*. Rarely, for purposes of surveying, is something outside the primitive circle given. If necessary, we project the lower half of the sphere by taking the zenith as second projection point, and we then

[1] For evidence see J. D. H. Donnay, *Spherical Trigonometry after the Cesàro Method* (1945), p. 7.

distinguish the two projections covering one another by giving them different indications — for example, crosses for upper faces and rings for lower ones (Gadolin, 1867).

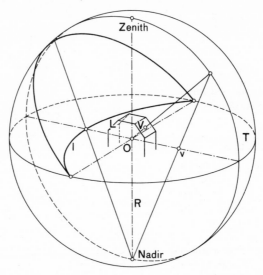

Fig. 9. The stereographic projection v of the face V and the projection l of the edge direction L on the horizontal projection plane T.

The circles of intersection of the coordinate and symmetry planes with the construction sphere, and the points of intersection of the crystallographic and symmetry axes with that sphere, are projected. Arrows outside the primitive circle indicate the positive crystallographic axes; an inversion point is sometimes represented by a dot. The rotation axes are represented by $\mathbb{0}$, $\triangledown$, $\diamondsuit$, and $\bigcirc$, the polar axes by $\blacklozenge$, $\blacktriangledown$, $\blacklozenge$, and $\blacklozenge$, and the rotatory inversion axes by $\triangledown$, $\diamondsuit$, and $\odot$.[1]

Symmetry Classes

A crystal may possess more than one symmetry element. Only a limited number of combinations is possible, however, and each combination possesses its special configuration. Thirty-two classes, in all, are possible (Hessel, 1830).

The symmetry of a crystal face is determined by the elements normal to it; in a plane (two-dimensionally), ten classes are possible.

[1] *The International Tables for X-ray Crystallography*, I (1952), represent $\bar{3}$ by $\blacktriangle$, $\bar{4}$ by $\blacklozenge$, and $\bar{6}$ by $\blacktriangle$.

Classes with only one rotation axis are called *cyclic* and are represented by 1, 2, 3, 4, and 6 (or, according to Schoenflies, C_1, C_2, C_3, C_4, and C_6); 1 may also be called the asymmetric class.

Classes with one rotation axis and some twofold axes normal to this axis are called dihedral and are represented by 222, 32, 422, and 622 (or, according to Schoenflies, D_2, D_3, D_4, and D_6). In the last three classes the first axis is called the *principal axis*.

The other classes with only rotation axes are called *endospheric* and are represented by T and O.

The eleven classes in question are called *holoaxial*.

Tables 1 and 2 give a survey of the classes.

Axial Sets (of Crystallographic Axes)

As a rule, the axial set is chosen in compliance with the following conditions: (1) existing or possible edges are chosen as axes, or (more completely expressed) four crystal faces are chosen as fundamental faces (principal law, p. 5); (2) the set — the axial directions as well as the lengths — complies with the symmetry of the class, with the understanding that no distinction is made between positive and negative axial directions.

In most classes it is possible, without considering the crystal itself and its faces, to choose *a priori* the axial set; in classes m, 2, and $2/m$ this is partly, in $\bar{1}$ and 1 not at all, possible. In order to prove this, we make use of the following properties:

1. (a) Symmetry planes and (b) normal planes to symmetry axes are possible crystal faces.

   a. If m is a symmetry plane and v_1 and v_2 are crystal faces, there are also the reflected faces v_1' and v_2'. The edges $v_1 v_1'$ and $v_2 v_2'$ determine a face coinciding with m.

   b. If n is an even-fold axis and v_1 and v_2 are crystal faces, there are also v_1' and v_2' at $180°$ from v_1 and v_2. The edges $v_1 v_1'$ and $v_2 v_2'$ determine a face normal to the axis. If n is a three-fold axis, the property cannot be derived from the principal law, but it follows from the structure of a crystal.[1]

2. (a) Symmetry axes and (b) normals to symmetry planes are possible crystal edges.

[1] See the hypothesis of Bravais (p. 99) and A. Bravais (1848) in Ostwalds Klassiker der exakten Wissenschaften, No. 90 (1897), p. 65; also P. Terpstra, *Leerboek der geometrische kristallografie* (1927), p. 76.

TABLE 1 **Systems and Classes**

Groth (1895), Fedorov (1893)	Int. Tables [1]	Schoen-flies [2]	Symmetry	Older Names (chiefly due to Schoenflies, 1891)
Cubic (Regular) System				
1. hexakis-octahedral	$m\,3\,m$	O_h	3 m 6 m	holohedry
2. hexakis-tetrahedral	$\bar 4\,3\,m$	T_d	3 m 6 m	tetrahedral hemihedry
3. pentagonal-icositetrahedral	$4\,3\,2$	O		enantiomorphic hemihedry
4. disdodecahedral	$m\,3$	T_h	3 m	paramorphic hemihedry
5. tetrak-pentag.-dodecahedral	$2\,3$	T		tetartohedry
Hexagonal System A				
6. dihex-bipyramidal	$6/m\,m\,m$	D_{6h}	3 m 3 m	holohedry
7. ditrig-bipyramidal	$\bar 6\,m\,2$	D_{3h}	m 3 m	trigonotype hemihedry
8. dihex-pyramidal	$6\,m\,m$	C_{6v}	m 3 m	hemimorphic hemihedry
9. hex-trapezohedral	$6\,2\,2$	D_6		enantiomorphic hemihedry
10. hex-bipyramidal	$6/m$	C_{6h}	m	paramorphic hemihedry
11. trig-bipyramidal	$\bar 6$	C_{3h}	m	trigonotype tetartohedry
12. hex-pyramidal	6	C_6		hemimorphic tetartohedry
Hexagonal System B (Trigonal System)				
13. ditrig-scalenohedral	$\bar 3\,m$	D_{3d}	3 m	(holohedry)
14. ditrig-pyramidal	$3\,m$	C_{3v}	3 m	hemimorphic hemihedry
15. trig-trapezohedral	$3\,2$	D_3		enantiomorphic hemihedry
16. rhombohedral	$\bar 3$	S_6		rhombohedral hemihedry
17. trig-pyramidal	3	C_3		hemimorphic tetartohedry

Groth (1895), Fedorov (1893)	Int. Tables [1]	Schoen-flies [2]		Symmetry							Older Names (chiefly due to Schoenflies, 1891)
Tetragonal System											
18. ditetr.-bipyramidal . . .	4/m m m	D_{4h}	J	◇	2	0	2	m	2 m	2 m	holohedry
19. tetr.-scalenohedral . . .	4̄ 2 m	D_{2d}		◈	2	0			2 m	2 m	sphenoidal hemihedry
20. ditetr.-pyramidal . . .	4 m m	C_{4v}		◆					2 m	2 m	hemimorphic hemihedry
21. tetr.-trapezohedral . .	4 2 2	D_4		◇	2	0	2				enantiomorphic hemihedry
22. tetr.-bipyramidal. . .	4/m	C_{4h}	J	◈				m			paramorphic hemihedry
23. tetr.-bisphenoidal . .	4̄	S_4		◇							sphenoidal tetartohedry
24. tetr.-pyramidal . . .	4	C_4	J	◆	2						hemimorphic tetartohedry
Orthorhombic System											
25. orthorh.-bipyramidal. . .	m m m	D_{2h}	J	◇		0		m	m	m	holohedry
26. orthorh.-pyramidal. . .	m m 2	C_{2v}		◑		0		m	m		hemimorphic hemihedry
27. orthorh.-bisphenoidal. .	2 2 2	D_2		◯		0	0				enantiomorphic hemihedry
Monoclinic System											
28. mon.-prismatic . . .	2/m	C_{2h}	J	◯		0		m			holohedry
29. mon.-domatic . . .	m	C_{1v}		◑				m			domatic hemihedry
30. mon.-sphenoidal. . .	2	C_2									hemimorphic hemihedry
Triclinic System											
31. tricl.-pinacoidal . . .	1̄	S_2	J								holohedry
32. tricl.-pedial . . .	1	C_1									hemihedry

[1] An explanation of the symbols will be found in *International Tables for X-ray Crystallography*, I (1952), 29.

[2] Alternative symbols are: 1, K_h; 3, K; 13, S_{8u}; 16, C_{3i}; 19, V_d, S_{4u}; 23, $\bar{C}_4$; 25, V_h; 27, V; 29, C_s, $\bar{C}_i$, C_{1h}; 31, C_i, $\bar{C}_2$. (h = horizontal; d = diagonal; v = vertical).

TABLE 2   **Stereographic Projections of the Classes**

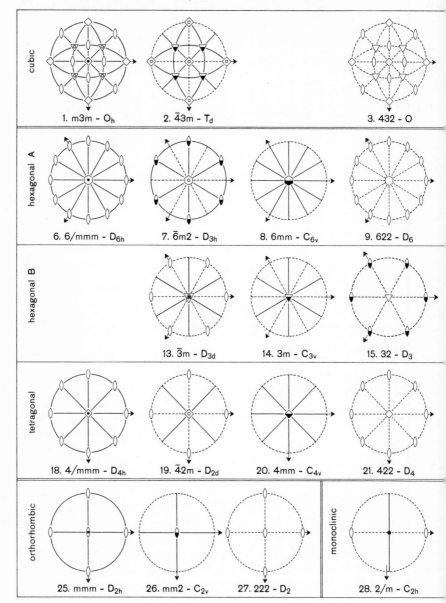

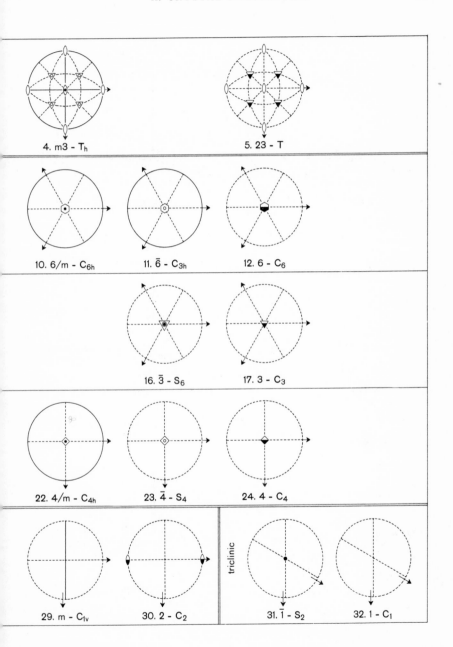

4. m3 - T$_h$

5. 23 - T

10. 6/m - C$_{6h}$

11. $\bar{6}$ - C$_{3h}$

12. 6 - C$_6$

16. $\bar{3}$ - S$_6$

17. 3 - C$_3$

22. 4/m - C$_{4h}$

23. $\bar{4}$ - S$_4$

24. 4 - C$_4$

29. m - C$_{1v}$

30. 2 - C$_2$

triclinic

31. $\bar{1}$ - S$_2$

32. 1 - C$_1$

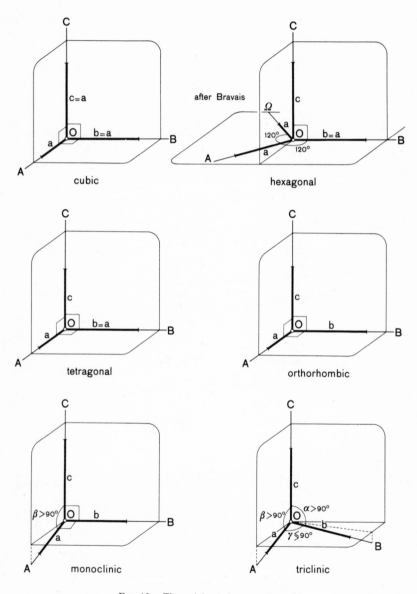

Fig. 10.   The axial sets in normal setting.

a. If n is an even-fold axis and r_1 and r_2 are edges, there are also r_1' and r_2' at 180° from r_1 and r_2. The faces r_1r_1' and r_2r_2' determine an edge coinciding with the axis. If n is a three-fold axis, the same as under 1b holds.

b. If m is a symmetry plane and r_1 and r_2 are edges, there are also the reflected edges r_1' and r_2'. The faces r_1r_1' and r_2r_2' determine an edge coinciding with the normal to m.

It is thus possible to arrive at six or seven different sets (Fig. 10). In addition to or instead of Bravais' four-axial set (1851), use is also made of Miller's three-axial set (1839) (Fig. 11) or sometimes of Schrauf's three-axial set (1861); the last, however (Fig. 12), does not comply with condition 2.

In Table 2 arrows indicate the non-vertical positive axes.

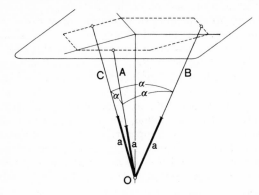

Fig. 11. Hexagonal axial set (Miller).

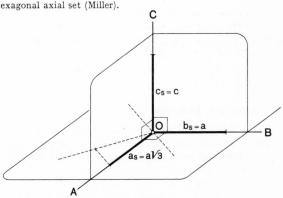

Fig. 12. Hexagonal axial set (Schrauf).

Systems

The classes for which a similar axial set can be chosen are arranged in a system. The hexagonal system is subdivided into parts A and B (or sometimes into hexagonal and trigonal systems).

Table 1 gives a survey. The names in the first column are those of Groth, the symbols in the second column are those of Hermann-Mauguin,[1] and the names in the last column are those of Schoenflies (with some deviations).

Groups and Sub-groups

In mathematics a *group* is a collection of group elements (quantities, actions) with the principal characteristic that the product of two elements is equal to one of the elements — that is, that two elements, applied one after the other, give the same result as one of the elements.

In crystallography the group elements are symmetry operations. So m and J each denote one operation, an n-fold axis $n - 1$ operations. The symmetry operations in each class are a finite group, in this case a point group, for such a group multiplies a point to a finite collection of points (cf. p. 96). This implies that all symmetry elements in a class have at least one point in common.

A group may comprise sub-groups; that is, some of the operations may themselves be a group. In class mmm, for example, there are identity, E (initial position), and seven operations: three rotations, $180_A°$, $180_B°$, and $180_C°$; three reflections, $refl_{AB}$, $refl_{BC}$, and $refl_{CA}$; and an inversion. A sub-group is found in class $mm\,2$: identity, E; one rotation, $180_C°$; and two reflections, $refl_{BC}$ and $refl_{CA}$. The other sub-groups are found in classes 222, $2/m$, m, 2, $\bar{1}$, and 1.

It appears that the operations in each of the thirty-two classes are a sub-group of those in $m3m$ or in $6/mmm$ or in both.[2] It also appears that in each system the group in one class contains the groups in the others as sub-groups; this class is called *holohedral* and the others *merohedral*. In hexagonal system B the class $\bar{3}m$ might be called holohedral.

Characteristic Domains

A characteristic domain is one which, under the symmetry operations of the class, is repeated so as to fill space completely without any gap. Table 4 gives the *projections* of characteristic domains;[3] within

---

[1] *International Tables for X-ray Crystallography*, I (1952), p. 44.

[2] A. Schleede and E. Schneider, *Röntgenspektroskopie und Kristallstrukturanalyse*, II (1929), p. 29; *Int. Tables*, I, p. 36.

[3] The monoclinic and triclinic drawings are further explained on p. 73.

a class they are mutually congruent or *enantiomorphic* accordingly as they can be brought to coincidence by symmetry operations of the first or second kind (p. 9).

In each class the characteristic domain has a definite magnitude; in some classes the boundaries can be chosen entirely or partly arbitrarily (for example, 1 and 4); symmetry elements can occur only at the boundaries.

It appears that within each system the characteristic domains in the merohedral classes are two or four times as large as in the holohedral class. The first ones are called *hemihedral*, the others *tetartohedral*. If the classes of hexagonal system B are considered as merohedrals

TABLE 3

| | holohedry | | merohedries | | | | | | | |
| | | | hemihedries | | | | | tetartohedries | | |
	general form		general form	hemi-morphic	para-morphic	enantio-morphic		general form	hemi-morphic	
cubic	48	$m3m$	24		$m3$	432	$\bar{4}3m$	12		23
hex. A	24	$6/mmm$	12	6mm	$6/m$	622	$\bar{6}m2$	6	6	$\bar{6}$
hex. B	12	$\bar{3}m$	6	3m		32	$\bar{3}$	3	3	
tetr.	16	$4/mmm$	8	4mm	$4/m$	422	$\bar{4}2m$	4	4	$\bar{4}$
orthorh.	8	mmm	4	mm2		222				
mon.	4	$2/m$	2	2			m			
tricl.	2	$\bar{1}$	1				1			

(Vertical labels across the hex. A / hex. B / tetr. rows: di… pyramids — bipyramids — trapezohedra — pyramids)

The number of faces of the general form in each class.

of 6/*mmm*, the characteristic domain can be eight times as large (*ogdohedry*).

The hemihedries may be called (Table 3) (1) *hemimorphic* (the principal axis is polar), (2) *enantiomorphic* (only the rotation axes of the holohedral classes occur, and there is no inversion point), and (3) *paramorphic* (only the principal axis and the normal symmetry plane occur; in the cubic system, in this case, three axes are considered as principal axes).

Forms

Objects that coincide by multiplication by the symmetry operations are called *equivalent*.

If the projection of a crystal face (initial face) falls within the projection of a characteristic domain, this face is multiplied, as it were kaleidoscopically, to a *general form*. If the projection falls on a boundary formed by a symmetry element, a *special form* with fewer faces occurs, but then each face shows proper symmetry. In a hemihedral class the general form possesses half the faces of the holohedral form of the same system, in a tetarhohedral a fourth, in an ogdohedral an eighth; hence the names of these classes. We may also express this otherwise: in a hemihedral class the general holohedral form splits up into two, four, or eight *correlate* forms. The same may be valid for special forms. Correlate forms are again mutually congruent or enantiomorphic.

The characteristic domains of the holohedral classes are trihedra. The stereographic projections are the projections of spherical triangles, the monoclinic and triclinic classes being considered, following Weiss (1815), as merohedrals of the orthorhombic holohedry. In each of these classes there are, then, seven essentially different positions of the projections of the initial face of a form — that is, within the spherical triangle, on one of the sides, or on one of the corners; each of the seven forms has a *proper name*.[1]

As a rule, these names move on into the merohedral classes; but, in order to distinguish the forms, we add *position names*.

In order to achieve this, we divide the sphere in the cubic system and in the systems with principal axes as shown in Fig. 13, and, if possible and necessary, we add three position names; these are determined by the situation of the upper faces, unless lower faces only are present:

[1] In the systems with principal axes, in a stereographic projection after Gadolin, the crosses and rings of a bipyramid coincide, those of a scalenohedron and rhombohedron alternate symmetrically, and those of a trapezohedron alternate unsymmetrically. In the last three systems pinacoidal faces are parallel to two crystallographic axes, domal and prismatic faces to one, and pyramid faces to none.

1. proto: The stereographic projection lies in the middle between crystallographic axes.

   deutero: The stereographic projections lie on crystallographic axes.

   trito: The stereographic projections are arbitrarily placed.

2. positive or negative.

3. right or left.

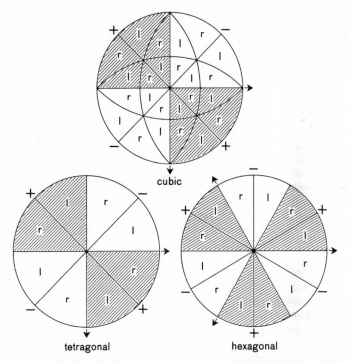

Fig. 13. Division of the sphere for the determination of position names; r = right; l = left.

In the orthorhombic, monoclinic, and triclinic systems, the position names are given by the position of one of the faces. The position of such a face is determined by the points of intersection with the crystallographic axes (on the A axis in front or behind, on the B axis right or left, on the C axis upper or lower). The parts of the position names placed in parentheses in Table 4 [1] may be omitted without ambiguity.

[1] In this table f. = in front; b. = behind; r. = right; l. = left; up. = upper; low. = lower.

A form complies with the symmetry of the class, and so does the axial set. From this it follows that the same figures occur in the symbols of all faces of one form, and only the sequence and the sign may differ. The symbol of a form is that of one of its faces, but the parentheses are replaced by braces; as a rule, the face in whose symbols most positive indices occur is chosen.

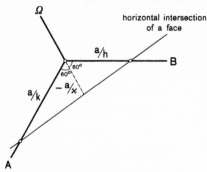

FIG. 14. For the areas of the three triangles:

$$\tfrac{1}{2}\,\frac{a}{k}\cdot\frac{\bar{a}}{\varkappa}\,\sin 60^\circ + \tfrac{1}{2}\,\frac{\bar{a}}{\varkappa}\cdot\frac{a}{h}\,\sin 60^\circ$$

$$= \tfrac{1}{2}\,\frac{a}{k}\cdot\frac{a}{h}\,\sin 120^\circ.$$

Hence $-h-k=\varkappa$
and $h+k+\varkappa=0$.

If in a face or form symbol no numbers are used, but the characters h, k, and l, then, in the cubic system, we impose $h \geqslant k \geqslant l \geqslant 0$; in the tetragonal system $h \geqslant k \geqslant 0$, and, for the l, always occurring as third index (the third axial length is independent of the other two), $l \geqslant 0$; in the orthorhombic, monoclinic, and triclinic systems, $h \geqslant 0$, $k \geqslant 0$, and $l \geqslant 0$.

The characters h, k, $\varkappa$, and l are used for the four-axial hexagonal cross, in which

$$h + k + \varkappa = 0 \ \text{(Fig. 14)}$$
$$h \geqslant k \geqslant 0;\ \varkappa \leqslant 0$$

hence $\bar{\varkappa} \geqslant h \geqslant k \geqslant 0$, and for l, always occurring as fourth index, $l \geqslant 0$. The symbols of faces of the general forms are given in Fig. 15.

In the *projections* of Table 4 all the forms that are possible in each class are stated.

Combinations of Forms

Most crystals are bounded by more than one form, sometimes by several forms,[1] but it is remarkable that the number of zones is mostly small.

Crystal Aggregates, Twins, Repeated Twins

Aggregates may be described as consisting of two or more single

[1] V. Goldschmidt, *Atlas der Krystallformen* (1913), gives for all minerals the forms and twins which have been observed, illustrating them at the same time.

P. Groth, *Chemische Krystallographie* (1906), describes natural and artificial crystals, with many pictures.

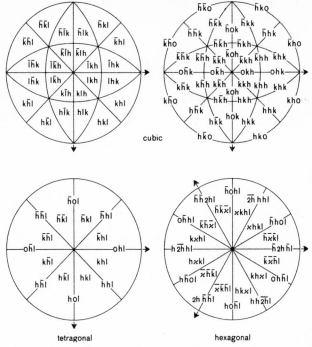

cubic

tetragonal

hexagonal

FIG. 15.

crystals (individuals), all of the same composition and the same modification.

The mutual position of two joined individuals can either be arbitrary or conform to a law — that is, can occur oftener than probability would lead us to expect.

The laws are nearly always such that both individuals possess a number of faces and edges in parallel. Genetically, one can say that in the one case the two individuals, originally separated, show arbitrary joining and that in the other case the development began from one germ (cf. also pp. 254 and 259).

The position conforming to a law can be one of the three following:

1. Each face and each edge of the first individual are parallel respectively to the corresponding face and edge of the second. Here one speaks of *parallel growth*, but this aggregate may be considered one crystal, for the structure is prolonged homogeneously throughout the two individuals. [continued on page 40]

TABLE 4 **Cubic System (Regular System)**

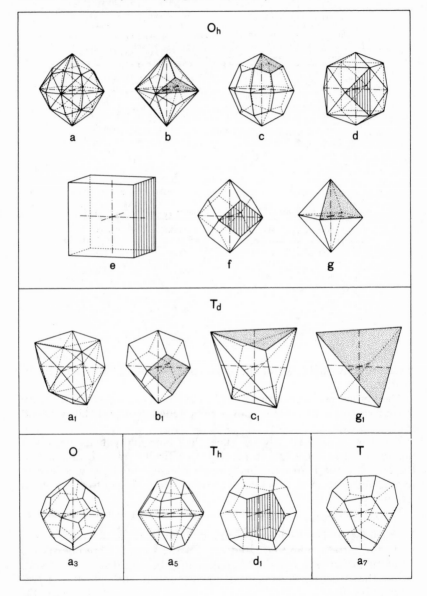

TABLE 4 **Cubic System (Regular System)**

O_h

Hexakis-octahedral class m 3 m — O_h
a	hexakis-octahedron	{h k l}
b	tris-octahedron	{h h k}
c	icositetrahedron	{h k k}
d	tetrakis-hexahedron	{h k 0}
e	hexahedron (cube)	{100}
f	rhombic dodecahedron	{110}
g	octahedron	{111}

T_d

Hexakis-tetrahedral class $\overline{4}$ 3 m — T_d
a_1	hexakis-tetrahedron	pos.	{h l k}
a_2	,,	,, neg.	{h $\overline{l}$ k}
b_1	deltoid-dodecahedron	pos.	{h k h}
b_2	,,	,, neg.	{h $\overline{k}$ h}
c_1	tris-tetrahedron	pos.	{h k k}
c_2	,,	,, neg.	{h $\overline{k}$ k}
g_1	tetrahedron	pos.	{111}
g_2	,,	neg.	{1$\overline{1}$1}

O

Pentagonal-icositetrahedral class 4 3 2 — O
a_3	pentagonal-icositetrahedron l.		{h k l}
a_4	,,	,, r.	{k h l}

T_h

Dis-dodecahedral class m 3 — T_h
a_5	dis-dodecahedron frontal.		{h k l}
a_6	,,	,, sagittal	{k h l}
d_1	pentagonal dodecahedron frontal		{h k 0}
d_2	,,	,, sagittal.	{k h 0}

T

Tetrahedral-pentagonal-dodecahedral class 2 3 — T
a_7	tetrahedral-pentagonal-dodecahedron	pos. r.		{h l k}
a_8	,,	,,	,, pos. l.	{k l h}
a_9	,,	,,	,, neg. l.	{h $\overline{l}$ k}
a_{10}	,,	,,	,, neg. r.	{k $\overline{l}$ h}

TABLE 4 (continued) **Hexagonal System A**

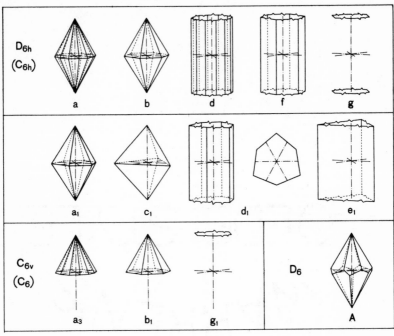

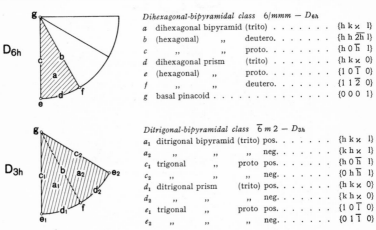

Dihexagonal-bipyramidal class 6/mmm — D_{6h}

a dihexagonal bipyramid (trito) . . . . {h k $\varkappa$ l}
b (hexagonal)   „   deutero. . . . . . . {h h $\overline{2h}$ l}
c   „   „   proto. . . . . {h 0 $\overline{h}$ l}
d dihexagonal prism   (trito) . . . . {h k $\varkappa$ 0}
e (hexagonal)   „   proto. . . . . {1 0 $\overline{1}$ 0}
f   „   „   deutero. . . . . . . {1 1 $\overline{2}$ 0}
g basal pinacoid . . . . {0 0 0 1}

Ditrigonal-bipyramidal class $\overline{6}$ m 2 — D_{3h}

a_1 ditrigonal bipyramid (trito) pos. . . . . . . {h k $\varkappa$ l}
a_2 „   „   „   neg. . . . . . . {k h $\varkappa$ l}
c_1 trigonal   „   proto pos. . . . . . . {h 0 $\overline{h}$ l}
c_2 „   „   „   neg. . . . . . . {0 h $\overline{h}$ l}
d_1 ditrigonal prism   (trito) pos. . . . . . . {h k $\varkappa$ 0}
d_2 „   „   „   neg. . . . . . . {k h $\varkappa$ 0}
e_1 trigonal   „   proto pos. . . . . . . {1 0 $\overline{1}$ 0}
e_2 „   „   „   neg. . . . . . . {0 1 $\overline{1}$ 0}

TABLE 4 (continued) Hexagonal System A

C6v

Dihexagonal-pyramidal class 6 mm — C_{6v}

a_3 dihexagonal pyramid (trito)	up.....	{h k ϰ 1}
b_1 (hexagonal)	„	deutero up.....	{h h $\overline{2h}$ 1}
c_3	„	„ proto up.....	{h 0 $\overline{h}$ 1}
g_1 basal pedion		up.....	{0 0 0 1}
a_4, b_2, c_4, g_2 similar, but lower.......			{. . . $\overline{1}$}

D6

Hexagonal-trapezohedral class 622 — D_6

A trapezohedron (trito)	r.........	{h k ϰ 1}
A_1	„	„ l.........	{ϰ̄ $\overline{k}$ $\overline{h}$ 1}

C6h

Hexagonal-bipyramidal class 6/m — C_{6h}

a_5 bipyramid trito	r...........	{h k ϰ 1}
a_6	„	„ l...........	{ϰ̄ $\overline{k}$ $\overline{h}$ 1}
d_3 prism	„	r...........	{h k ϰ 0}
d_4	„	„ l...........	{ϰ̄ $\overline{k}$ $\overline{h}$ 0}

C3h

Trigonal-bipyramidal class $\overline{6}$ — C_{3h}

a_7 trigonal bipyr. (trito)	pos. r......	{h k ϰ 1}
a_8	„	„ „ neg. l......	{k h ϰ 1}
a_9	„	„ „ pos. l......	{ϰ̄ $\overline{k}$ $\overline{h}$ 1}
a_{10}	„	„ „ neg. r......	{$\overline{k}$ ϰ̄ $\overline{h}$ 1}
b_3	„	„ deutero counter-axial..	{h h $\overline{2h}$ 1}
b_4	„	„ „ axial......	{$\overline{h}$ 2h $\overline{h}$ 1}
d_5	„	prism (trito) pos. r......	{h k ϰ 0}
d_6	„	„ „ neg. l......	{k h ϰ 0}
d_7	„	„ „ pos. l......	{ϰ̄ $\overline{k}$ $\overline{h}$ 0}
d_8	„	„ „ neg. r......	{$\overline{k}$ ϰ̄ $\overline{h}$ 0}
f_1	„	„ deutero counter-axial..	{1 1 $\overline{2}$ 0}
f_2	„	„ „ axial......	{$\overline{1}$ 2 $\overline{1}$ 0}

C6

Hexagonal-pyramidal class 6 — C_6

a_{11} pyramid trito up.	r.........	{h k ϰ 1}
a_{12}	„	„ low. r.........	{h k ϰ $\overline{1}$}
a_{13}	„	„ up. l.........	{ϰ̄ $\overline{k}$ $\overline{h}$ 1}
a_{14}	„	„ low.........	{ϰ̄ $\overline{k}$ $\overline{h}$ $\overline{1}$}

TABLE 4 (continued) **Hexagonal System B (Trigonal System)**

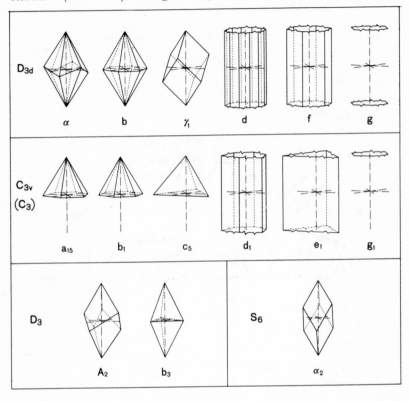

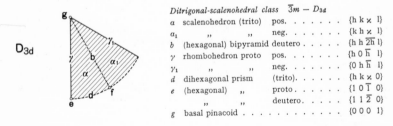

Ditrigonal-scalenohedral class $\overline{3}m - D_{3d}$

a	scalenohedron (trito)	pos.	{h k x l}
a_1	,,	,, neg.	{k h x l}
b	(hexagonal) bipyramid	deutero	{h h $\overline{2h}$ l}
γ	rhombohedron proto	pos.	{h 0 $\overline{h}$ l}
γ_1	,,	,, neg.	{0 h $\overline{h}$ l}
d	dihexagonal prism	(trito).	{h k x 0}
e	(hexagonal) ,,	proto.	{1 0 $\overline{1}$ 0}
	,,	,, deutero.	{1 1 $\overline{2}$ 0}
g	basal pinacoid	. . . .	{0 0 0 1}

TABLE 4 (continued) Hexagonal System B (Trigonal System)

Ditrigonal-pyramidal class 3m — C₃ᵥ

a_{15}	ditrigonal pyramid	(trito)	pos. up.	. . .	{h k ϰ l}
a_{17}	,,	,,	neg. up.	. . .	{k h ϰ l}
b_1	(hexagonal)	,,	deutero up.	. . . .	{h h $\overline{2h}$ l}
c_6	trigonal	,,	proto pos. up.	. . .	{h 0 $\overline{h}$ l}
c_7	,,	,,	,, neg. up.	. . .	{0 h $\overline{h}$ l}
d_1	ditrigonal prism	(trito)	pos.	. . . . .	{h k ϰ 0}
d_2	,,	,,	,, neg.	. . . . .	{k h ϰ 0}
e_1	trigonal	,,	proto pos.	. . . . .	{1 0 $\overline{1}$ 0}
e_2	,,	,,	,, neg.	. . . . .	{0 1 $\overline{1}$ 0}
g_1	basal pedion	,,	up.	. . . . .	{0 0 0 1}

a_{16}, a_{18} ,b_2, c_6, c_8, g_2 similar, but lower. . . . { . . . $\overline{1}$}

Trigonal-trapezohedral class 32 — D₃

A_2	trigonal trapezohedron (trito) pos. r.	. .	{h k ϰ l}
A_3	,,	,, ,, neg. l.	. .	{k h ϰ l}
A_4	,,	,, ,, pos. l.	. .	{ϰ̄ k̄ h̄ l}
A_5	,,	,, ,, neg. r.	. . .	{k̄ ϰ̄ h̄ l}
b_3	,,	bipyramid deutero counter-axial.		{h h $\overline{2h}$ l}
b_4	,,	,, deutero axial		{h̄ 2h h̄ l}
d_9	ditrigonal prism (trito) counter-axial	. .	{h k ϰ 0}
d_{10}	,,	,, ,, axial		{ϰ̄ k̄ h̄ 0}
f_1	trigonal prism deutero counter-axial.	. .	{h h $\overline{2h}$ 0}
f_2	,,	,, ,, axial		{h̄ 2h h̄ 0}

Rhombohedral class $\overline{3}$ — S₆

a_2	rhombohedron trito pos. r.		{h k ϰ l}
a_3	,,	,, ,, l.	{ϰ̄ k̄ h̄ l}
a_4	,,	,, ,, neg. l.	{k h ϰ l}
a_5	,,	,, ,, r.	{k̄ ϰ̄ h̄ l}
β	,,	deutero counter-axial. .	{h h $\overline{2h}$ l}
β_1	,,	,, axial	{2h h̄ h̄ l}
d_3	(hexagonal) prism trito r.		{h k ϰ 0}
d_4	,,	,, ,, l.	{ϰ̄ k̄ h̄ 0}

Trigonal-pyramidal class 3 — C₃

a_{19}	trigonal pyramid (trito)	pos. r. up.	. .	{h k ϰ l}
a_{21}	,,	,,	,, neg. l. up.	. .	{k h ϰ l}
a_{23}	,,	,,	,, pos. l. up.	. .	{ϰ̄ k̄ h̄ l}
a_{25}	,,	,,	,, neg. r. up.	. .	{k̄ ϰ̄ h̄ l}
b_5	,,	,,	deutero counter-axial		{h h $\overline{2h}$ l}
b_7	,,	,,	,, axial		{h̄ 2h h̄ l}
d_5	,,	prism	trito pos. r.	. . .	{h k ϰ 0}
d_6	,,	,,	,, neg. l.	. . .	{k h ϰ 0}
d_7	,,	,,	,, pos. l.	. . .	{ϰ̄ k̄ h̄ 0}
d_8	,,	,,	,, neg. r.	. . .	{k̄ ϰ̄ h̄ 0}

a_{20}, a_{22}, a_{24}, a_{26}, b_6, b_8, c_6, c_8, g_2 similar, but
lower . . . . { . . . $\overline{1}$}

TABLE 4 (continued) **Tetragonal System**

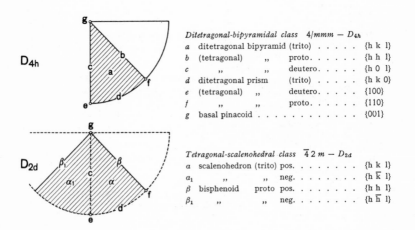

D4h

Ditetragonal-bipyramidal class 4/mmm — D_{4h}
a   ditetragonal bipyramid (trito) . . . . .   {h k l}
b   (tetragonal)   ,,   proto. . . . . .   {h h l}
c   ,,   ,,   deutero. . . . .   {h 0 l}
d   ditetragonal prism   (trito) . . . . .   {h k 0}
e   (tetragonal)   ,,   deutero. . . . .   {100}
f   ,,   ,,   proto. . . . . .   {110}
g   basal pinacoid . . . .   {001}

Tetragonal-scalenohedral class $\overline{4}\,2\,m$ — D_{2d}
α   scalenohedron (trito) pos. . . . .   {h k l}
$α_1$,,   ,,   neg. . . . .   {h $\overline{k}$ l}
β   bisphenoid   proto pos. . . . .   {h h l}
$β_1$,,   ,,   neg. . . . .   {h $\overline{h}$ l}

TABLE 4 (continued) **Tetragonal System**

C_{4v}

Ditetragonal-pyramidal class 4 mm — C_{4v}

a_1 ditetragonal pyramid (trito)	up.	. . .	{h k l}
b_1 (tetragonal)	,,	proto	up. . . .	{h h l}
c_1 ,,	,,	deutero	up. . . .	{h 0 l}
g_1 basal pedion			up. . . .	{0 0 1}
a_2, b_2, c_2, g_2 similar, but lower				{. . l̄}

D_4

Tetragonal-trapezohedral class 422 — D_4

A trapezohedron (trito) l.	{h k l}
A_1 ,, ,, r.	{k h l}

C_{4h}

Tetragonal-bipyramidal class 4/m — C_{4h}

a_3 bipyramid trito l.	{h k l}
a_4 ,, ,, r.	{k h l}
d_1 prism ,, l.	{h k 0}
d_2 ,, ,, r.	{k h 0}

S_4

Tetragonal-bisphenoidal class $\overline{4}$ — S_4

a_2 bisphenoid trito pos. l.	{h k l}
a_3 ,, ,, ,, r.	{k h l}
a_4 ,, ,, neg. r.	{h k̄ l}
a_5 ,, ,, ,, l.	{k h̄ l}
γ ,, deutero frontal	{h 0 l}
γ_1 ,, ,, sagittal.	{0 h l}

C_4

Tetragonal-pyramidal class 4 — C_4

a_5 pyramid trito up. l.	{h k l}
a_6 ,, ,, low. l.	{h k l̄}
a_7 ,, ,, up. r.	{k h l}
a_8 ,, ,, low. r.	{k h l̄}

TABLE 4 (continued) **Orthorhombic System**

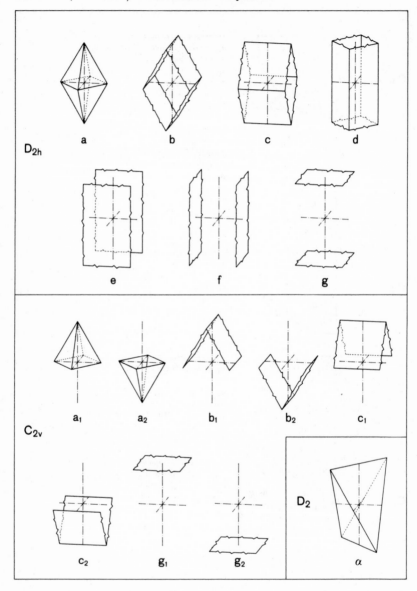

TABLE 4 (continued) **Orthorhombic System**

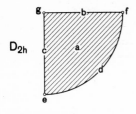

Orthorhombic-bipyramidal class   mmm — D_{2h}

a	bipyramid	(f. r. up.)	{h k l}
b	brachy-dome	(r. u.).	{0 k l}
c	macro-dome	(f. u.).	{h 0 l}
d	prism	(f. r.)	{h k 0}
e	macro-pinacoid	(f.)	{100}
f	brachy-pinacoid	(r.)	{010}
g	basal pinacoid	(u.).	{001}

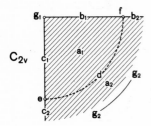

Orthorhombic-pyramidal class   mm 2 — C_{2v}

a_1	pyramid	(f. r.) up.	{h k l}
a_2	,,	(f. r.) low.. . . .	{h k $\bar{l}$}
b_1	he-domemi-brachy	(r.) up.	{0 k l}
b_2	,, ,,	(r.) low.. . . .	{0 k $\bar{l}$}
c_1	hemi-macro-dome	(f.) up.	{h 0 l}
c_2	,, ,, ,,	(f.) low.. . . .	{h 0 $\bar{l}$}
g_1	basal pedion	up.	{001}
g_2	,, ,,	low.. . . .	{00$\bar{1}$}

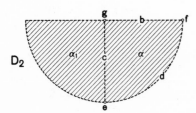

Orthorhombic-bisphenoidal class   222 — D_2

a_1	bisphenoid	(f. u.) r.	{h k l}
a_1	,,	(f. u.) l	{h $\bar{k}$ l}

TABLE 4 (continued) **Monoclinic System**

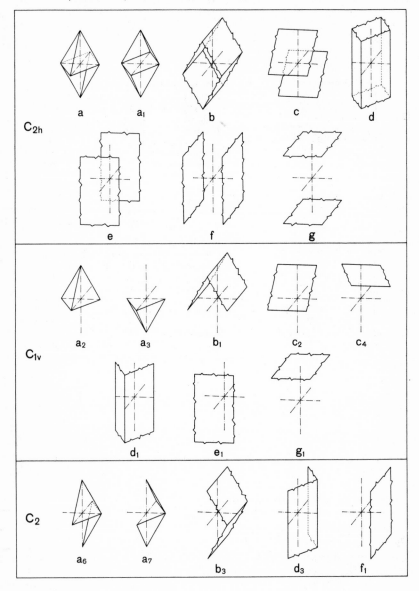

TABLE 4 (continued) **Monoclinic System**

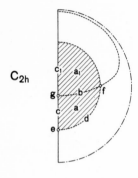

C₂ₕ

Monoclinic-prismatic class 2/m − C₂ₕ

a	hemi-pyramid	(r. u.) f.	{h k l}
a₁	,, ,,	(r. u.) b.	{h̄ k l}
b	clino-dome	(r. u.)	{0 k l}
c	hemi-ortho-dome	(u.) f.	{h 0 l}
c₁	,, ,, ,,	(u.) b.	{h̄ 0 l}
d	prism	(f. r.)	{h k 0}
e	ortho-pinacoid	(f.)	{100}
f	clino-pinacoid	(r.)	{010}
g	basal pinacoid	(u.)	{001}

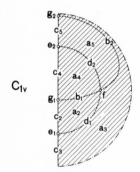

C₁ᵥ

Monoclinic-domatic class   m − C₁ᵥ

a₂	tetarto-pyramid	(r.) f. u.	{h k l}
a₄	,, ,,	(r.) b. u.	{h̄ k l}
b₁	hemi-clino-dome	(r.) u.	{0 k l}
c₂	tetarto-ortho-dome	f. u.	{h 0 l}
c₄	,, ,, ,,	b. u.	{h̄ 0 l}
d₁	hemi-prism	(r.) f.	{h k 0}
d₂	,, ,,	(r.) b.	{h̄ k 0}
e₁	ortho-pedion	f.	{100}
e₂	,, ,,	b.	{1̄00}
g₁	basal pedion	u.	{001}

a₃, a₅, b₂, c₃, c₅, g₂ similar, but lower . . . . { . .1̄}

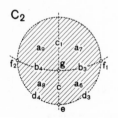

C₂

Monoclinic-sphenoidal class 2 − C₂

a₆	tetarto-pyramid	(u.) f. r.	{h k l}
a₇	,, ,,	(u.) b. r.	{h̄ k l}
a₈	,, ,,	(u.) f. l.	{h k̄ l}
a₉	,, ,,	(u.) b. l.	{h̄ k̄ l}
b₃	hemi-clino-dome	(u.) r.	{0 k l}
b₄	,, ,, ,,	(u.) l.	{0 k̄ l}
d₃	hemi-prism	(f.) r.	{h k 0}
d₄	,, ,,	(f.) l.	{h k̄ 0}
f₁	clino-pedion	r.	{010}
f₂	,, ,,	l.	{01̄0}

TABLE 4 (continued) **Triclinic System**

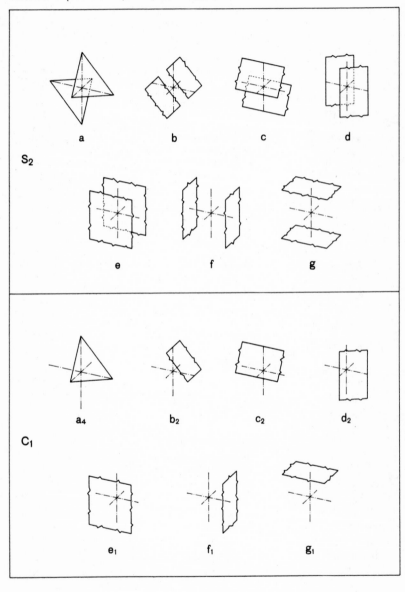

TABLE 4 (continued) **Triclinic System**

S_2

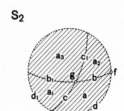

Triclinic-pinacoidal class $\bar{1} - S_2$

a	tetarto-pyramid	(u.) f. r..	$\{h\ k\ l\}$
a_1	,,	,,	(u.) f. l..	$\{h\ \bar{k}\ l\}$
a_2	,,	,,	(u.) b. r..	$\{\bar{h}\ k\ l\}$
a_3	,,	,,	(u.) b. r..	$\{\bar{h}\ \bar{k}\ l\}$
b	hemi-brachy-dome	(u.) r.	$\{0\ k\ l\}$
b_1	,,	,, ,,	(u.) l..	$\{0\ \bar{k}\ l\}$
c	hemi-macro-dome	(u.) f..	$\{h\ 0\ l\}$
c_1	,,	,, ,,	(u.) b.	$\{\bar{h}\ 0\ l\}$
d	hemi-prism	(f.) r.	$\{h\ k\ 0\}$
d_1	,,	,,	(f.) l..	$\{h\ \bar{k}\ 0\}$
e	macro-pinacoid	(f.).	$\{100\}$
f	brachy-pinacoid	(r.).	$\{010\}$
g	basal pinacoid	(u.)	$\{001\}$

C_1

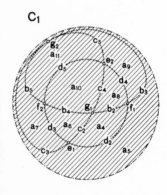

Triclinic-pediaі class $1 - C_1$

a_4	ogdo-pyramid	f. r. u.	$\{h\ k\ l\}$
a_6	,, ,,	f. l. u..	$\{h\ \bar{k}\ l\}$
a_8	,, ,,	b. r. u.	$\{\bar{h}\ k\ l\}$
a_{10}	,, ,,	b. l. u.	$\{\bar{h}\ \bar{k}\ l\}$
b_2	tetarto-brachy-dome	r. u.	$\{0\ k\ l\}$
b_4	,, ,,	l. u.	$\{0\ \bar{k}\ l\}$
c_2	tetarto-macro-dome	f. u.	$\{h\ 0\ l\}$
c_4	,, ,, ,,	b. u..	$\{\bar{h}\ 0\ l\}$
d_2	tetarto-prism	f. r..	$\{h\ k\ 0\}$
d_3	,, ,,	f. l..	$\{h\ \bar{k}\ 0\}$
d_4	,, ,,	b. r.	$\{\bar{h}\ k\ 0\}$
d_5	,, ,,	b. l.	$\{\bar{h}\ \bar{k}\ 0\}$
e_1	macro-pedion	f.	$\{100\}$
e_2	,, ,,	b.	$\{\bar{1}00\}$
f_1	brachy-pedion	r.	$\{010\}$
f_2	,, ,,	l.	$\{0\bar{1}0\}$
g_1	basal pedion	u.	$\{001\}$

a_5, a_7, a_9, a_{11}, b_3, b_5, c_3, c_5, g_2 similar, but lower $\{00\bar{1}\}$

2. One edge of the first individual is parallel to the corresponding edge of the second; for the rest, the mutual position is arbitrary (definition of *crystallographic fiber*). Examples: serpentine asbestos and, especially, nemalite, a variety of brucite.
3. The mutual position of the two individuals is fixed, but not parallel. This position is described by a so-called *twin law*.

In nearly all cases of twinning, one individual can be brought into coincidence with the other, either by rotation through 180° (*hemitropism*) round an axis, the *twin axis*, or by reflection across a plane, the *twin plane*; if the crystal possesses an inversion point, both twin axis and twin plane are present. Both elements are nearly always crystallonomic. It may be observed that an even-fold symmetry axis or a symmetry plane of the crystal cannot occur as twin axis or twin plane respectively, for the individuals would then occupy a parallel position.

The two individuals can either have grown together in a flat plane,

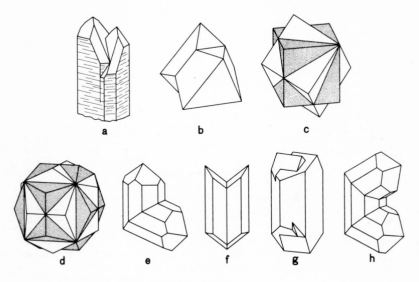

FIG. 16. (*a*) Parallel growth of quartz. (*b*) Cubic contact twin (spinel law): two octahedra, twin plane (111), composition plane (111). (*c*) Cubic penetration twin (fluorite law): two cubes, twin axis [111]. (*d*) Cubic penetration twin (pyrite law; iron cross): two pentagonal dodecahedra, twin plane (110). (*e*) Tetragonal contact twin of rutile (elbow twin): twin plane and composition plane (101). (*f*) Monoclinic contact twin of gypsum (swallowtail): twin plane and composition plane (100). (*g*) Monoclinic penetration twin of orthoclase (Carlsbad twin): twin axis *C* axis. (*h*) Tetragonal repeated twin of rutile (cf. *e*).

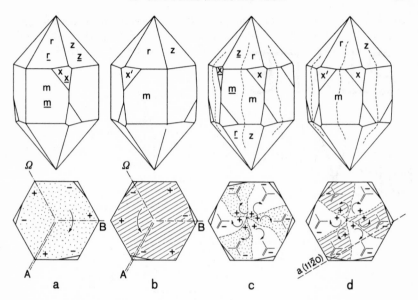

Fig. 17. The two principal twins of quartz. (a) Right-handed crystal. The ends of the positive horizontal crystallographic axes are charged positively after the crystal has cooled. (b) Left-handed crystal. The charge is opposite to that of a. But physicists assume for this crystal the reflected axial set of a so that the rule of a remains valid. [See W. G. Cady, *Piezoelectricity* (1946), p. 406.] (c) Penetration twin (Dauphiné law): either two right-handed or two left-handed individuals, twin axis C axis. Twinning can be recognized (pyro)electrically, not optically. (d) Penetration twin (Brazil law): one right-handed and one left-handed individual, twin plane $a(11\bar{2}0)$. Twinning can be recognized either optically — for example, with sections 1 mm thick, cut normal to the C axis (rotation of the vibration plane in opposite direction) — or (pyro)electrically.

the *composition plane*, or have grown one through the other in an irregular way. In the first case one speaks of a *contact*, in the second of a *penetration*, twin. If often happens that twin plane and composition plane coincide.

Twins often show re-entrant angles and faces, which in various places are striated in different directions. Under the polarization microscope the extinction directions (p. 206) of the individuals are generally different.

Repetition of twinning on the same law produces a *repeated twin*. Repeated twins, considered as homogeneous, often show (apparently or really) higher symmetry than the single individuals (*mimetic* repeated twins).

A twin shows two orientations (of the structure), a repeated twin more than two. If the individuals are placed one next to another as lamellae, and if the orientations of lamellae 1, 3, etc, are the same, just as those of 2, 4, etc. are, one speaks of a *polysynthetic twin.*

Figs. 16, 17, and 18 show some of the commonest aggregates.[1]

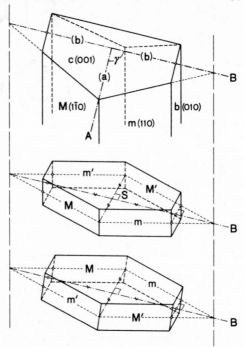

Fɪɢ. 18.   Triclinic contact twin of plagioclase (pericline law): twin axis *B* axis; the composition plane *S* is the "rhombic section," a non-crystallonomic plane such that the line of intersection with the face *b* (010) is normal to the *B* axis. [See Dana-Ford, *A Textbook of Mineralogy* (1932), p. 543.] For the construction of *S* see p. 72.

B. Crystallographic Calculations [2]

Analytic Relations

Faces and Zones

The face $(h\,k\,l)$ cuts off intercepts from the axes in the ratio $pa : qb : rc$ (p. 6):

$$h : k : l = \frac{1}{p} : \frac{1}{q} : \frac{1}{r}$$

[1] See the footnote on p. 24.

[2] Th. Liebisch, *Geometrische Krystallographie* (1881), a standard work; B. Hecht, *Anleitung zur Krystallberechnung* (1893), the most remarkable and compact summary; B. Gossner, *Kristallberechnung und Kristallzeichnung* (1914).

The equation of the face (A axis $\equiv X$ axis, etc.) is

$$\frac{h}{a} x + \frac{k}{b} y + \frac{l}{c} z = \text{constant}$$

and of the parallel plane through O is

$$\frac{h}{a} x + \frac{k}{b} y + \frac{l}{c} z = 0$$

Two faces, h_1 ($h_1k_1l_1$) and h_2 ($h_2k_2l_2$), intersect in an edge $[uvw]$, the equation of which is derived from

$$\frac{h_1}{a} x + \frac{k_1}{b} y + \frac{l_1}{c} z = 0 \quad \text{and} \quad \frac{h_2}{a} x + \frac{k_2}{b} y + \frac{l_2}{c} z = 0$$

$$\frac{x}{z} = \frac{a}{c} \frac{\begin{vmatrix} k_1 & l_1 \\ k_2 & l_2 \end{vmatrix}}{\begin{vmatrix} h_1 & k_1 \\ h_2 & k_2 \end{vmatrix}} \quad \text{and} \quad \frac{y}{z} = \frac{b}{c} \frac{\begin{vmatrix} l_1 & h_1 \\ l_2 & h_2 \end{vmatrix}}{\begin{vmatrix} h_1 & k_1 \\ h_2 & k_2 \end{vmatrix}}$$

We call

$$\begin{vmatrix} k_1 & l_1 \\ k_2 & l_2 \end{vmatrix} \equiv u; \quad \begin{vmatrix} l_1 & h_1 \\ l_2 & h_2 \end{vmatrix} \equiv v; \quad \begin{vmatrix} h_1 & k_1 \\ h_2 & k_2 \end{vmatrix} \equiv w.$$

Then

$$u : v : w = \frac{x}{a} : \frac{y}{b} : \frac{z}{c}$$

$\frac{x}{a}$, $\frac{y}{b}$, and $\frac{z}{c}$ are the coordinates of any point of the line of intersection expressed in axial lengths; u, v, and w are therefore the indices of the line of intersection (p. 7), and its equation is

$$\frac{x}{ua} = \frac{y}{vb} = \frac{z}{wc}$$

u, v, and w are easily obtained by cross multiplication (Von Lang, 1866); write down each face symbol twice, and omit the two end columns:

$$\frac{h_1}{h_2} \begin{matrix} k_1 \\ k_2 \end{matrix} \times \begin{matrix} l_1 \\ l_2 \end{matrix} \times \begin{matrix} h_1 \\ h_2 \end{matrix} \times \begin{matrix} k_1 \\ k_2 \end{matrix} \begin{matrix} l_1 \\ l_2 \end{matrix}$$
$$\underbrace{}_{u} \underbrace{}_{v} \underbrace{}_{w}$$

Three Faces in One Zone (Tautozonal Faces)

If three faces intersect in parallel lines, or, in other words, if the three planes through O have a common line of intersection, then the condition is

$$\begin{vmatrix} h_1 & k_1 & l_1 \\ h_2 & k_2 & l_2 \\ h_3 & k_3 & l_3 \end{vmatrix} = 0$$

which may be written as $h_3 u + k_3 v + l_3 w = 0$ (*zone condition*).

If we use four-axial symbols in the hexagonal set (p. 7), the equation is

$$h_3 u + k_3 v + \varkappa_3 \omega + l_3 w = 0$$

for we have, in the three-axial set,

$$3h_{III} u_{III} + 3k_{III} v_{III} + 3l_{III} w_{III} = 0$$

This formula may be written in another form as

$$h_{III}(2u_{III} - v_{III}) + k_{III}(2v_{III} - u_{III})$$
$$+ (- h_{III} - k_{III}) (- u_{III} - v_{III}) + 3l_{III} w_{III} = 0$$

and we have, in the four-axial set (cf. p. 7),

$$h_{IV} u_{IV} + k_{IV} v_{IV} + \varkappa_{IV} \omega_{IV} + l_{IV} w_{IV} = 0$$

If $(h_1 k_1 l_1)$, $(h_2 k_2 l_2)$, and $(h_3 k_3 l_3)$ are tautozonal, so are the faces $(h_1 h_2 h_3)$, $(k_1 k_2 k_3)$, and $(l_1 l_2 l_3)$; in this way, numerous relations can be deduced from the determinant.[1]

Two edges, $[u_1 v_1 w_1]$ and $[u_2 v_2 w_2]$, may determine face $(h k l)$. Then

$$hu_1 + kv_1 + lw_1 = 0$$
$$hu_2 + kv_2 + lw_2 = 0$$

$$h : k : l = \begin{vmatrix} v_1 & w_1 \\ v_2 & w_2 \end{vmatrix} : \begin{vmatrix} w_1 & u_1 \\ w_2 & u_2 \end{vmatrix} : \begin{vmatrix} u_1 & v_1 \\ u_2 & v_2 \end{vmatrix}$$

h, k, and l can easily be found by cross multiplication:

$$\begin{matrix} u_1 & v_1 & w_1 & u_1 & v_1 & w_1 \\ u_2 & v_2 & w_2 & u_2 & v_2 & w_2 \end{matrix}$$
$$\underbrace{\quad}_{h} \quad \underbrace{\quad}_{k} \quad \underbrace{\quad}_{l}$$

Three edges lie in the same face — that is, are *coplanar* — when

$$\begin{vmatrix} u_1 & v_1 & w_1 \\ u_2 & v_2 & w_2 \\ u_3 & v_3 & w_3 \end{vmatrix} = 0$$

Duality of Faces and Edges

Duality exists between faces and edges; that is, to each relation between faces and edges we can associate a second relation, by reading edges instead of faces and faces instead of edges. Example: the directions

[1] J. D. H. Donnay, Am. Min. 19 (1934), 593.

of two faces determine the direction of an edge, and the directions of two edges determine the direction of a face.

Analytically, the duality follows from $hu + kv + lw = 0$; this formula remains the same if h, k, and l are replaced by u, v, and w, and vice versa.

All Faces (hkl) in a Zone $[uvw]$

The following expression is valid:

$$\begin{vmatrix} h_1 & k_1 & l_1 \\ h_2 & k_2 & l_2 \\ \lambda h_1 + \mu h_2 & \lambda k_1 + \mu k_2 & \lambda l_1 + \mu l_2 \end{vmatrix} \equiv 0$$

Comparing this with the zone condition, we see that $(h\,k\,l)$ is tautozonal with $(h_1\,k_1\,l_1)$ and $(h_2\,k_2\,l_2)$ if

$$h = \lambda h_1 + \mu h_2$$
$$k = \lambda k_1 + \mu k_2$$
$$l = \lambda l_1 + \mu l_2$$

λ and μ are arbitrary numbers.

Complication (Addition Rule)

Derivation of the symbol of a new tautozonal face $(h\,k\,l)$ in the above-mentioned way is called *complication* (V. Goldschmidt, 1897), especially when $\lambda = \mu = 1$ — that is, when the corresponding indices are added without anything else. In that case we speak of *replacement* of the edge between the old faces by the new face.

The edge is *truncated* if the new face forms equal angles with the two old ones, as it does,[1] for example, when the old faces belong to the same form (Viola, 1905).[2]

Splitting a Symbol (Subtraction Rule)

By complication of (111) and (023), for example, the faces (134) and (356) can be found in the zone determined by those faces:

$$h_3 = 1 \cdot 1 + 1 \cdot 0 = 1 \qquad h_4 = 3 \cdot 1 + 1 \cdot 0 = 3$$
$$k_3 = 1 \cdot 1 + 1 \cdot 2 = 3 \qquad k_4 = 3 \cdot 1 + 1 \cdot 2 = 5$$
$$l_3 = 1 \cdot 1 + 1 \cdot 3 = 4 \qquad l_4 = 3 \cdot 1 + 1 \cdot 3 = 6$$

Reversing the procedure, we can split the symbols (134) and (356):

$$134 \begin{cases} 111 \\ 023 \end{cases} \qquad 356 \begin{cases} 333 \equiv 3 \cdot (111) \\ 023 \end{cases}$$

[1] P. Terpstra and R. ter Veld, Am. Min. 31 (1946) 386.
[2] L. Weber, Z. f. Krist. 55 (1919), 594.

By splitting symbol (*hkl*) in two ways, we indicate two zones that determine the face (*hkl*) (Fig. 19).

By adequate splitting we can finally bring it about that no other indices than 1, 0, and Ī occur in the new symbols. These symbols belong to the twenty-six faces which may be derived in a simple manner from the fundamental faces by the zone relation and which are determined by the zones of the so-called *system of the nine zones* [1] (Fig. 20).

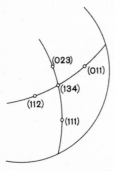

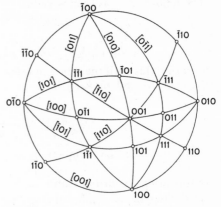

FIG. 19. Complication of (134) from (111) + (023) and from (112) + 2·(011), or splitting of (134) into two pairs.

FIG. 20.   The "system of the nine zones."

Equivalence of the Two Formulations of the Principal Law (Neumann)

If, when applying the second formulation (p. 7), we start from four faces with integral indices — for example, (100), (010), (001), and (111) — it follows from cross multiplication that the symbols of the edges also contain integral indices, as do all further deduced faces and edges. And each face with a symbol consisting of integral numbers may be deduced in this way, for by adequate splitting the zone relation with the original faces can be shown.

Rows, Nets, and Lattices [2]

General

A *row* is a one-dimensional collection of equidistant points; a *net* (point net) is a two-dimensional collection of points arranged as the intersection points of two *ranges* of equidistant (parallel) lines (generating

[1] P. Terpstra, *Kristallometrie* (1946), in which this system is called the "normal pattern."

[2] A. Bravais (1848) in Ostwalds Klassiker der exakten Wissenschaften, No. 90 (1897); P. Niggli, *Handbuch der Experimentalphysik*, VII, 1 (1928).

lines); a *lattice* is a three-dimensional collection of points arranged as the intersection points of three ranges of equidistant planes (generating planes).

Lattice, net, and row are infinite; the points of each are mutually indistinguishable, *identical;* the environment of all points is the same and is oriented in the same way (parallel). According to the variation of symmetry, there are one kind of row, five kinds of nets, and fourteen kinds of lattices (cf. p. 94).

The distance between two neighboring points in a row is called the *identity period.*

A line through two net points is called a *net line;* the lattice points lying on a net line form a row; a net line parallel to a given net line can be drawn through each net point, and these two net lines contain identical rows. If lines parallel to a given net line are drawn through all net points, these lines form a range of equidistant net lines. Two ranges of net lines, all the intersecting points of which coincide with all net points, are called *conjugate* ranges. The distance between two neighboring lines of a range is called the *spacing.*

A line through two lattice points is called a *lattice line;* the lattice points lying on a lattice line form a point row. Through each point of a lattice there is a lattice line parallel to a given lattice line; all these lattice lines are indistinguishable, identical; and the whole is called a spatial range.

A plane through three points is called a *lattice plane.* The lattice points lying on a lattice plane form a point net. A lattice plane parallel to a given lattice plane can be put through each point of a lattice, all these planes being identical and forming a range. The distance between two neighboring planes of a *range* is called the *spacing.*

Three ranges of lattice planes, the intersection points of which coincide with all lattice points, are called conjugate ranges. The generating ranges are therefore also conjugate, and all conjugate ranges may be considered as generating ones.

Three lattice planes are called conjugate if each one belongs to one of three conjugate ranges. The intersection lines (being lattice lines) of three conjugate lattice planes are called *conjugate lattice lines.*

A *sub-lattice* is a lattice composed of some of the points of a lattice. If we consider, not the absolute dimensions of a lattice, but only the ratios of the dimensions (that is, the shape of the lattice), then a lattice plane of a lattice coincides or is parallel with a lattice plane in each sub-lattice; and, vice versa, a lattice plane in a sub-lattice is also a lattice plane in the original lattice; and in a sub-lattice we can always indicate a sub-lattice that is equal and parallel to the original lattice (Fig. 21).

Lattice and sub-lattice have *the same metrics;* that is, corresponding constants are in simple (rational) relation, and quantities indicated in one of them by rational numbers are expressed in the other also by rational numbers.[1]

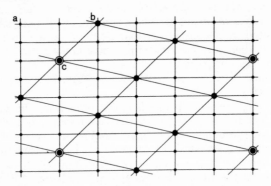

FIG. 21.   (Two-dimensional) lattice *a* • and sub-lattice *b* • ; *c* ◯, sub-lattice of *b*, is of the same shape as *a* and parallel to it.

The identity space, or *primitive cell*, in a row, is a line which has the length of the identity distance (Fig. 22); in a net it is a parallelogram congruent with and parallel to a parallelogram bounded by two pairs of neighboring lines of two conjugate ranges of net lines; in a lattice it is the parallelepiped congruent with and parallel to a parallelepiped bounded by three pairs of neighboring planes of three conjugate ranges of lattice planes. Nothing is said about the position of such a cell.

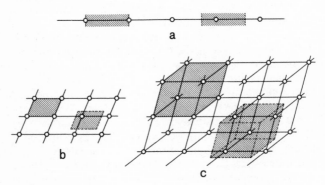

FIG. 22.   Primitive cells: (*a*) a one-dimensional, (*b*) a two-dimensional, (*c*) a three-dimensional lattice. The position of the cell is arbitrary.

[1] P. Niggli, *Handbuch der Experimentalphysik*, VII, 1 (1928), p. 16.

Mathematical Lattice

If one of the points of a lattice is taken as origin O, three conjugate lattice planes through O as coordinate planes, and hence their intersection lines—being three conjugate lattice lines—as coordinate axes, and if, furthermore, the three identity distances along the axes are taken as absolute axial lengths, such a lattice is called a mathematical lattice, and each lattice point has three integral numbers as coordinates, their symbols being $[[m\ n\ p]]$.

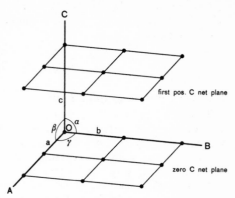

If a sub-lattice is taken as a mathematical lattice, or — which is the same — if in the original lattice three non-conjugate lattice lines are chosen as axes, then some coordinates of lattice points are fractional or mixed numbers.

Fig. 23.   Two C net planes in the direct lattice.

The plane through O of a range of lattice planes is called a *zero plane*. The coordinate planes and the lattice planes parallel to them are called *net planes*, the coordinate plane OAB the *zero C net plane*, the *neighboring planes* of these the first positive and the first negative C net plane, etc. (Fig. 23).

Direct Crystallographic Lattice

The symbols of the crystal edges contain three whole numbers, and so do the points of a mathematical lattice.

To a crystal (the direct sheaf) we add, in the following way, a mathematical lattice, and we call this the *direct crystallographic lattice*.

The origin O may coincide with the center; the lattice axes are parallel to the crystallographic axes A, B, and C; the identity lengths along the axes are in the proportion of the axial lengths a, b, and c [1] (or they may be taken equal to a_0, b_0, c_0; cf. p. 99); and the coordinates of an arbitrary point are indicated as $[[uvw]]$ or $[uvw]$.

---

[1] There are therefore as many different kinds of direct lattices as there are systems.

The older literature, especially, makes use also of topic axial lengths. The ratios of these are the same as those of the relative axial lengths — that is, those of the edges of the elementary cell (p. 99) of the direct lattice if the volume of that cell is made the same as the molecular volume (molecular weight divided by specific gravity). Cf. Encykl. der math. Wiss., Vol. V, I (1905), p. 410.

For this lattice the *radius vector* to [[*uvw*]] — that is, the line from *O* to that point — is parallel with the edge [*uvw*], which follows from the definition of the edge symbol (p. 7). If the coordinates *u*, *v*, and *w* have a common factor *D*, the lattice point is not the neighboring point of *O* on the radius vector, but the coordinates of the neighboring point are in that case

$$\frac{u}{D}, \ \frac{v}{D}, \ \frac{w}{D}$$

Indirect Crystallographic Lattice

In the indirect sheaf (p. 3), the crystal faces are represented by their normals and the edges by the planes to which they are normal; and the symbols (*hkl*) of the lines comprise three integers.

As we added a direct crystallographic lattice to the direct sheaf, so, in an analogous way, we add to the indirect sheaf an *indirect crystallographic lattice*. The origin *O** may coincide with the center, and the axial directions *A**, *B**, and *C** are parallel to the normals to (100), (010), and (001) — that is, to the normals to the pinacoids — whereas the ratios of the axial lengths, *a** : *b** : *c**, are determined by the fact that a point of the normal to (111) has to have the coordinates [[111]].[1] The coordinates of an arbitrary point are indicated by [[*hkl*]] or (*hkl*).

It can be shown (p. 52) that this lattice has the property that the radius vector to [[*hkl*]] is parallel to the normal to the crystal face (*hkl*) and, especially, that the symbol of the neighboring point of the origin of *O** is equal to that of the face.

Relation Between Direct and Indirect Lattice

With regard to the circle with radius ρ around *M* (Fig. 24), *Q* is the *pole* (point) of line *AP* and *P* the pole (point) of line *BQ*; *AP* is the *polar line* of point *Q* and *BQ* that of point *P*. We have $MQ \times MP = \rho^2$. With regard to a sphere, the same applies for the normal planes in *P* and *Q*.

In the direct lattice there is always a range of lattice planes of which the planes are parallel to the crystal face (*hkl*). One of

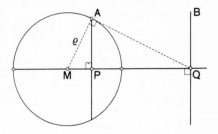

FIG. 24.   Poles and polar lines in regard to a circle.

---

[1] There are therefore as many different kinds of indirect lattices as there are systems.

the two neighboring planes of the origin O of this range intersects the axes in the points

$$\frac{a}{h}, \quad \frac{b}{k}, \quad \text{and} \quad \frac{c}{l}\,^1$$

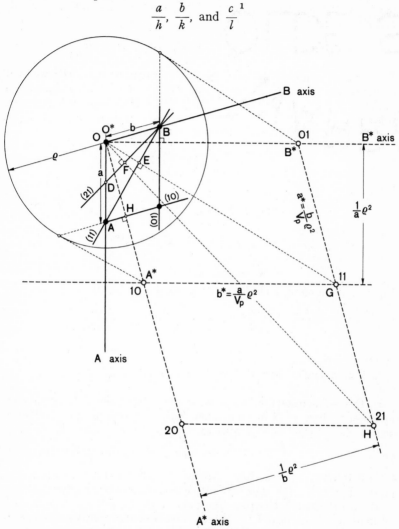

FIG. 25. A two-dimensional lattice ● and the lattice ○ which is polar to it with regard to a circle with radius ρ; $v_p = ab \sin \gamma$, the area of an elementary cell.

[1] A. Bravais in Ostwalds Klassiker, No. 90, p. 54; M. J. Buerger, *X-ray Crystallography* (1942), p. 8.

In Fig. 25, which, for the sake of clearness, has been drawn for a two-dimensional instead of for a three-dimensional direct lattice, the polar points of the neighboring lines of (10) and (01) are indicated as A^* and B^* respectively.

$$O^*A^* = a^* = \frac{\rho^2}{a \sin \gamma} \text{ and } O^*B^* = b^* = \frac{\rho^2}{b \sin \gamma}$$

These polar axial lengths may be the coordinates of G, and we shall demonstrate that O^*G is normal to AB, the neighboring line of the origin of O in the range (11), and that $OE \times O^*G = \rho^2$, and that thus G is the polar point of (11). Now $\triangle OAB \sim \triangle O^*B^*G$ (one angle equal and two sides proportional); the similarity factor is

$$\frac{\rho^2}{ab \sin \gamma} \left(\equiv \frac{\rho^2}{v_p} \right)$$

hence

$$O^*G = \frac{\rho^2}{ab \sin \gamma} \times AB$$

$$OA \perp O^*B^* \text{ and } OB \perp O^*A^*$$

hence

$$AB \perp O^*G$$

Further, the area of $\triangle OAB$ equals $\frac{1}{2} ab \sin \gamma$ and $\frac{1}{2} OE \times AB$, so that

$$OE = \frac{ab \sin \gamma}{AB} = \frac{ab \sin \gamma}{\dfrac{ab \sin \gamma}{\rho^2} \times O^*G} = \frac{\rho^2}{O^*G}$$

or $OE \times O^*G = \rho^2$.

H is, in a similar way, the polar point of BD, etc.

If, three-dimensionally, we construct the poles, not only of the two neighboring lines of O in each range (hkl), but also of the interjacent lattice planes which are parallel to them and which intersect the axes in the points $\dfrac{a}{nh}$, $\dfrac{b}{nk}$, and $\dfrac{c}{nl}$ (n is an integer), then the polar points form a lattice, the *polar lattice* (Bravais, 1848). If the normals to the pinacoid faces are taken in this lattice as axes, the polar lattice is identical with the indirect lattice. The polar axes A^*, B^*, and C^* are then normals to the planes of the direct axes, and the positive direction is taken so that $A^* \wedge A < 90°$, $B^* \wedge B < 90°$, and $C^* \wedge C < 90°$.

The direct lattice, on the other hand, is the polar lattice of the indirect lattice. From this the duality of crystal faces and edges follows clearly again.

The value of ρ is arbitrary; if we take $\rho = 1$ (not 1 cm!), we have a special polar lattice, called *reciprocal*. In geometric crystallography only directions and ratios are of importance; the value of ρ is therefore of no interest.

If two radius vectors, 1 and 2, enclose the angle (12), we have

$$\sin^2 (12) = \begin{vmatrix} \cos (11) & \cos (12) \\ \cos (21) & \cos (22) \end{vmatrix}$$

Analogously, in three dimensions, Sin (123) is defined by

$$\text{Sin}^2 (123) \equiv \begin{vmatrix} \cos (11) & \cos (12) & \cos (13) \\ \cos (21) & \cos (22) & \cos (23) \\ \cos (31) & \cos (32) & \cos (33) \end{vmatrix}$$

For the axial set it becomes

$$\text{Sin}^2 (ABC) \equiv \begin{vmatrix} 1 & \cos \gamma & \cos \beta \\ \cos \gamma & 1 & \cos \alpha \\ \cos \beta & \cos \alpha & 1 \end{vmatrix}$$

Sin (ABC) is taken as positive if the direction of the circulation $A \rightarrow B \rightarrow C$, seen from O, is clockwise. The volume of the elementary cell is then

$$v_p = abc \, \text{Sin} \, (ABC)$$
$$= abc \, \sqrt{1 - \cos^2 \alpha - \cos^2 \beta - \cos^2 \gamma + 2 \cos \alpha \cos \beta \cos \gamma}$$

The elements of the indirect lattice, which are marked with an asterisk, are

$$a^* = \frac{bc \sin \alpha}{v_p} \rho^2 = \frac{\sin \alpha}{a \, \text{Sin} \, (ABC)} \rho^2; \text{ cycl.}$$

$$\sin \alpha^* = \frac{\text{Sin} \, (ABC)}{\sin \beta \sin \gamma}; \text{ cycl. (cf. p. 59)}$$

$$\cos \alpha^* = \frac{\cos \beta \cos \gamma - \cos \alpha}{\sin \beta \sin \gamma}; \text{ cycl.}$$

and therefore

$$a^* : b^* : c^* = \frac{\sin \alpha}{a} : \frac{\sin \beta}{b} : \frac{\sin \gamma}{c}$$

The elements of the direct lattice, expressed in those of the indirect lattice, are, analogously,

$$a = \frac{b^* c^* \sin \alpha^*}{v_p^*} \rho^2, \text{ etc.}$$

Some mixed formulas [1] follow:

$$a\,a^* = \frac{\sin \alpha}{\mathrm{Sin}\,(ABC)}\,\rho^2;\ \text{cycl.}$$

$$\mathrm{Sin}\,(ABC) = \sin \alpha^* \sin \beta \sin \gamma = \sin \alpha \sin \beta^* \sin \gamma = \sin \alpha \sin \beta \sin \gamma^*$$

$$\mathrm{Sin}\,(A^*\,B^*\,C^*) = \frac{\mathrm{Sin}^2\,(ABC)}{\sin \alpha \sin \beta \sin \gamma}$$

$$v_p\,v_p^* = \rho^6$$

There is always complete duality; the formulas remain valid if the characters with asterisks are replaced by similar characters without asterisks, and vice versa.

The distance from O to the neighboring plane of the range (hkl) is equal to the spacing of the planes of the range. The *principal property* of direct and indirect lattices, which is regularly applied when we examine crystal structures (p. 112), reads as follows: the spacing of the lattice planes in one lattice multiplied by the length of the corresponding radius vector in the other lattice is constant $(= \rho^2)$.

If, in the direct lattice, three new lattice lines through O are taken (namely, those to $[[u_A\,v_A\,w_A]]$, $[[u_B\,v_B\,w_B]]$, and $[[u_C\,v_C\,w_C]]$), the new symbol of a point $[[u\,v\,w]]$ may become $[[U\,V\,W]]$. This change in axes requires a corresponding one in the indirect lattice; the new axes are then the radius vectors to $[[h_A\,k_A\,l_A]]$, $[[h_B\,k_B\,l_B]]$, and $[[h_C\,k_C\,l_C]]$, and the old symbol $[[h\,k\,l]]$ becomes the new symbol $[[H\,K\,L]]$.

The following transformation formulas are now valid:[2]

$$U = h_A u + k_A v + l_A w \qquad H = u_A h + v_A k + w_A l$$
$$V = h_B u + k_B v + l_B w \qquad K = u_B h + v_B k + w_B l$$
$$W = h_C u + k_C v + l_C w \qquad L = u_C h + v_C k + w_C l$$

$$u = u_A U + u_B V + u_C W \qquad h = h_A H + h_B K + h_C L$$
$$v = v_A U + v_B V + v_C W \qquad k = k_A H + k_B K + k_C L$$
$$w = w_A U + w_B V + w_C W \qquad l = l_A H + l_B K + l_C L$$

In these formulas

$$h_B = \frac{-\begin{vmatrix} v_A\,w_A \\ v_C\,w_C \end{vmatrix}}{\begin{vmatrix} u_A\,v_A\,w_A \\ u_B\,v_B\,w_B \\ u_C\,v_C\,w_C \end{vmatrix}};\ v_C = \frac{-\begin{vmatrix} h_A\,l_A \\ h_B\,l_B \end{vmatrix}}{\begin{vmatrix} h_A\,k_A\,l_A \\ h_B\,k_B\,l_B \\ h_C\,k_C\,l_C \end{vmatrix}};\ \text{etc.}$$

---

[1] Calculations of approximate values by A. L. Patterson, Am. Min. 37 (1952), p. 207.

[2] A. Bravais (1848) in Ostwalds Klassiker, No. 90 (1897), p. 56.

Calculation of Angles

With the Aid of Lattice Calculation from the Direct or Indirect Crystal Elements (g-method) [1]

If r_1 and r_2 are radius vectors in a lattice, we call $r_1 r_2 \cos (r_1 r_2) \equiv g_{12}$. From this it follows that

$$g_{aa} = a^2; \qquad g_{ab} = g_{ba} = ab \cos \gamma; \text{ cycl.}$$
$$g_{aa}^* = a^{*2}; \qquad g_{ab}^* = g_{ba}^* = a^* b^* \cos \gamma^*; \text{ cycl.}$$

From the direct crystal elements the following may be calculated:

$$g_{aa}^* = \frac{\sin^2 \alpha}{a^2 \operatorname{Sin}^2 (ABC)} \rho^4; \quad g_{ab}^* = \frac{\cos \alpha \cos \beta - \cos \gamma}{ab \operatorname{Sin}^2 (ABC)} \rho^4; \text{ cycl.}$$

Expressed in g's, this is

$$g_{aa}^* = \frac{\begin{vmatrix} g_{bb} & g_{bc} \\ g_{cb} & g_{cc} \end{vmatrix}}{\begin{vmatrix} g_{aa} & g_{ab} & g_{ac} \\ g_{ba} & g_{bb} & g_{bc} \\ g_{ca} & g_{cb} & g_{cc} \end{vmatrix}} \rho^4; \quad g_{ab}^* = \frac{- \begin{vmatrix} g_{ba} & g_{bc} \\ g_{ca} & g_{cc} \end{vmatrix}}{\begin{vmatrix} g_{aa} & g_{ab} & g_{ac} \\ g_{ba} & g_{bb} & g_{bc} \\ g_{ca} & g_{cb} & g_{cc} \end{vmatrix}} \rho^4; \text{ cycl.}[2]$$

The numerator is the sub-determinant of the denominator of the element g_{ab}, corresponding to g_{ab}^*; the denominator is v_p^2. All formulas are dual with regard to the g's and g^*'s.

The length of the radius vector to $[[u\,v\,w]]$ in the direct lattice is then

$$r_{uvw}^2 = u^2 g_{aa} + v^2 g_{bb} + w^2 g_{cc} + 2\,uv g_{ab} + 2\,vw g_{bc} + 2\,wu g_{ca}$$

and the length of the radius vector to $[[h\,k\,l]]$ in the indirect lattice is

$$r_{hkl}^{*2} = h^2 g_{aa}^* + k^2 g_{bb}^* + l^2 g_{cc}^* + 2\,hk g_{ab}^* + 2\,kl g_{bc}^* + 2\,lh g_{ca}^*$$

The angle $(r_1 r_2)$ between the radius vectors to $[[u_1 v_1 w_1]]$ and $[[u_2 v_2 w_2]]$ — that is, between the edges $[u_1 v_1 w_1]$ and $[u_2 v_2 w_2]$ — follows from

$$r_1 r_2 \cos (r_1 r_2) = u_1 u_2 g_{aa} + v_1 v_2 g_{bb} + w_1 w_2 g_{cc} + (u_1 v_2 + u_2 v_1) g_{ab}$$
$$+ (v_1 w_2 + v_2 w_1) g_{bc} + (w_1 u_2 + w_2 u_1) g_{ca}$$

The angle $(r_1 r_2)$ between the faces $(h_1 k_1 l_1)$ and $(h_2 k_2 l_2)$ is, analogously,

$$r_1^* r_2^* \cos (r_1^* r_2^*) = h_1 h_2 g_{aa}^* + k_1 k_2 g_{bb}^* + l_1 l_2 g_{cc}^* + (h_1 k_2 + h_2 k_1) g_{ab}^*$$
$$+ (k_1 l_2 + k_2 l_1) g_{bc}^* + (l_1 h_2 + l_2 h_1) g_{ca}^*$$

---

[1] Zeitschrift für Kristallographie A 101 (1939), p. 317.
[2] In geometric crystallography we are concerned with the ratios only; common factors, as in this case the denominators, are omitted.

The angle $(r\,r^*)$ between a radius vector $[[u\,v\,w]]$ in the direct and a radius vector $(h\,k\,l)$ in the indirect lattice—that is, the angle between the edge $[u\,v\,w]$ and the face $(h\,k\,l)$—follows from

$$r_{uvw}\,r^*_{hkl}\cos{(r\,r^*)} = (uh + vk + wl)\,\rho^2$$

With the Aid of Spherical Trigonometry

General

The intersection of the surface of a sphere and a plane containing its center is a *great circle;* the intersection of the surface and an arbitrary plane is a small circle. The meridians on the terrestrial globe are great circles; the parallels of latitude, with the exception of the equator, are small circles. A great circle is determined by two points on the sphere except when these points are opposites.

Of the *spherical triangle ABC* (Fig. 26) the sides a, b, and c are great

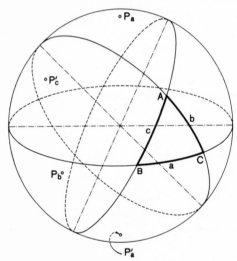

FIG. 26.   The elements of the triangle $P_aP_bP_c$ are supplementary to those of *abc*.

circles; the angles are called α, β, and γ.

The properties of spherical triangles are related to those of plane triangles; the latter may even be considered as spherical triangles on a sphere with infinite radius. The sides as well as the angles are expressed in degrees; a triangle with a 90° side is called right-sided, with a 90° angle right-angled.

A great circle possesses two *poles*, P and P' (Fig. 26); one pole of the side of a triangle lies with the triangle on the same half of the sphere. The poles of triangle ABC are P_a, P'_a; P_b, P'_b; and P_c, P'_c. The elements of the polar triangle $P_aP_bP_c$ are supplementary to those of the triangle ABC (cf. p. 58) in such a way that a side of ABC is supplementary to the corresponding angle of $P_aP_bP_c$, and vice versa.

The planes of the direct sheaf, the origin O of which is placed in the center of the sphere, intersect the sphere in great circles. Angles between edges can therefore be calculated as sides, angles between faces as angles, and angles between edges and faces as altitudes in a spherical triangle.

The edges of the indirect sheaf, the origin O^* of which is also thought of as in the center of the sphere, are normals to the planes of the direct sheaf, so that their points of intersection are the poles of the sides of the spherical triangle mentioned before. In the polar triangle angles between crystal faces can be calculated as sides, angles between edges as angles, and angles between faces and edges as altitudes.

The stereographic projection and graphic calculation (cf. p. 68) are very valuable for these calculations.

We derive some formulas and demonstrate the relation between the angles of the direct and those of the indirect sheaf (Fig. 27).

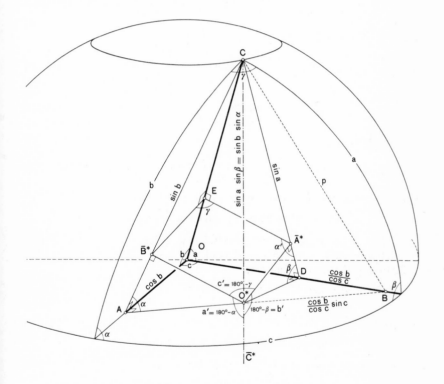

FIG. 27.

Arbitrary Spherical Triangle

The corners of the triangle are joined to the center of the sphere, and the normal $CO*$ to the plane AOB is drawn in the trihedron $OABC$. We also draw $O*A \perp OA$, $O*D \perp OB$, $O*\bar{A}* \perp CD$, and $O*\bar{B}* \perp CA$. Then the three lines $O*\bar{A}*$, $O*\bar{B}*$, and $O*\bar{C}*$ (the opposite to $O*C$) are normals to the planes of the trihedron; and, if we consider $OABC$ to be a direct axial set, $O*A*B*C*$ is the indirect (polar) set.

Because $O*\bar{A}* \perp OCD$ and $O*\bar{B}* \perp OCA$, $CO \perp O*\bar{A}*$ and $CO \perp O*\bar{B}*$, it is seen that $CO \perp$ plane $O*\bar{A}*E\bar{B}*$ and, by inspection, that $c' = 180° - \gamma$, cycl., and that $\alpha' = 180° - a$, cycl. Let OC be the unit of length; then $AC = \sin b$, and $OA = \cos b$; furthermore, $CD = \sin a$, $O*C = \sin b \sin \alpha$, and $O*C = \sin a \sin \beta$. Hence the sine rule:

$$\frac{\sin a}{\sin \alpha} = \frac{\sin b}{\sin \beta} \left(\text{and also} = \frac{\sin c}{\sin \gamma} \right)$$

In $\triangle OAB$ the side

$$OB = \frac{\cos b}{\cos c} \quad \text{and} \quad AB = \frac{\cos b}{\cos c} \cdot \sin c$$

Hence in $\triangle OBC$

$$p^2 = 1 + \left(\frac{\cos b}{\cos c} \right)^2 - 2 \cdot 1 \cdot \frac{\cos b}{\cos c} \cdot \cos a$$

and in $\triangle ABC$

$$p^2 = \sin^2 b + \left(\frac{\cos b}{\cos c} \sin c \right)^2 - 2 \sin b \cdot \frac{\cos b}{\cos c} \sin c \cdot \cos \alpha$$

From these equations we derive the first cosine rule:

$$\cos a = \cos b \cos c + \sin b \sin c \cos \alpha; \text{ cycl.}$$

In the polar trihedron $O*\bar{A}*\bar{B}*\bar{C}*$ the sides a', b', and c' equal, respectively, $180° - \alpha$, $180° - \beta$, and $180° - \gamma$.

Applying the first cosine rule,

$$\cos (180° - \alpha) = \cos (180° - \beta) \cos (180° - \gamma)$$
$$+ \sin (180° - \beta) \sin (180° - \gamma) \cos (180° - a)$$

we get the second cosine rule:

$$\cos \alpha = - \cos \beta \cos \gamma + \sin \beta \sin \gamma \cos a$$

Two other useful formulas are (Fig. 28):

$$\cos x \sin c = \cos a \sin q + \cos b \sin p$$

$$\cos (14) \text{ Sin } (234) + \cos (24) \text{ Sin } (314) + \cos (34) \text{ Sin } (124) = \text{Sin } (123)$$

The first is known as Stewart's theorem. The second gives the connection between the six angles found between four crystal faces. To prove this, draw the radii to the center O of the sphere, erect a normal plane to the radius to 4, and express the volume of the tetrahedron $(O\,123)$ as equal to the sum of the volumes of three tetrahedra.

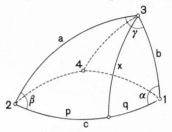

FIG. 28. General spherical triangle.

If we turn to the crystallographic axial sets (p. 5), the directions of A, B, and C in the direct set are indicated by OA, OB, and OC (Fig. 27), the directions of A^*, B^*, and C^* in the indirect set by the opposites of $O^*\bar{A}^*$, $O^*\bar{B}^*$, and $O^*\bar{C}^*$. Hence α, β, and γ in the direct set are identical with $a, b,$ and c and α^*, β^*, and γ^* in the indirect set with $a'\,(=180° - \alpha)$, $b'\,(=180° - \beta)$, and $c'\,(=180° - \gamma)$. The first cosine rule then yields the following:

$$\cos \alpha = \cos \beta \cos \gamma + \sin \beta \sin \gamma \cos (180° - \alpha^*)$$

$$\cos \alpha^* = \frac{\cos \beta \cos \gamma - \cos \alpha}{\sin \beta \sin \gamma}$$

$$1 - \sin^2 \alpha^* = \frac{\cos^2 \beta \cos^2 \gamma + \cos^2 \alpha - 2 \cos \alpha \cos \beta \cos \gamma}{\sin^2 \beta \sin^2 \gamma}$$

$$\sin^2 \alpha^* = \frac{1 - \cos^2 \alpha - \cos^2 \beta - \cos^2 \gamma + 2 \cos \alpha \cos \beta \cos \gamma}{\sin^2 \beta \sin^2 \gamma}$$

$$\sin \alpha^* = \frac{\text{Sin}\,(ABC)}{\sin \beta \sin \gamma} \quad [\text{cf. p. 53}]$$

Special formulas, derived from the general ones, follow.

Right-angled Spherical Triangle (Fig. 29)

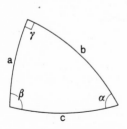

$$\cos c = \cos a \cos b = \text{cotg}\,\alpha \,\text{cotg}\,\beta$$

$$\cos a = \frac{\cos \alpha}{\sin \beta}$$

$$\sin \alpha = \frac{\sin a}{\sin c}$$

$$\cos \alpha = \frac{\tan b}{\tan c}$$

$$\tan \alpha = \frac{\tan a}{\sin b}$$

FIG. 29. Spherical triangle with one angle 90°.

Right-sided Spherical Triangle (Fig. 30)

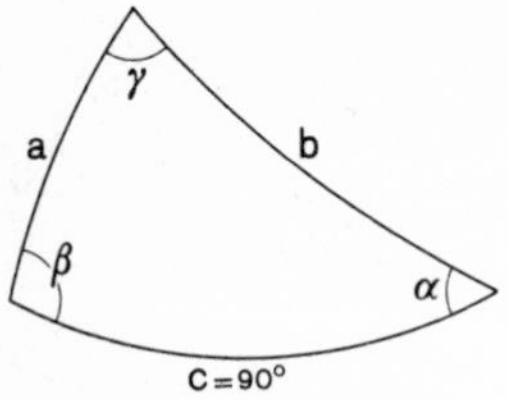

$$\cos \gamma = -\cos \alpha \cos \beta = -\cot g\, a \cot g\, b$$

$$\cos \alpha = \frac{\cos a}{\sin b}$$

$$\sin a = \frac{\sin \alpha}{\sin \gamma}$$

$$\cos a = -\frac{\tan \beta}{\tan \gamma}$$

$$\tan a = \frac{\tan \alpha}{\sin \beta}$$

FIG. 30. Spherical triangle with one side 90°.

In Connection with Theodolite Measurements

In measurements made with a theodolite goniometer (see p. 4), the *positions* of the faces are found. The position of a face is given in spherical coordinates φ and ρ of the intersection point of the normal to the face with the construction sphere. φ is the *azimuth*, measured from the right-handed point of the horizontal circle to the front; ρ is the *angle from the zenith*.

Two formulas are of great importance for spherical calculations.

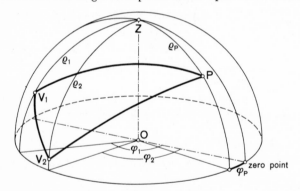

FIG. 31. P is the pole of the great circle through V_1 and V_2.

If V_1 and V_2 (Fig. 31) are the intersection points of the normals to these faces, then, in the triangle $V_1 V_2 Z$,

$$\cos (V_1 V_2) = \cos \rho_1 \cos \rho_2 + \sin \rho_1 \sin \rho_2 \cos (\varphi_1 - \varphi_2)$$

If we introduce

$$\tan \psi = \tan \rho_1 \cos (\varphi_1 - \varphi_2)$$

this expression becomes convenient for logarithmic treatment, and the result is

$$\cos (V_1 V_2) = \frac{\cos \rho_1 \cos (\rho_2 - \psi)}{\cos \psi}$$

A second formula expresses the coordinates of P, the pole of the great circle through V_1 and V_2, in terms of the coordinates of V_1 and V_2. In the right-sided spherical triangles $V_1 PZ$ and $V_2 PZ$

$$\cotg PZ = \cotg \rho_P = - \tan \rho_1 \cos (\varphi_1 - \varphi_P) = - \tan \rho_2 \cos (\varphi_2 - \varphi_P)$$

Hence

$$\tan \varphi_P = - \frac{\tan \rho_1 \cos \varphi_1 - \tan \rho_2 \cos \varphi_2}{\tan \rho_1 \sin \varphi_1 - \tan \rho_2 \sin \varphi_2}$$

$$\cotg \rho_P = - \tan \rho_1 \cos (\varphi_1 - \varphi_P) = - \tan \rho_2 \cos (\varphi_2 - \varphi_P)$$

If V_1 and V_2 are situated on the horizontal circle, then, respectively,

$$\varphi_P = \varphi_1 \pm 90° \quad \text{and} \quad \varphi_P = \varphi_2 \pm 90°$$

If the crystal tilts about a horizontal axis φ_S through the angle τ, the new position of a face can be derived as follows (Fig. 32):

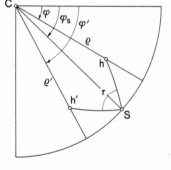

After tilting the point $h (\varphi, \rho)$ may have the position $h' (\varphi', \rho')$; thus $hS = h'S$. Then, in the right-sided spherical triangle CSh,

$$\tan \rho = \frac{\tan CSh}{\sin (\varphi_S - \varphi)}$$

$$\cos (\varphi_S - \varphi) = \frac{\cos hS}{\sin \rho}$$

Fig. 32. Tilting h round CS to h' through an angle τ.

The angle CSh and the side hS can be calculated from this.

In the right-sided spherical triangle CSh'

$$\tan h'S = \frac{\tan (\varphi' - \varphi_S)}{\sin (\tau - CSh)}; \quad \cos (\tau - CSh) = \frac{\cos \rho'}{\sin h'S}$$

After inserting the values of CSh and hS, we can calculate φ' and ρ'. If $\cos \rho'$ is found to be negative and h, after tilting, to be situated on the lower hemisphere, we can proceed to the opposite face (φ'', ρ''), whereby

$$\varphi'' = \varphi' + 180° \quad \text{and} \quad \rho'' = 180° - \rho'$$

Anharmonic Ratios

General

If four radius vectors in a plane, passing through one point O, are numbered in an arbitrary sequence as 1, 2, 3, and 4, and if we take the symbol sin (12) to be the sine of the angle through which 1 has to pass in a certain sense—for example, anti-clockwise—to coincide with 2, then

$$\frac{\sin (12) \ \sin (34)}{\sin (23) \ \sin (14)}$$

is called an *anharmonic ratio* of the sines; the value of the anharmonic ratio in question may be called δ.

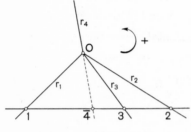

If the opposite of radius vector 4 is called negative (designation $\bar{4}$), the value of

$$\frac{\sin (12) \ \sin (3\bar{4})}{\sin (23) \ \sin (1\bar{4})}$$

also equals δ; that is, the value does not change if the opposite of one or more radius vectors is taken (Fig. 33).

FIG. 33.   Anharmonic ratios.

The value of the anharmonic ratio of the intercepts on an arbitrary transversal line is also δ, for the areas of the triangles formed have the same ratio as the bases (Fig. 33); therefore

$$\frac{\sin (12) \ \sin (34)}{\sin (23) \ \sin (14)} = \frac{\text{int.} (12) \ \text{int.} (34)}{\text{int.} (23) \ \text{int.} (14)} = \delta$$

The value of the anharmonic ratio does not change if the intercepts are taken on another transversal line, nor does it change if the entire figure is subjected to a parallel or central projection.

Anharmonic Ratios in Lattices

If four radius vectors from O^* to $(h_1 \ k_1 \ l_1)$ etc. in the indirect lattice are situated in one plane, the four crystal faces therefore being *tautozonal*, and if we extend the radius vectors to the lattice points of which the first coordinates are equal—for example, to the product $h_1 h_2 h_3 h_4$—the end points fall on a lattice line which is parallel to the plane $B^*O^*C^*$ (Fig. 34).

These points are projected $// \ C^*$ on the plane $A^*O^*B^*$; the symbols

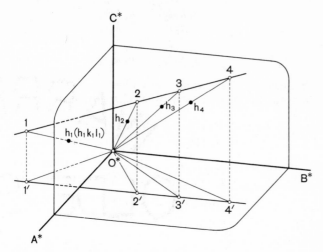

FIG. 34. The symbol of 1 is $[[h_1h_2h_3h_4 \quad k_1h_2h_3h_4 \quad l_1h_2h_3h_4]]$, that of 1′ is
$[[h_1h_2h_3h_4 \quad k_1h_2h_3h_4 \quad 0]]$, etc.

of these projections are then $(h_1h_2h_3h_4 \; k_1h_2h_3h_4 \; 0)$, etc. The distances between the projections are $(k_2h_1h_2h_3 - k_1h_2h_3h_4) \; b^*$, etc. Then

$$\delta = \frac{\sin (12) \; \sin (34)}{\sin (23) \; \sin (14)} = \frac{\text{dist } (1'2') \; \text{dist } (3'4')}{\text{dist } (2'3') \; \text{dist } (1'4')}$$

$$= \frac{\{(h_2h_3h_4k_1 - h_1h_3h_4k_2)b^*\} \; \{(h_1h_2h_4k_3 - h_1h_2h_3k_4)b^*\}}{\{(h_1h_3h_4k_2 - h_1h_2h_4k_3)b^*\} \; \{(h_2h_3h_4k_1 - h_1h_2h_3k_4)b^*\}}$$

$$= \frac{\begin{vmatrix} h_1 \; k_1 \\ h_2 \; k_2 \end{vmatrix} \begin{vmatrix} h_3 \; k_3 \\ h_4 \; k_4 \end{vmatrix}}{\begin{vmatrix} h_2 \; k_2 \\ h_3 \; k_3 \end{vmatrix} \begin{vmatrix} h_1 \; k_1 \\ h_4 \; k_4 \end{vmatrix}}$$

If we project $// \; A^*$, or if another than the first index is made equal in all symbols, we have such expressions as

$$\delta = \frac{\begin{vmatrix} k_1 \; l_1 \\ k_2 \; l_2 \end{vmatrix} \begin{vmatrix} k_3 \; l_3 \\ k_4 \; l_4 \end{vmatrix}}{\begin{vmatrix} k_2 \; l_2 \\ k_3 \; l_3 \end{vmatrix} \begin{vmatrix} k_1 \; l_1 \\ k_4 \; l_4 \end{vmatrix}}$$

which may all be noted as

$$\delta = \frac{\begin{vmatrix} h_1 & k_1 & l_1 \\ h_2 & k_2 & l_2 \end{vmatrix} \begin{vmatrix} h_3 & k_3 & l_3 \\ h_4 & k_4 & l_4 \end{vmatrix}}{\begin{vmatrix} h_2 & k_2 & l_2 \\ h_3 & k_3 & l_3 \end{vmatrix} \begin{vmatrix} h_1 & k_1 & l_1 \\ h_4 & k_4 & l_4 \end{vmatrix}}$$

whereby in each matrix the same column has to be omitted.
Sometimes the formulas are somewhat changed, as in

$$\delta = \frac{\sin (12) \sin (34)}{\sin (23) \sin (14)} = \frac{\sin (12) \sin (14-13)}{\sin (13-12) \sin (14)}$$

$$= \frac{\sin (12) \sin (14) \cos (13) - \sin (12) \cos (14) \sin (13)}{\sin (13) \cos (12) \sin (14) - \cos (13) \sin (12) \sin (14)}$$

$$= \frac{\cotg (13) - \cotg (14)}{\cotg (12) - \cotg (13)}$$

Hence

$$\delta \cotg (12) - (1 + \delta) \cotg (13) + \cotg (14) = 0$$

With the aid of these relations (Gauss 1830, Miller 1839) it is possible to calculate the indices of a face if this is situated in *one zone* with three other faces, the symbols of which, as well as the angles between all faces, are known. Furthermore, an angle can be calculated if all symbols and two angles between four tautozonal faces are given. With the aid of the direct lattice, analogous formulas can be derived for four coplanar edges.

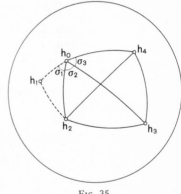

The *general case*, in which four arbitrary faces with their enclosed angles are given and the two angles of a fifth face with two of the given faces are also given, and from which the symbol of the fifth face is to be

FIG. 35.

calculated, may also be solved with the aid of anharmonic ratios without calculation of crystal elements or other constants.

If the faces h_0, h_2, h_3, and h_4, with their angles (Fig. 35), and the angles of h_1 with h_0 and h_2, are given, we first calculate, with the aid of the formulas of spherical trigonometry (p. 58), the angles σ_1, σ_2, and σ_3 between the zone circles in h_0.

In h_0 [1] we have

$$\frac{\sin \sigma_1 \sin \sigma_3}{\sin \sigma_2 \sin (\sigma_1 + \sigma_2 + \sigma_3)} \equiv \frac{\sin (102) \sin (304)}{\sin (203) \sin (104)}$$

$$= \frac{\begin{vmatrix} h_1 & k_1 & l_1 \\ h_0 & k_0 & l_0 \\ h_2 & k_2 & l_2 \end{vmatrix} \begin{vmatrix} h_3 & k_3 & l_3 \\ h_0 & k_0 & l_0 \\ h_4 & k_4 & l_4 \end{vmatrix}}{\begin{vmatrix} h_2 & k_2 & h_2 \\ h_0 & k_0 & l_0 \\ h_3 & k_3 & l_3 \end{vmatrix} \begin{vmatrix} h_1 & k_1 & l_1 \\ h_0 & k_0 & l_0 \\ h_4 & k_4 & l_4 \end{vmatrix}}$$

and in h_2 we have a similar formula. From these two equations the ratios $h_1 : k_1 : l_1$ may be derived.[2]

Transformation Formulas

In this section we indicate old axial lengths by a, b, c, and new ones by A, B, C, old indices by small letters and new ones by capitals. Furthermore, hkl is identical with $nh\ nk\ nl$ and HKL with $nH\ nK\ nL$.

Of the following cases, I and II are important special cases; the others are general cases from which the special cases may easily be derived.

I. It is given that the axial directions remain the same, but that face $(e\,f\,g)$ changes into $(E\,F\,G)$. Any face (hkl) changes into $(H\,K\,L)$, whereby

$$H = \frac{E}{e}\,h; \quad K = \frac{F}{f}\,k; \quad L = \frac{G}{g}\,l$$

II. It is given that the new axial directions are the old edges $[u_1v_1w_1]$, $[u_2v_2w_2]$, and $[u_3v_3w_3]$, and that $(e\,f\,g)$ changes into $(E\,F\,G)$; $(h\,k\,l)$ then changes into $(H\,K\,L)$, whereby

$$H = \frac{hu_1 + kv_1 + lw_1}{eu_1 + fv_1 + gw_1}\,E$$

$$K = \frac{hu_2 + kv_2 + lw_2}{eu_2 + fv_2 + gw_2}\,F$$

$$L = \frac{hu_3 + kv_3 + lw_3}{eu_3 + fv_3 + gw_3}\,G$$

---

[1] For the derivation of this formula see Proceedings of the Koninklijke Nederlandse Akademie van Wetenschappen, Amsterdam, 49 (1946), 369.

[2] Acta Crystallographica 1 (1948), 97.

III. It is given that the old faces $(h_1k_1l_1)$, $(h_2k_2l_2)$, $(h_3k_3l_3)$, and $(h_4k_4l_4)$ change into $(H_1K_1L_1)$, etc.;[1] (hkl) then changes into (HKL), whereby

$$H = u_A h + v_A k + w_A l$$
$$K = u_B h + v_B k + w_B l$$
$$L = u_C h + v_C k + w_C l$$

Hence $[u_A v_A w_A]$ is the new axis $[100]$, the old face (100) is the new $(u_A u_B u_C)$, etc. The coefficients u_A etc. are the old indices of the new axes, and they form the so-called transformation matrix:

$$\begin{Vmatrix} u_A & v_A & w_A \\ u_B & v_B & w_B \\ u_C & v_C & w_C \end{Vmatrix}$$

which may also be written as

$$u_A v_A w_A \,/\, u_B v_B w_B \,/\, u_C v_C w_C$$

The coefficients are calculated:

$$u_A = \begin{vmatrix} k_2 & l_2 \\ k_3 & l_3 \end{vmatrix} P_1^* H_1 + \begin{vmatrix} k_3 & l_3 \\ k_1 & l_1 \end{vmatrix} P_2^* H_2 + \begin{vmatrix} k_1 & l_1 \\ k_2 & l_2 \end{vmatrix} P_3^* H_3$$

$$u_B = \quad ,, \quad P_1^* K_1 + \quad ,, \quad P_2^* K_2 + \quad ,, \quad P_3^* K_3$$

$$u_C = \quad ,, \quad P_1^* L_1 + \quad ,, \quad P_2^* L_2 + \quad ,, \quad P_3^* L_3$$

$$v_A = \begin{vmatrix} l_2 & h_2 \\ l_3 & h_3 \end{vmatrix} P_1^* H_1 + \begin{vmatrix} l_3 & h_3 \\ l_1 & h_1 \end{vmatrix} P_2^* H_2 + \begin{vmatrix} l_1 & h_1 \\ l_2 & h_2 \end{vmatrix} P_3^* H_3$$

$$v_B = \quad ,, \quad P_1^* K_1 + \quad ,, \quad P_2^* K_2 + \quad ,, \quad P_3^* K_3$$

$$v_C = \quad ,, \quad P_1^* L_1 + \quad ,, \quad P_2^* L_2 + \quad ,, \quad P_3^* L_3$$

$$w_A = \begin{vmatrix} h_2 & k_2 \\ h_3 & k_3 \end{vmatrix} P_1^* H_1 + \begin{vmatrix} h_3 & k_3 \\ h_1 & k_1 \end{vmatrix} P_2^* H_2 + \begin{vmatrix} h_1 & k_1 \\ h_2 & k_2 \end{vmatrix} P_3^* H_3$$

$$w_B = \quad ,, \quad P_1^* K_1 + \quad ,, \quad P_2^* K_2 + \quad ,, \quad P_3^* K_3$$

$$w_C = \quad ,, \quad P_1^* L_1 + \quad ,, \quad P_2^* L_2 + \quad ,, \quad P_3^* L_3$$

In this calculation

$$P_1^* = \frac{\begin{vmatrix} H_2 & K_2 & L_2 \\ H_3 & K_3 & L_3 \\ H_4 & K_4 & L_4 \end{vmatrix}}{\begin{vmatrix} h_2 & k_2 & l_2 \\ h_3 & k_3 & l_3 \\ h_4 & k_4 & l_4 \end{vmatrix}}; \quad P_2^* = \frac{\begin{vmatrix} H_1 & K_1 & L_1 \\ H_3 & K_3 & L_3 \\ H_4 & K_4 & L_4 \end{vmatrix}}{\begin{vmatrix} h_1 & k_1 & l_1 \\ h_3 & k_3 & l_3 \\ h_4 & k_4 & l_4 \end{vmatrix}}; \quad P_3^* = \frac{\begin{vmatrix} H_1 & K_1 & L_1 \\ H_2 & K_2 & L_2 \\ H_4 & K_4 & L_4 \end{vmatrix}}{\begin{vmatrix} h_1 & k_1 & l_1 \\ h_2 & k_2 & l_2 \\ h_4 & k_4 & l_4 \end{vmatrix}}$$

---

[1] The derivation is given in Acta Crystallographica 2 (1949), 322.

IV. If transformations are given of (a) three faces and one edge, (b) two faces and two edges, (c) one face and three edges, (d) four edges, each case may be reduced to III with the aid of cross-multiplications.

V. In the four-axial symbols according to Bravais, the third index of a face symbol is omitted, and for the edge symbol $[uv\omega w]$ we read $[u-\omega \; v-\omega \; w]$; the symbols then refer to the axial set ABC (p. 7).

VI. From the general formulas it follows that, when changing from the hexagonal axial set of Bravais (face symbol $hk\varkappa l$) to that of Miller (pqr), or vice versa, we derive

$$p = 2h + k + l = h - \varkappa + l \qquad h = p - q$$
$$q = -h + k + l = k - h + l \qquad k = q - r$$
$$r = -h - 2k + l = \varkappa - k + l \qquad \varkappa = r - p$$
$$l = p + q + r$$

For the elements of the axial sets we have

$$\sin \tfrac{1}{2}\alpha = \frac{3}{2\sqrt{3 + \left(\frac{c}{a}\right)^2}} \qquad \frac{c}{a} = \sqrt{\frac{9}{4 \sin^2 \tfrac{1}{2}\alpha} - 3}$$

For the change from the axial set of Bravais ($h\; k\; \varkappa\; l$) to that of Schrauf ($h_s\; k_s\; l_s$), or vice versa (p. 19), the following formulas are valid:

$$h_s = 2h + k \qquad h = \tfrac{1}{2}(h_s - k_s)$$
$$k_s = k \qquad k = k_s$$
$$l_s = l \qquad \varkappa = \tfrac{1}{2}(-h_s - k_s)$$
$$l = l_s$$

VII. If by a first transformation $h\ldots$ changes into $H\ldots$ and by a second $H\ldots$ changes into $H'\ldots$, the matrix of p. 66 can be applied for the first transformation and for the second:

$$\begin{Vmatrix} u'_A & v'_A & w'_A \\ u'_B & v'_B & w'_B \\ u'_C & v'_C & w'_C \end{Vmatrix}$$

For the transformation of $h\ldots$ into H' the product matrix [1] is valid:

$$\begin{Vmatrix} u_A u'_A + u_B v'_A + u_C w'_A & v_A u'_A + v_B v'_A + v_C w'_A & w_A u'_A + w_B v'_A + w_C w'_A \\ u_A u'_B + u_B v'_B + u_C w'_B & v_A u'_B + v_B v'_B + v_C w'_B & w_A u'_B + w_B v'_B + w_C w'_B \\ u_A u'_C + u_B v'_C + u_C w'_C & v_A u'_C + v_B v'_C + v_C w'_C & w_A u'_C + w_B v'_C + w_C w'_C \end{Vmatrix}$$

[1] P. Terpstra, *Kristallometrie* (1946), p. 99.

Calculations with the Aid of Projections

Projection Methods

There are four classical projection methods, all of which, in principle, were given by Neumann (1823) for use in crystallography.[1]

I. A (horizontal) plane is erected at a distance R from the center of the sheaf. The intersection points of the sheaf lines and the intersection lines of the sheaf planes are their projections: (a) the direct sheaf: *linear* projection method; (b) the indirect sheaf: *gnomonic* projection method.

II. A sphere with radius R is drawn round the center, and a stereographic projection—with the nadir or zenith as viewpoint—on the (horizontal) equator plane is derived from the intersections of the sheaf lines and sheaf planes with the sphere: (a) the direct sheaf: *cyclographic* projection method; (b) the indirect sheaf: *stereographic* projection method.

According to I, the zone axes (edges) and crystal faces are projected as points and straight lines, respectively (a), or vice versa (b). The drawbacks of these methods are that the projections of a crystal face and the opposite face coincide, and that very large pieces of drawing paper are needed for the projection of sheaf lines and planes with small inclination. If II is used, the projections become points and circles (arcs of circle); the advantages are that angles remain unaltered and that a much greater area of the sphere can be projected on a convenient size.

The stereographic projection is in general use, but for special purposes the gnomonic projection may have the advantage.

Stereographic Projection

General

A crystal face is projected as a point, an edge (zone axis) as a circle, the *zone circle*, intersecting the primitive circle in two diametrical points (p. 11). The normals to crystal faces lying in one zone are situated in a plane, the *zone plane;* the projections of these crystal faces fall on the zone circle. The position of a crystal face is given by the spherical coordinates φ and ρ (p. 60). The constructions required may be carried

---

[1] The stereographic projection was applied in astronomy by Hipparchus, in spherical trigonometry by A. Metius (1627); the gnomonic projection was applied in 1612 in astronomy by C. Grienberger.

Cf. A. Hutchinson, Zeitschrift für Kristallographie 46 (1909), 238.

out with the aid of compasses and ruler,[1] but generally a *stereographic net* is used. This consists of the projection of a number of meridians and parallels of latitude on the construction sphere, as on the globe, but with the north pole and the south pole on the primitive circle (Fig. 36). The

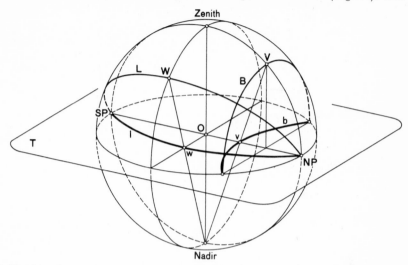

FIG. 36.   Construction of the stereographic net: the meridian *L* and the parallel of latitude *B* projected as *l* and *b* respectively on the projection plane *T* with the nadir as projection point.

radius of the net is conveniently taken as 10 cm, the circles are drawn every 2°, and the accuracy obtainable is about 1°. The net is usually applied as a pad for the sheet of transparent paper on which the drawing is constructed; paper and net can rotate separately round the common center.

Use of the Stereographic Net

1. Drawing of point *p* (position φ, ρ)

Mark off the angle φ along the primitive circle, beginning at the zero point and proceeding clockwise (Fig. 37), rotate the drawing until the mark falls on the equator, and mark off the point *p* at $\rho°$ from the center along the equator.

---

[1] H. E. Boeke, *Die Anwendung der stereographischen Projektion bei kristallographischen Untersuchungen* (1911); H. Tertsch, *Stereographische Projektion in der Kristallkunde* (1954).

2. Polar circle π polar to the point p

Rotate the drawing until p falls on the equator (Fig. 38), and draw the meridian circle π which is at a distance of 90° from p.

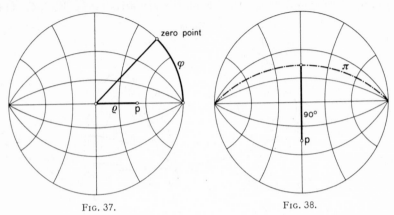

FIG. 37.   FIG. 38.

3. Great circle through a and b

Rotate the drawing until a and b fall on a meridian (Fig. 39).

4. Angle $\psi°$ between a and b

Place a and b on a meridian, and read the angle $\psi°$ along this circle (Fig. 39).

5. Pole p of a great circle π

Place the great circle on a meridian of the net, and mark off p along the equator at a distance of 90° (Fig. 38).

6. Angle $\psi°$ between two great circles δ and ε

Mark off points A and B at 90° from the point of intersection of the circles, T (Fig. 40), by placing the circles successively on meridian circles of the net; then place T on the equator, and read the angle $\psi°$ between A and B. If one of the points A and B falls outside the primitive circle, the supplement of the angle is measured.

7. Small circle with radius $\alpha°$ round p

(a) Place p on the equator, and mark off $\alpha°$ at both sides of p, thereby finding a_1 and a_2 (Fig. 41). The midpoint m of a_1 and a_2 is the center of the circle asked for.

(b) If a_1 or a_2 or both fall outside the primitive circle, place p on a meridian, and mark off $\alpha°$. Then rotate the drawing until p falls on a second meridian, and again mark off $\alpha°$. This may be repeated until enough points are found to construct the required circle or to draw it by hand.

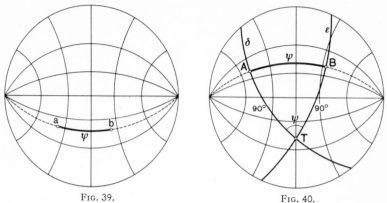

FIG. 39.   FIG. 40.

8. Great circle which comprises p and encloses $\psi°$ with great circle θ

Place p on the equator (Fig. 42), draw the polar circle π, and mark off on this circle $\psi°$ on both sides of the point of intersection of π with θ, thereby obtaining a_1 and a_2. The great circles through pa_1 and pa_2 are those asked for.

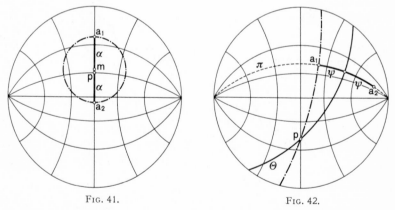

FIG. 41.   FIG. 42.

9. Great circles δ_1 and δ_2 drawn through p and enclosing angle $\psi°$ with a given great circle θ

Circle round from the pole t of θ with $\varphi°$ (Fig. 43), determine the intersection points d_1 and d_2 of this small circle with the polar circle π of p. Then d_1 and d_2 are the poles of the required circles δ_1 and δ_2.

10. Determination of "rhombic section" S in a plagioclase crystal (triclinic)

The intersection line of S with $b(010)$ lies in the face b and is normal to the B axis (Fig. 44). The intersection point P of this line, therefore, is situated on the polar circles of b and $\bar{B}$ (cf. p. 42), and the projection of S is the pole of the meridian through P and $\bar{B}$.

The intersection line with $b(010)$ encloses the angle σ with the A axis.

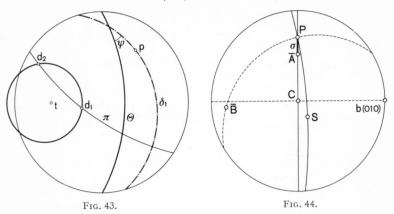

FIG. 43.   FIG. 44.

11. Tilting

If we turn the globe $\alpha°$ round its horizontal axis (tilting), each point on the surface describes an arc of $\alpha°$ on its own parallel of latitude.

If we rotate the drawing round the center until the axis of tilting is normal to the equator of the net, then each point, as it tilts through $\alpha°$ (Fig. 45), describes an arc of $\alpha°$ on its own parallel of latitude.

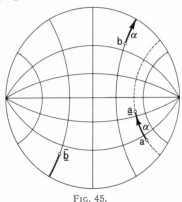

FIG. 45.

12. Points outside the primitive circle

If, after tilting, b falls outside the primitive circle (Fig. 45), the *opposite point* $\bar{b}$ can be indicated inside the primitive circle.

In all our constructions we may make use of this opposite point. For example, the great circle through a and b goes through a and $\bar{b}$; since the spherical triangles abc and $ab\bar{c}$ are complementary, and their elements either equal or supplementary, the elements of abc can easily be derived from those of $a\bar{b}\bar{c}$.

In order to bring the projection of the whole sphere within the primitive circle, we can project the lower hemisphere from the zenith and the upper hemisphere from the nadir (p. 11). But in such a representation points and arcs may coincide. Hence it is sometimes convenient to make an adjustment to the projection in the following way.

We may project the upper half stereographically and the lower half in a conventional way — for example, by rotating each point of the sphere, in its vertical plane, round the zenith point to the equatorial projection plane. The distortion is then great, especially in the neighborhood of the nadir, the nadir point itself projecting as the boundary circle of the projection; but the entire surface of the sphere is represented in a clear way. This method has been applied for some figures of Table 4 (pp. 37 and 39).

Gnomonic Projection

General

At a distance R from the center of the direct sheaf the projection plane is taken as horizontal. The intersections of the normals to the crystal faces are then the gnomonic projections of these faces, and those

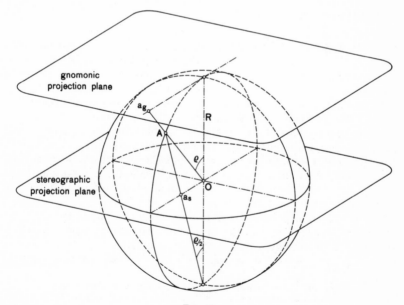

Fig. 46.

of the planes normal to the edges — that is, the zone planes — are the gnomonic projections of the edges (zone axes).

The faces in a zone are projected on the projection of the zone axis — that is, on a straight line. Fig. 46 gives the stereographic and the gnomonic projection of crystal face *a*. If one makes the projection planes coincide, the gnomonic projection of a face or a zone can easily be derived from the stereographic projection (Fig. 47).

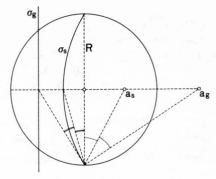

FIG. 47.   Relation of the stereographic projections a_s and σ_s to the gnomonic projections a_g and σ_g.

We may use, for our constructions, a net resembling the stereographic net, but for accurate work, for which the gnomonic method is very suitable, we should do better with a ruler (and compasses). [1]

Goldschmidt's Application

V. Goldschmidt chooses as gnomonic projection plane a plane normal to the *C* axis, but he pictures it at such a distance that it coincides with the first C^* net plane (p. 49) of the indirect lattice; in other words, he makes the indirect lattice of such dimensions that the net plane in question lies above O^* at a distance R (Fig. 48).

If, in the indirect lattice, the radius vectors to the lattice points are drawn, the points of intersection with the projection plane are the gnomonic projections of the crystal faces, the symbols of which correspond to those of the lattice points. The projections of the faces having 1 as third index form in the projection plane a net with a^* and b^* as axial lengths and γ^* as axial angle; Goldschmidt calls these axial lengths p_0 and q_0. The first two indices in the symbols therefore indicate the coordinates, expressed in p_0 and q_0.

The intersection points of the radius vectors to points in other net planes are also indicated in the projection plane by coordinates, which are equal to the first two indices but are then divided by the number of the net plane — that is, by the third index. Thus the projection of

[1] V. Goldschmidt, *Ueber Projektion und graphische Krystallberechnung* (1887); H. E. Boeke, *Die gnomonische Projektion in ihrer Anwendung auf kristallographische Aufgaben* (1913).

(232) is the point of which the coordinates are 1 and 3/2 (Fig. 48). The face symbols, in which the last index has been made 1 and after that omitted, are then two-fold and are called *Goldschmidt symbols*.

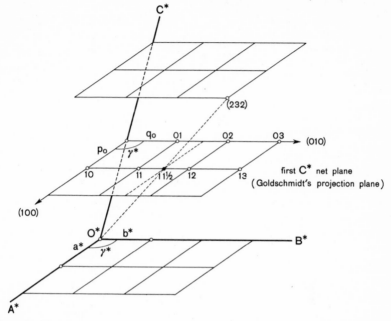

FIG. 48. If the first C^* net plane coincides with the gnomonic projection plane, the projections of the crystal faces are indicated by coordinates, expressed in a^* and b^*, which are equal to the Goldschmidt indices.

If, in the gnomonic projection, the sites of four faces — for example, of (001), (010), (001), and (111) — are known, the net in the first C^* net plane can be drawn and all points provided with Goldschmidt symbols. The gnomonic projection of a face (*hkl*) is now situated on the spot whose coordinates are $\dfrac{h}{l}$ and $\dfrac{k}{l}$. If $l = 0$, the projection is situated at infinity on the line from the origin of the net to the point [[*hk*]].

Other Projections

Linear Projection

The gnomonic projection is formed by the points and lines of intersection of the indirect sheaf with the projection plane, the linear one by those of the direct sheaf; each projection is polar to the other. The linear projection has been especially developed by Quenstedt (1873).

Cyclographic Projection

In a manner analogous to that mentioned above, this projection is the polar figure of the stereographic projection.

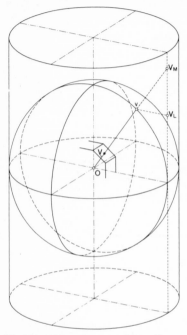

FIG. 49.   Poles of a crystal face V on the Mercator (V_M) and on the Lambert (V_L) projection. The cylinder is cut along a generator and then flattened out.

Angle Projection (Winkelprojektion)

This is like the stereographic projection, but the viewpoint is on the zenith-nadir line about 0.7 R below the last point. The area distortion is now minimal.

Orthogonal Projection

This is like the stereographic projection, but the viewpoint is at infinity on the zenith-nadir line. The method may be applied to crystal-optical problems in connection with the polarizing microscope.

Triangular Projection

For cubic crystals this is the gnomonic projection on one of the octahedral faces; for other crystals it is a conventional projection resembling the gnomonic one.[1]

Cylindrical Projection

Mercator's projection is angle-true from any point.[2] Lambert's projection is area-true.[3] Cf. Fig. 49.

Stereographic Projection (Stereogram) of a Crystal [4]

General

We shall deal only with the general, triclinic case, the special cases being simplifications of the general one. Hexagonal crystals referred to four axes are considered, for calculations, as being referred to the three axes A, B, and C (p. 7).

---

[1] P. Niggli, *Lehrbuch der Mineralogie und Kristallchemie* (1941), p. 169.

[2] The angle OvV_M is not $180°$! See V. A. Vening Meinesz, *Kort overzicht der kartografie* (1950), p. 35.

[3] Used by B. G. Escher, *Algemene mineralogie en kristallografie* (1950).

[4] For references see the footnote on p. 69.

We speak of a *normal projection* when the projection plane is normal to the C axis and therefore horizontal (cf. p. 5). By tilting and rotation other projections can be reduced to normal ones or derived from normal ones.

The Direct Elements

The positions of the four fundamental faces or of the three pinacoid faces and any arbitrary face are given.

For other cases see p. 87.

In a normal projection $a(100)$ and $b(010)$ are situated on the primitive circle, b being taken at the right side (Fig. 50). The primitive circle is

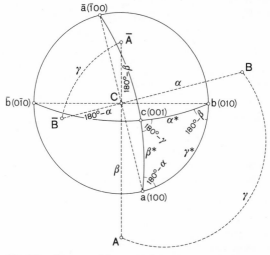

FIG. 50. Stereographic projection of the direct and the indirect axes, the axial angles, and the pinacoids.

the projection of the edge ab, therefore also of the C axis, and the points of intersection with the sphere are consequently the poles of the primitive circle. The $\bar{A}$ axis is situated in the sagittal plane, $180° - \beta$ from C, the $\bar{B}$ axis $180° - \alpha$ from C and γ from $\bar{A}$. The faces b and c lie on the polar circle of $\bar{A}$, a and c on the polar circle of $\bar{B}$. The *direct axial angles* (their supplements) are the angles between the great circles mentioned and also the angles between the points of intersection of the axes.

The *direct axial lengths* can be found in two ways.

1. A crystal face, imagined outside the center of the sheaf, determines triangles on the coordinate planes, which are called *index triangles*. The sides of the index triangles are crystal edges. In this way, BC in

Fig. 51 is the edge between the pinacoidal face $a(100)$ and the unit face $e(111)$, OB is the edge between $c(001)$ and $a(100)$, and the angle of the edges is α_c.

The projection of $e(111)$ lies within the *fundamental triangle abc* (Fig. 52), the arcs of circle in the figure are the projections of the edges in Fig. 51, and the angles of the index triangles are therefore equal to those in the projection.

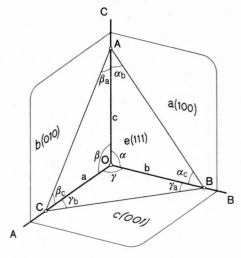

Fig. 51.

If a, b, c, and e are given, the angles of the index triangles can be read, the triangles themselves can be constructed in true proportion, and the axial lengths can be measured.

It follows from the triangles that

$$\frac{a}{b} = \frac{\sin \gamma_a}{\sin \gamma_b}; \quad \frac{c}{b} = \frac{\sin \alpha_c}{\sin \alpha_b}$$

If the projection of any face (hkl) is indicated, the axial lengths can be determined in a similar way. The index triangles are then those of Fig. 53, and the formulas become

$$\frac{a/h}{b/k} = \frac{\sin \gamma'_a}{\sin \gamma'_b}$$

$$\frac{c/l}{b/k} = \frac{\sin \alpha'_c}{\sin \alpha'_b}$$

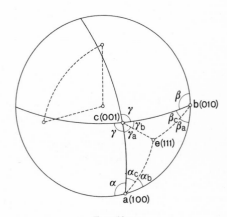

Fig. 52.

2. The face $e(111)$ cuts off a, b, and c from the axes (Fig. 54). If the normal OE to e encloses angles ε_1, ε_2, and ε_3 with the axes, then (Miller's equations, 1839)

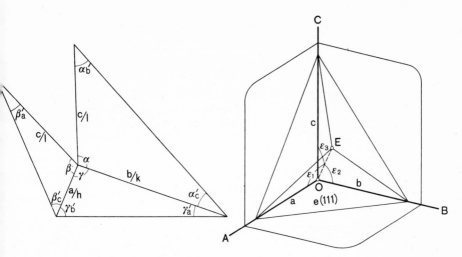

Fig. 53. Full-size drawing of the index triangles of the face (*hkl*).

Fig. 54.

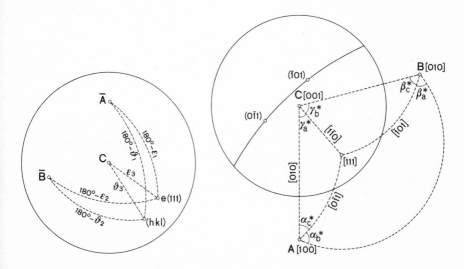

Fig. 55.

Fig. 56. The angles of the indirect index triangles — that is, of the triangles determined on the indirect coordinate planes by the plane normal to [111].

$$\cos \varepsilon_1 = \frac{OE}{a}; \ \cos \varepsilon_2 = \frac{OE}{b}; \ \cos \varepsilon_3 = \frac{OE}{c}$$

$$a : b : c = \frac{1}{\cos \varepsilon_1} : \frac{1}{\cos \varepsilon_2} : \frac{1}{\cos \varepsilon_3}$$

The angles ε may be read from the projection (Fig. 55).

If any face $h(hkl)$ is given, the axial lengths can be determined in the same way from the angles ϑ, which the normal to h makes with the axes. Then (Fig. 55)

$$\frac{a}{h} : \frac{b}{k} : \frac{c}{l} = \frac{1}{\cos \vartheta_1} : \frac{1}{\cos \vartheta_2} : \frac{1}{\cos \vartheta_3}$$

The Indirect Elements

α^* is the angle between the normals to (010) and (001) and therefore also arc bc (Fig. 50); β^* and γ^* are analogous.

The indirect axial lengths in the indirect index triangles can be constructed in the same way as the direct axial lengths in the direct index triangles. The point $[111]$ is the pole of the zone through $(\bar{1}01)$ and $(0\bar{1}1)$, for (Fig. 56)

$$\begin{vmatrix} \bar{1} & 0 \\ 0 & \bar{1} \end{vmatrix} \times \begin{vmatrix} 1 & \bar{1} \\ 1 & 0 \end{vmatrix} \times \begin{vmatrix} 0 & 1 \\ \bar{1} & 1 \end{vmatrix} \equiv [111]$$

The angles α_b^* etc. may also be measured as the arcs between faces (see Fig. 57).

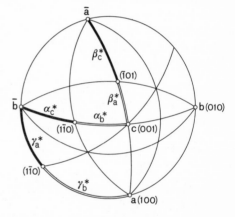

FIG. 57. Reading off the base angles of the indirect index triangles within the primitive circle.

Drawing a Stereogram

The direct crystal elements are given.

Axes and pinacoid faces

The C axis lies in the center of the primitive circle, $\bar{A}$ on the sagittal line, $180° - \beta°$ from C; $\bar{B}$ lies at $180° - \alpha°$ from C and at $\gamma°$ from $\bar{A}$ (construction 7, p. 70). The pinacoid faces are the poles of the great circles $\bar{A}\bar{B}$, $\bar{B}C$, and $C\bar{A}$ (Fig. 50).

Unit (parametral) face $e(111)$.

In order to find α_b and β_a, we construct two index triangles (p. 77), those with the angles α and β (Fig. 51). By drawing through a a great circle enclosing α_b°, and through b a great circle enclosing β_a° with the primitive circle, we find the position of e (111) in the stereogram. As a check, we may also determine other angles in the index triangles and mark them off in the projection (Fig. 52).

Arbitrary face (hkl)

(hkl), like $e(111)$, can be found in a direct way if we draw two index triangles and mark off the angles α'_b and β'_a in a and b respectively (p. 78).

If we draw the faces in this way, the zone relation often disappears owing to inaccuracies in measurement and drawing. In order to avoid this serious drawback, we usually determine the situation of (hkl) as the intersection point of two zone circles. To this end, as soon as the positions of the fundamental faces are known, we apply the system of the nine zones (p. 46). Fig. 58 gives the sequence of application. In order to trace further the two zones of which (hkl) is the point of intersection, we may, in the first place, consult figures already constructed (Figs. 59 and 60), for the zone relation is independent of the crystal elements and therefore of the special situation of the fundamental faces.

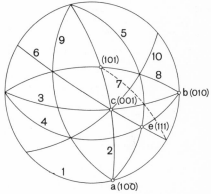

FIG. 58.   Drawing the "system of the nine zones" when the fundamental faces are given.

If the face (hkl) is not indicated in Fig. 59 or 60, we can trace the two required zones by *splitting* the symbol into two pairs with lower indices (p. 45) and, if necessary, continuing the splitting until symbols of the faces of the system of the nine zones, and no others, have been obtained.

In a third way of tracing the two required zones, we use the gnomonic projection according to Goldschmidt's application (p. 74). Because only the zone relation, which is independent of the crystal elements, is asked for, we construct the gnomonic projection in which $p_0 = q_0$ and $\gamma^* = 90°$. The required face (hkl) can immediately be drawn as the point whose coordinates are $\dfrac{h}{l}$ and $\dfrac{k}{l}$; the required zone lines, which in this projection are straight lines, can easily be found.

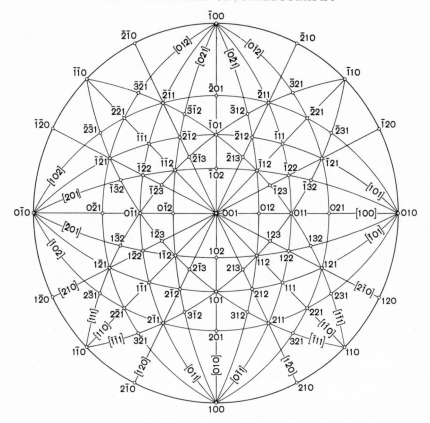

Fig. 59. The zone relation of a number of faces.

Example: In the stereogram of Fig. 61 the location of (324) may be asked for.

We draw the gnomogram of the system of the nine zones and choose $p_0 = q_0$ (for example, 10 cm) and $\gamma^* = 90°$ (Fig. 61, left).

In this figure (324) is drawn as the point with coordinates $3/4$ and $2/4$. Zone line I is drawn through the two points 10 and 01, which are known, zone line II through the point of intersection of I with zone line 00−11 and the infinite point in the direction (100); (324) is situated on this zone line. According to Fig. 61, left, (324) is situated on zone line III of 0$\bar{1}$−11. The point of intersection of II and III is the projection of (324).

In the stereogram we therefore find the location of (324) by drawing the same zones in the same sequence (Fig. 61, right).

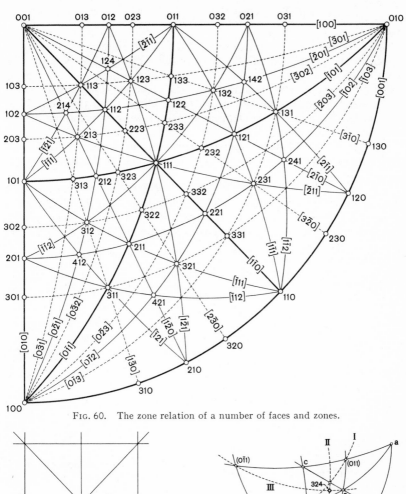

FIG. 60.   The zone relation of a number of faces and zones.

FIG. 61.

C. Crystal Drawing [1]

General

Of a stereometric crystal drawing it is always required that parallel edges in the crystal be parallel lines in the drawing. The ratio of the lengths of the edges — that is, the shape of the faces — is generally of less interest unless the symmetry has to be expressed.[2] From this it follows that only a *parallel projection* is allowed. Furthermore, it is preferable that edges do not appear in the drawing as points and faces do not appear as lines.

The projection plane is placed either horizontally or vertically, in the latter case either frontally or sometimes parallel to the *B* axis, which is then not quite frontal.

The projecting lines may fall normal to the projection plane (*orthographic* projection) or obliquely (*clinographic projection*). If, in the latter case, the projection plane is both a vertical and a frontal plane, and if the projecting radii are in the sagittal plane, we speak of a *semi-clinographic* projection.

Table 5 gives a synopsis.

Regiographic Drawing

The drawing is composed of the directions of the edges; their lengths

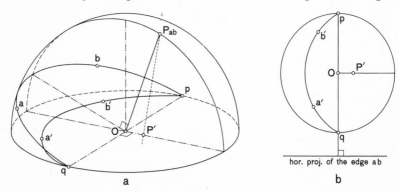

Fig. 62.   (a) P' is the projection of the pole P_{ab} of the zone circle ab; the line OP' is normal to the chord pq.   (b) The edge direction ab, projected normally on to the projection plane, is normal to the chord pq.

[1] V. Goldschmidt, *Ueber Projektion und graphische Krystallberechnung* (1887), with technical directions on p. 7; T. V. Barker, *Graphical and Tabular Methods in Crystallography* (1922); P. Terpstra, *Kristallometrie* (1946), p. 268; L. Burmeister, Zeitschrift für Kristallographie 57 (1922), 1 (history).

[2] H. Heritsch, "Porträtgetreue Kristallbilder aus der stereographischen Projektion," Tschermaks Mitteilungen 2 (1950), 67.

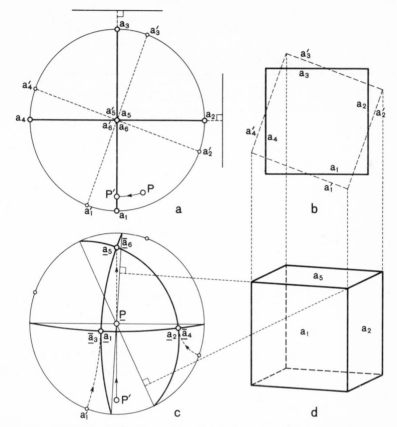

FIG. 63. Regiographic drawing of a cube. In a and c, P and a_{1-6} are normal stereographic projections, P' and a'_{1-6} rotated projections, and $\underline{P}$ and $\underline{a}_{1-6}$ rotated and tilted projections.

are rather arbitrary, but sometimes it is desirable to make the drawing display the symmetry of the crystal. The direction of an edge — for example, that of the edge ab in Fig. 62 — is obtained from the stereogram as the normal to the chord pq of the zone circle.

The construction of a drawing of an arbitrary view (normal to plane P, as a rule with position $\varphi = 80°$ and $\rho = 70°$; Fig. 63) proceeds as follows. Design first the normal stereographic projection (Fig. 63-a), derive therefrom the top view (Fig. 63-b), rotate the stereogram (and the top view) until the new plane of projection P falls on the sagittal line, and tilt about the frontal line until P lies in the center (Fig. 63-c).

Compose the view from 63-c and rotated 63-b by deriving the directions from the former and the lengths of the edges from the latter.

TABLE 5 **Projections and Drawings**

Projection method	Projection plane	Projecting lines	Setting of the crystal	Distortion of the axial cross	Drawing	Applied by	
ortho-graphic	horizontal	normal to the projection plane, therefore vertical	normal	c shortened to a point	top view		
			rotated and tilted	a, b, and c shortened	any view	Haidinger Miers Hecht	(1822, 1825) (1887) (1893)
clino-graphic	vertical and frontal	oblique to the projection plane	rotated	only c full length	semi-oblique view	Haüy Naumann	(1801, 1822) (1830)
	vertical and parallel to the B axis	not in the sagittal and not in the horizontal plane	normal	b and c full length	oblique view	Kopp Niggli	(1849) (1941)

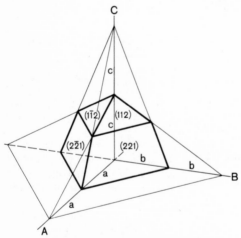

FIG. 64.   Axonometric drawing of some faces.

Axonometric Drawing

The crystallographic axial set is projected; the indices of the faces then give the points of intersection with the axes; the edges, in the exact direction and also in the right place, are found from the intersections of the faces with the coordinate planes (Fig. 64). This method was formerly applied generally.

The method of obtaining the projection of the axial set is described in the textbooks.[1]

[1] F. C. Phillips, *An Introduction to Crystallography* (1956), p. 46; A. E. H. Tutton, *Crystallography and Practical Measurement* (1922), Ch. 25.

D. Problems in Geometric Crystallography [1]

General

A crystal description comprises: (a) the symmetry; (b) the direct crystal elements; (c) the symbols of the faces (and edges); (d) the angles between the faces (between the edges and between the faces and edges); (e) the normal stereographic projection; (f) a drawing (arbitrary view).

The Symmetry

The symmetry of well-developed crystals can often be derived with some certainty from the positions of the faces, but usually physical tests have also to be employed:

1. Etch figures: See p. 261.
2. Optical phenomena: Cubic crystals are isotropic, those with a principal axis are optically uniaxial, and the others are biaxial. For parallel and inclined extinction see p. 208. Rotation of the vibration plane occurs only in certain classes (p. 213).
3. Differences in hardness: See p. 236.
4. Piezoelectric phenomena occur only in crystals without an inversion point, and they occur in all such crystals except those from class 432 (p. 220).
5. X-ray diagrams, especially Laue diagrams and retigrams: It is not possible to find in this way whether an inversion point is present or not (p. 127).
6. Magnetic phenomena.

The Direct Crystal Elements

The elements of a triclinic crystal involve *five data:* three axial angles and two ratios of axial lengths — for example, $\dfrac{a}{b}$ and $\dfrac{c}{b}$. For a derivation we therefore need five independent angle measurements between faces, three of which are not lying in one zone. Three measurements are required for a monoclinic crystal, two for an orthorhombic crystal, one for a crystal with a principal axis, and none for a regular crystal.

If, for a triclinic crystal, five angles are measured between four indexed faces,[2] of which no three faces are situated in one zone, the calculation of the elements requires much work. We may follow a *mathematical method* by expressing the cosines of the five angles in g^*'s (p. 55), calculating the five unknowns

---

[1] P. Terpstra, *A Thousand and One Questions on Crystallographic Problems* (1952).

[2] These four faces cannot be indexed in an entirely arbitrary way. Cf. A. Brezina, *Methodik der Krystall-Bestimmung* (1884), p. 205.

$$\frac{g_{11}^*}{g_{22}^*}, \quad \frac{g_{33}^*}{g_{22}^*}, \quad \frac{g_{12}^*}{g_{22}^*}, \quad \frac{g_{23}^*}{g_{22}^*}, \quad \frac{g_{31}^*}{g_{22}^*}$$

and deriving the direct elements from the g^*'s.

If the five angles which have been measured are those between the four fundamental faces or between the coordinate planes and (hkl), the sixth angle can be calculated (p. 58), and the indirect elements follow from

$$ha^* : kb^* : lc^* = \begin{vmatrix} \cos \vartheta_1 & \cos \gamma^* & \cos \beta^* \\ \cos \vartheta_2 & 1 & \cos \alpha^* \\ \cos \vartheta_3 & \cos \alpha^* & 1 \end{vmatrix} : \begin{vmatrix} 1 & \cos \vartheta_1 & \cos \beta^* \\ \cos \gamma^* & \cos \vartheta_2 & \cos \alpha^* \\ \cos \beta^* & \cos \vartheta_3 & 1 \end{vmatrix}$$

$$: \begin{vmatrix} 1 & \cos \gamma^* & \cos \vartheta_1 \\ \cos \gamma^* & 1 & \cos \vartheta_2 \\ \cos \beta^* & \cos \alpha^* & \cos \vartheta_3 \end{vmatrix}$$

the angles being indicated as on p. 80. Then the direct elements may be derived therefrom with the aid of the formulas on p. 53.

The result can be attained more quickly by a *crystallographic method*. In the special case that the five angles measured are those between the coordinate planes and $e(111)$ or $h(hkl)$, a graphic determination is carried out with the aid of the index triangles (p. 77), or the elements are calculated with the aid of the formulas on p. 78.

The general case, whereby the angles between four arbitrary faces are measured, can be reduced to the special case by Websky's method [1] or by the method described below.[2]

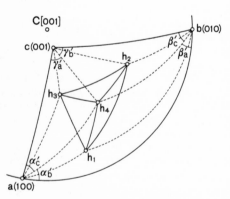

FIG. 65.

The angles between $h_1 h_2 h_3 h_4$ (Fig. 65) may be given. With the aid of spherical trigonometry the angles between the edges can be calculated. Thereafter we calculate the zone circles $h_1 a$, $h_2 b$, $h_3 c$, $h_4 a$, $h_4 b$, and $h_4 c$ and apply in h_1 the formula found on p. 65. Then the angles $h_3 h_1 a$ and $h_4 h_1 a$ are known. Application of the formula in h_4 to the four arcs to h_1, h_2, h_3, and a gives also the angle $a h_4 h_1$.

[1] See Th. Liebisch, *Geometrische Krystallographie* (1881), p. 160.
[2] Acta Crystallographica 1 (1948), 97.

In the spherical triangle ah_1h_4 one side and two adjacent corners are known, and ah_4 can be calculated; bh_4 and ch_4 may be determined in a similar way. Then for the spherical triangle abh_4 the sides ah_4 and bh_4 and the enclosed angle are known, and the angles α'_b and β'_a can be calculated. The remaining four base angles of the index triangles can be similarly calculated. The direct elements follow from these angles (p. 78).

If more than five angle measurements have been carried out on a triclinic crystal, two cases may be distinguished:

1. We have measured n angles, and the results of the measurements comply with $n - 5$ conditions. Finally there are five independent data. The most probable values for the angles can be determined with the aid of balancing methods.

The case is of importance when the six angles between four crystal faces forming a tetrahedron have been measured. Then the angles comply with the condition of p. 58. The *balancing method* has been worked out by Beckenkamp, and he has given rules for its application.[1] The result is used for the accurate determination of the angles at two different temperatures when we wish to find the variability of the crystal elements resulting from thermal expansion.

2. We have measured n angles, and the results of the measurements comply with fewer than $n - 5$ conditions. According to which five data are chosen the results will vary slightly.

We may then consider the angles as functions of the g^*'s,[2] and with the aid of least squares we calculate their most probable values, deriving therefrom the most probable elements.

To this end we deduce from five angles first the five values of *approximated* g^*'s (g_{22}^* is taken as 1) and with their aid the approximated values of the other angles. If the faces are numbered, the approximated angle $(r_1^* r_2^*)$ follows (p. 55) from

$$r_1^* r_2^* \cos (r_1^* r_2^*) = g_{12}^* = h_1 h_2 g_{aa}^* + k_1 k_2 + l_1 l_2 g_{cc}^*$$
$$+ (h_1 k_2 + h_2 k_1) g_{ab}^* + (k_1 l_2 + k_2 l_1) g_{bc}^* + (l_1 h_2 + l_2 h_1) g_{ca}^*$$

The *corrections* dg_{aa}^* etc., which have to be applied to the g^*'s, follow from the *normal equations*

[1] J. Beckenkamp, *Statische und kinetische Kristalltheorien*, I (1913), p. 45; P. Groth, *Physikalische Krystallographie* (1905), p. 612.

[2] Enc. d. math. Wiss. V, (1905), 428; P. Niggli, *Handbuch der Experimentalphysik*, VII, 1 (1928), p. 35 (with literature survey); A. Brezina, *Methodik der Kristall-Bestimmung* (1884).

$$[A\delta] - [AA]dg^*_{aa} - [AC]dg^*_{cc} - [AD]dg^*_{ab} - [AE]dg^*_{bc} - [AF]dg^*_{ca} = 0$$
$$[C\delta] - [CA] \text{ ,, } - [CC] \text{ ,, } - [CD] \text{ ,, } - [CE] \text{ ,, } - [CF] \text{ ,, } = 0$$
$$[D\delta] - [DA] \text{ ,, } - [DC] \text{ ,, } - [DD] \text{ ,, } - [DE] \text{ ,, } - [DF] \text{ ,, } = 0$$
$$[E\delta] - [EA] \text{ ,, } - [EC] \text{ ,, } - [ED] \text{ ,, } - [EE] \text{ ,, } - [EF] \text{ ,, } = 0$$
$$[F\delta] - [FA] \text{ ,, } - [FC] \text{ ,, } - [FD] \text{ ,, } - [FE] \text{ ,, } - [FF] \text{ ,, } = 0$$

in which

$$[A\delta] = A_{12}\,\delta_{12} + A_{13}\,\delta_{13} + \ldots\ldots$$
$$[AC] = A_{12}\,C_{12} + A_{13}\,C_{13} + \ldots\ldots$$

$$A_{12} = \left(\frac{h_1^2}{2r_1^{*2}} + \frac{h_2^2}{2r_2^{*2}} - \frac{h_1 h_2}{r_1^* r_2^* \cos(r_1^* r_2^*)}\right) \cot g\,(r_1^* r_2^*)$$

$$D_{12} = \left(\frac{h_1 k_1}{r_1^{*2}} + \frac{h_2 k_2}{r_2^{*2}} - \frac{h_1 k_2 + h_2 k_1}{r_1^* r_2^* \cos(r_1^* r_2^*)}\right) \cot g\,(r_1^* r_2^*)$$

$\delta_{12} =$ the difference between the measured and the approximated angle, expressed in radians, five of these differences being equal to zero.

The Symbols of the Faces

If the direct crystal elements and two angles of known faces (for example, pinacoid faces) with the face of which the symbol is unknown are given, the angles of the index triangles can be calculated with the aid of spherical triangle formulas, and the indices can be derived therefrom (p. 78).

If the elements are not known but the required face is situated in two zones determined by known faces, the symbols of the zones and also of the face can be calculated by cross-multiplication.

If the face lies in one zone with three known faces, and if the enclosed angles are given, the formula on p. 64 may be applied.

If four arbitrary faces with their enclosed angles, as well as two angles between the required face and two of the other faces, are given, we follow the procedure of p. 64.

The calculations can be carried out much more quickly by a graphical method, and this usually gives sufficient accuracy.

If the direct lattice is suspended freely at O, and if, at the points of intersection of the axes with a sphere with center O, weights ua, vb, and wc are suspended, the radius vector to $[[u\ v\ w]]$ comes to a vertical position, and the same applies to the indirect lattice and $[[h\ k\ l]]$. In this way we might determine *experimentally* the directions of the edge $[u\ v\ w]$ and of the normal to $(h\ k\ l)$ or, contrariwise, the symbols of these directions.[1]

---

[1] A. Möbius, *Der barycentrische Calcül* (1827).

The Angles Between the Faces (Between the Edges and Between the Faces and the Edges)

If the crystal elements are unknown, the quickest way to attain our goal is by means of spherical trigonometry. If, for example, five angles between the four faces r, x, a, and s of axinite [1] are given and the sixth angle ax (Fig. 66) is asked for, three sides of the spherical triangle rxs are known, and angle s_1 can therefore be calculated (p. 58). In the same way, in the spherical triangle rsa, angle s_2 can be calculated; so angle s_3 also is known. Then in the spherical triangle asx the side xa can be derived, and we find $a \wedge x = 32°30'8''$.

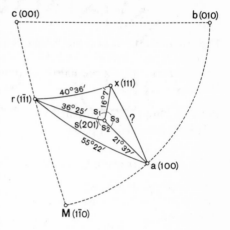

The six cosines of the angles between four faces comply with the equation [2]

$$\begin{vmatrix} 1 & \cos(12) & \cos(13) & \cos(14) \\ \cos(21) & 1 & \cos(23) & \cos(24) \\ \cos(31) & \cos(32) & 1 & \cos(34) \\ \cos(41) & \cos(42) & \cos(43) & 1 \end{vmatrix} = 0$$

If the direct crystal elements are known, one may calculate the g's and $g*$'s and then the angles (p. 55). For two faces, $(h_1k_1l_1)$ and $(h_2k_2l_2)$, one might apply the formula

$$\cos(h_1h_2) = \frac{T_{12}^2}{T_{11} T_{22}}$$

in which, for example, T_{12}^2 equals the value of the determinant

$$T_{12}^2 = \begin{vmatrix} \dfrac{h_1}{a} & & \\ \dfrac{k_1}{b} & \mathrm{Sin}^2 (ABC) & \\ \dfrac{l_1}{c} & & \\ 0 & \dfrac{h_2}{a} \quad \dfrac{k_2}{b} \quad \dfrac{l_2}{c} \end{vmatrix}$$

---

[1] J. D. Dana, *A System of Mineralogy* (1914), p. 527.
[2] T. Liebisch, *Geometrische Krystallographie* (1881), p. 78.

The expression for cos $(h_1 h_2)$ is far from simple;[1] for cubic crystals, however, this expression is reduced to

$$\cos (h_1 h_2) = \frac{h_1 h_2 + k_1 k_2 + l_1 l_2}{\sqrt{(h_1^2 + k_1^2 + l_1^2)} \sqrt{(h_2^2 + k_2^2 + l_2^2)}}$$

The Normal Stereographic Projection

On p. 80 we described the derivation from the direct elements. By rotation and tilting a normal projection can be derived from any given projection (p. 72).

The Drawing of an Arbitrary View

This is described on p. 84.

E. Geometric Crystal Determination

Because the angles between faces are, in general, characteristic, it is obviously possible to use them for the *identification* and *determination* of a crystal.

One difficulty is that we need well-developed small crystals, in order to obtain satisfactorily accurate angle values (for example, to 5'), and tables containing the required angle values of the crystals of all known compounds. Even more difficult, for the low-symmetry crystal, is the choice of the same crystal axes as were followed in the construction of the tables.

A group of institutes is at the moment engaged in compiling tables according to the system proposed by Barker,[2] and methods of choosing the axes correctly are described.[3] The determination is carried out according to the magnitudes of *three angles:* in the first place (001) $\wedge$ (101), then (100) $\wedge$ (110), and (010) $\wedge$ (011).[4]

---

[1] P. Niggli, *Handbuch der Experimentalphysik*, VII, 1 (1928), p. 31; numerical values on pp. 116 ff.

[2] T. V. Barker, *Systematic Crystallography* (1930).

[3] P. Terpstra, *Kristallometrie* (1946), Ch. 6.

[4] M. W. Porter, R. C. Spiller, *The Barker Index of Crystals*, I and II (1951 and 1956).

Part II | Structural Crystallography

A. History [1]

Jamitzer (1568) published some speculations about the structure of crystals; so did Guglielmini (1688), who also gave some calculations. Huygens (1690) assumed calcite, $CaCO_3$, to be built up of small, equal, and parallel rotation ellipsoids (Fig. 67).

Westfeld (1767) and Gahn and Bergman (1773) supposed small cleavage rhombohedra to be the building stones of calcite; Gahn succeeded in constructing a scalenohedron by piling them in a parallel manner (Fig. 68). The characteristics of this *parallelepipedal* arrangement are that the

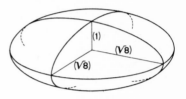

FIG. 67.

building stones are all the same, are parallel, lie in straight rows, and are not shifted with respect to each other; so it is possible to explain the equivalence of the cleavage planes, these being the planes along which the rhombohedra are joined.

Haüy declared this theory to be valid for all crystals and refined it (1783). The small particles first form the nucleus, which is a large cleavage particle bounded by the primary form (*forme primitive*). A mantle of cleavage particles can then be put round the nucleus, each layer showing a *regular decrease*, whereby a crystal boundary occurs, which takes a different shape, a secondary form (*forme secondaire;* Fig. 69).

This kind of construction is possible, however, only with small *parallelepipeds* and can therefore be applied only to crystals having three directions of cleavage.

If there were fewer directions of cleavage, Haüy assumed the missing ones; if there were more, he assumed that the particles,

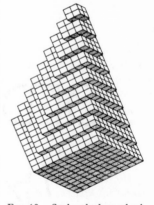

FIG. 68. Scalenohedron of calcite, built up of small cleavage rhombohedra, arranged in a parallelepipedal order.

[1] For literature see p. 1.

bounded by all directions of cleavage (*molécules intégrantes*, which were said to occur in the solution and in the melt), first formed small parallelepipeds (*molécules soustractives*, which determined the decrease and thus were the actual construction units).

The theory explained the occurrence of the faces of the forms in the right places with respect to one another (for example, eight equivalent octahedral faces always bevel the corners of the cube) and revealed the principal law (Fig. 69).

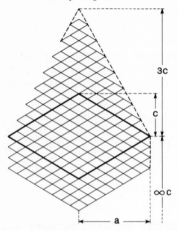

Haüy assumed fourteen kinds of nuclei, but Bernhardi indicated (1807) that six were sufficient. These six are identical with our six parallelepipeds on the sets of crystallographic axes (Fig. 10)!

Haüy's conceptions, which may be considered the base of scientific crystallography, gave rise to much further scientific work. The equivalence of the fourth cleavage direction of fluorite (CaF_2) proved to be difficult for the theory; a parallel piling of cleavage octahedra causes a porous crystal, differing in principle from that constructed with parallelepipeds. The rigidity and angularity of the building particles also seemed implausible at the time when Dalton drew up his atomic theory. In 1813 Wollaston assumed small spheres to be the building particles. In 1824 Seeber spoke only about centers of gravity of the particles and expressed the idea that these centers in a crystal are arranged in a parallelepipedal way, or, in modern terms, that they form a *lattice*.

FIG. 69. Nucleus (heavily outlined) with mantle, showing two kinds of decrease; in one case the axial ratio is 3 : 1, in the other ∞ : 1; with each regular decrease the ratio is measurable.

Characteristic of a lattice are (1) the arrangement mentioned, (2) the parallel orientation of the particles, (3) their equal and parallel environments.

In 1835 Frankenheim inquired how many (micro-)symmetrically different lattices were theoretically possible, and he concluded that there were fifteen; but in 1848 Bravais ascertained that there are, two-dimensionally, five (Fig. 70) and, three-dimensionally, fourteen (Fig. 73).

The macro symmetries of the fourteen lattices are those of the holohedral classes. In order to explain the symmetry of crystals of the merohedral classes, one assumed that the lower symmetry was the result of a low symmetry of the building particles themselves. This only shifted the problem, however, and did not explain the structure.

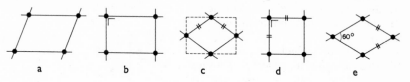

FIG. 70.   The five two-dimensional lattices (nets).

Sohncke (1879) extended the theory by assuming that congruent environments are equal even when their orientations are rotated with respect to each other. Thus he arrived at sixty-five configurations, varying according to their micro symmetry. If not only rotated environments, but also reflected environments, which in other respects are equal, are admitted, one obtains 230 cases, the *point systems* (Fedorov, 1885; Schoenflies, 1889; Barlow, 1894).[1]

B. Structure Theory

Fundamental Hypothesis

The supposition that, when crystallization takes place undisturbed, each equal particle (atom or ion or molecule) will create for itself an equal environment is very simple and plausible and forms the basis of the entire theory of structure.

By "environment" we understand the totality of points and distances minus the atom under consideration, and this totality is three-dimensionally infinite (cf. p. 98).

Two environments (in general, bodies) are called equal if all atoms and their distances occurring in one of them are equal to those in the other (p. 8).

In general, the fundamental assumption appears to be true; but in some cases equal atoms may possess two or more kinds of environment in the same crystal — in graphite, for example (p. 149).

Symmetry

In order to examine the equality of the environments of two equal atoms, we suppose one atom to be brought to the place of the other

---

[1] A. E. H. Tutton, *Crystallography and Practical Crystal Measurement* (1922), p. 565, gives the principles of the derivations and also explains Fedorov's conception of the *Sterohedron*.

and then see whether or not the two environments also — that is, all other atoms — can be brought to coincidence. If they can, the environments are equal.

An act by which coincidence is obtained is called a *symmetry operation.*

Coincidence can be obtained by parallel displacement (*translation*), rotation, reflection, inversion, and their combinations: screw motion, glide reflection, and those already indicated on p. 9. These operations can be described with the aid of symmetry elements: a translation element consists of the direction and the magnitude of the translation; screw motion is connected with a screw axis, and glide reflection with a glide reflection plane. Fig. 71 shows some of these elements.

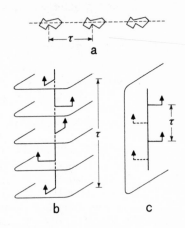

FIG. 71.   Demonstration of some symmetry elements: (*a*) translation τ; (*b*) screw axis with translation component $\tau/4$; (*c*) glide reflection plane with translation component $\tau/2$.

Infinite Groups and Their Symmetry Elements

A finite body can have only the symmetry of a point group; the symmetry elements are therefore rotation axes, reflection planes, rotatory inversion axes, and inversion points. There are thirty-two different combinations of these elements, each possessing a special frame of symmetry elements (symmetry classes, p. 12).

If other elements also occur, such as translations or elements containing

TABLE 6

one-dimensional	two-dimensional	three-dimensional
with row translations (2 kinds) [1]	with row translations (7) [2] with net translations (17) [3]	with row translations (75) [4] with net translations (80) [4] with lattice translations (230)

[1] Zeitschrift für Kristallographie 71 (1929), 81.
[2] Zeitschrift für Kristallographie 63 (1926), 255.
[3] Zeitschrift für Kristallographie 60 (1924), 278, 283.
[4] Zeitschrift für Kristallographie 69 (1929), 250.

a translation component, the group, and also the symmetric body concerned, are infinite. The translations and the translation components of such a group are one-, two-, or three-dimensional, and the translations are equal, respectively, to the identity periods of a row, a net, and a lattice. The number of possible combinations of these symmetry elements is indicated in Table 6.

Space Groups

There are 230 different three-dimensional groups (*space groups*), each characterized by a special frame of symmetry elements. If, in such a frame, an initial point is taken, this is multiplied by the symmetry elements to a *point system;* each of the points is surrounded equally in the broad sense indicated on p. 95. Taking a second initial point gives a second point system, the points of which all possess the same environment, but the environments of the points of the first point system differ from those of the second. If the initial point is situated on a symmetry element (except a screw axis or a glide plane), we obtain a less dense point system, but now the points possess their own symmetry (cf. the special forms on p. 22).

The sub-group of the translations multiplies the initial point to a lattice (of *identical points*). Each of the points (*equivalent points*) caused

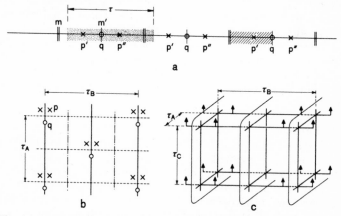

a

b   **c**

Fig. 72. (a) One-dimensional line group with mirror points m and m', a primitive cell (with length equal to the translation τ), a characteristic domain (length $\tau/2$), a general point system p and a special one q. The point system p may be regarded as consisting of two congruent lattices (rows) p' and p'' while the point system q consists of one congruent lattice. The structure may be described as consisting of three congruent interpenetrating rows in parallel orientation. (b) Plane group (two-dimensional) with reflection lines (solid) and glide reflection lines (broken) with a general point system p and a special one q. (c) Space group with reflection planes and a general point system.

by some other element is multiplied by this sub-group to a congruent and parallel lattice. Each point system can therefore be described as being composed of a number of congruent interpenetrating lattices in parallel orientation.

If one or more point systems are present in a space group, each may be described as being composed of lattices, all being geometrically congruent and penetrating one another in parallel orientation (Fig. 72).

Structures

The two demands (1) that equal atoms have equal environments and (2) that a virtually infinite number of individuals of each kind of atoms be present can be complied with by a three-dimensional crystal only if it possesses the symmetry of one of the 230 space groups — that is, if the atoms form a *structure*.

By "structure" we understand the totality of point systems, each of which is therefore formed by one kind of atom. The definition of a crystal drawn up by Groth in 1904 reads: *The atoms in a crystal form a structure complying with the symmetry of a space group. Each kind of atom forms a point system, and each of these point systems can be described as being composed of one or more lattices. All lattices are congruent and interpenetrating in parallel orientation.*

From this theory it follows that a structure, and therefore a crystal, is supposed to be three-dimensionally infinite. There is nothing in this idea that conflicts with the physical, atomic standpoint, for (1) to the great majority of the atoms the boundaries of the crystal, compared with their mutual distances, are very remote, and (2) if the crystal is allowed to grow, the boundaries can always be displaced, whereby the properties of the crystal, or rather of the crystalline matter, do not change.

Bravais Lattices

All the lattices from which all the point systems of a structure can be considered to be composed are congruent and parallel. The entire structure is known if the form and the dimensions of one lattice (that is, of its primitive cell) and the coordinates of all the atoms occurring in this primitive cell are known. If we indicate in this cell an arbitrary point — for example, the center of gravity — which we call the Bravais point, and in each of the other cells the corresponding Bravais point, these points also form a congruent and parallel lattice. This lattice we call the *Bravais lattice*. The site of the Bravais lattice depends on which lattice was considered originally, but this is of no importance; only the shape and the dimensions of the Bravais lattice are characteristic. The shape and the dimensions of a primitive cell are determined by the sub-group of the translations, the symmetry of the content of the cell by other symmetry elements of the space group. It can also be said that the translations determine the repetition *pattern*, other symmetry elements the *motif*, of the structure.

Bravais' Hypothesis

This hypothesis reads: crystal faces are lattice planes, and crystal edges are lattice lines in the Bravais lattice; in general, crystal faces and edges are close-packed lattice planes and lines respectively.[1]

Crystallographic axes, therefore, are also lattice lines in the Bravais lattice; the smallest translations along these axes (the identity periods, the repetition periods) are the *absolute axial lengths* a_0, b_0, and c_0, often summarily named a, b, and c, and the parallelepiped having these axial lengths as edges, and hence having constants equal to or closely related to the crystal elements, is the *elementary cell*, or, simply, the unit cell, or cell. There are therefore as many kinds of cells as there are axial sets — namely, six or seven.

If the crystallographic axes are conjugate lattice lines (p. 47), the elementary cell is a primitive cell (P); if they are not conjugate, the elementary cell is multiply primitive. In this case we shall name the sub-lattice of the Bravais lattice, the elementary cell of which is indeed a primitive cell, the *elementary Bravais lattice*. These elementary lattices will be considered first when we discuss the determination of structure; each one possesses the macro symmetry (p. 94) of a holohedral class, and their primitive cells are elementary cells; that is, the edges fall along the crystallographic axes, and the lengths of the edges are the absolute axial lengths.

The remaining Bravais lattices belong to the same symmetry classes, but possess another (micro) symmetry, and each may be described as an interpenetration of a few congruent, parallel, elementary Bravais lattices.

The manner of interpenetration is indicated by the positions of the points of the interpenetrating lattices. If, for example, there is a lattice penetrating in the center of the elementary cell of the elementary Bravais lattice, this cell and the entire Bravais lattice are indicated as I (*innenzentrirt*, body-centered). Other ways of interpenetration are F, A,[2] B,[2] C, and R (Fig. 73).

As a demonstration of the ideas mentioned above, a primitive cell has been indicated in the two-dimensional group of Fig. 74, whose

---

[1] J. D. H. Donnay and D. Harker formulate the hypothesis more sharply: Am. Min. 22 (1937), 446 (see also p. 258).

[2] A and B may be distinguished only in the orthorhombic, monoclinic, and triclinic systems and indicate that the vertical front planes and side planes, respectively, are centered.

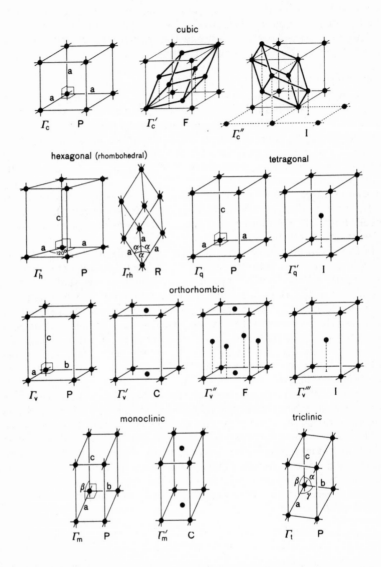

FIG. 73. The fourteen lattices (Bravais lattices); the elementary cells are faintly outlined, the primitive cells of Γ'_c and Γ''_c heavily outlined. The indication Γ is according to Schoenflies. The full lines between two points, considered as free vectors, are the representations of translations of the space groups.

lattice is of the type of c in Fig. 70. The Bravais points in the primitive cells compose the Bravais lattice. In this lattice the lattice lines which are parallel or perpendicular to the mirror lines have been chosen as

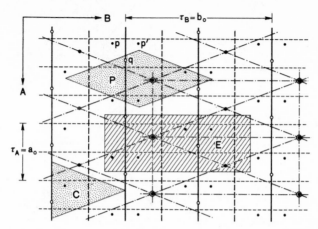

Fig. 74.   Demonstration of the different terms used in the text. In practice (cf. International Tables I) the Bravais points are taken on inversion points or on other symmetry elements.
— reflection line; — — — glide reflection line; • $p\ p'$ point system p; ○ point system q;
● Bravais points; ◯ points of the elementary Bravais lattice; >●< Bravais lattice;
— · — · — elementary Bravais lattice; P primitive cell; E elementary cell; C characteristic domain.

crystallographic axes, and the identity distances along these axes are the absolute axial lengths a_0 and b_0.

Since the sides of an elementary cell are parallel to the crystallographic axes and possess the lengths a_0 and b_0, this cell is twice as large as the primitive one, is doubly primitive. The centers of gravity of the elementary cells compose the elementary Bravais lattice; hence this lattice has half the point density of the Bravais lattice.

The Bravais lattice may also be described as composed of two interpenetrating elementary Bravais lattices; in our case the interpenetration is of the F type.

If we wished to distinguish a characteristic domain (cf. p. 20), this domain would possess the area of half a primitive cell.

Either the direct lattice (p. 49) is congruent (similar) with the elementary Bravais lattice, or one is a sub-lattice of the other (p. 47). If the elementary cell of a crystal is known, we may, obviously, identify the direct lattice with the elementary Bravais lattice, thus making the

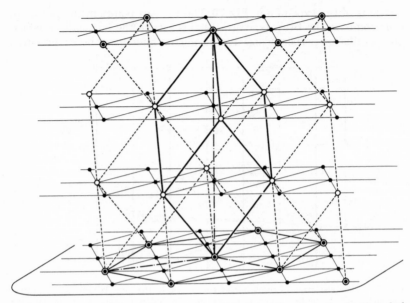

Fig. 75.   The lattices Γ_h and Γ_{rh} are each a sub-lattice of the other; the rhombohedral lattice $\odot + \bigcirc$ is a sub-lattice of the hexagonal $\odot + \bigcirc + \bullet$; the hexagonal $\odot$ is a sub-lattice of the rhombohedral $\odot + \bigcirc$.

ratios of the relative axial lengths equal to those of the absolute axial

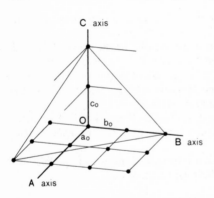

Fig. 76.   The intercepts on the axes in the Bravais lattice (and therefore also in the direct lattice) of a crystal face are in a rational ratio to each other when measured in axial lengths.

lengths. If these ratios are not the same (in other words, if the elementary Bravais lattice is a sub-lattice of the direct one), the relation between the ratios is very simple and is, in any case, measurable; and, because "the metrics for both are the same," the one as well as the other may be used for geometric calculations.

Henceforth we shall assume as a rule that the direct lattice and the elementary Bravais lattice are congruent.

There are six (or seven) kinds of elementary Bravais lattice, their number varying as the rhombohedral lattice is or is not distinguished from the hexagonal. Sometimes application of the rhombohedral lattice is desirable; but, since the two lattices are each other's sub-lattices (Fig. 75), in geometric crystallography there is no need to apply the rhombohedral lattice.

Bravais' hypothesis explains the occurrence of flat crystal faces and straight edges. The principal law is also explained, for a lattice plane divides an identity period on a lattice line (for example, on a crystallographic axis) into rational parts (Fig. 76).

Derivation and Description of the Space Groups

The translations of a space group multiply a symmetry element to an infinite number of parallel, identical elements. These, together with the subsequent elements present, which are also parallel, form a *range*. As an example, a reflection plane becomes a range of equidistant reflection planes if we apply a translation normal to the plane; between these there are always subsequent parallel reflection planes; and the whole is called a range of reflection planes (Fig. 77).

A *homomorphic* symmetry element corresponds to each range — that is, an element equal and parallel to the elements of the range but without translation component. The homomorphic element of a range of glide reflection planes is therefore a reflection plane.

If through any given point the homomorph of each of the ranges in a space group is placed, one of the thirty-two point groups is found. This point group is called *homomorphous* with the space group.

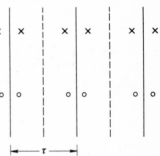

FIG. 77. A reflection plane and a translation perpendicular to it are multiplied to an infinite number of reflection planes (solid lines), but involve also subsequent planes (broken lines), as appears from the symmetry of *two* general point systems.

A structure possesses the symmetry of a space group; macroscopically one observes the symmetry of the homomorphic point group.

Corresponding conditions prevail for the relative position of the ranges in the derivation of all space groups as for the homomorphic symmetry elements in the derivation of all possible point groups (derivation according to Niggli).[1]

Each symmetry class "contains" those space groups which are homomorphous with the point group of the class.

---

[1] P. Niggli, *Geometrische Kristallographie des Diskontinuums* (1919).

A complete description of all space groups is given in the International Tables.[1] In these tables two kinds of symbols are given: (1) according to Schoenflies, those homomorphous with a point group are indicated by the symbol of the class and a serial number; (2) according to Hermann-Mauguin, the elementary Bravais lattice and some typical ranges are stated.

C. Determination of the Structure [2]

Diffraction of X-rays by Matter

Structures are determined with the aid of X-rays, sometimes with electron or neutron rays. The first determinations were carried out by W. H. Bragg and his son W. L. Bragg in 1913, after M. Laue had proved (in 1912) that X-rays are diffracted by the atoms (the electrons of the atoms) in a crystal, and that the diffracted rays interfere and therefore appear in some directions with a good, observable intensity.

We speak of diffraction if, under the influence of the incident (primary) beam, the atoms themselves become the sources of wavelets having the same wavelength as the entering radiation, and if the diffracted (secondary) waves are coherent.

As it is not possible to make X-rays converge with lenses, and as the primary beam is therefore rather weak and the secondary weaker still, it is sometimes only after several hours' exposure that an effect on the photographic film is observable.

Diffraction by an Electron [3]

If a parallel beam of unpolarized monochromatic X-ray light with amplitude A_p falls on an electron, then, in a direction making an angle 2θ with the primary beam, and at point P (at a distance R) we observe a wave whose average amplitude (averaged over all directions of polarization of the incident light vector) A_s' is

$$A_s' = \frac{1}{R} \frac{e^2}{mc^2} \sqrt{\frac{1 + \cos^2 2\theta}{2}} A_p$$

in which expression

e = charge of an electron
m = mass of an electron
c = velocity of light

---

[1] International Tables for X-ray Crystallography, I (1952).

[2] J. M. Bijvoet, N. H. Kolkmeyer, and C. H. MacGillavry, *X-ray Analysis of Crystals* (1951); N. F. M. Henry, H. Lipson, and W. A. Wooster, *The Interpretation of X-ray Diffraction Photographs* (1951); D. McLachlan, *X-ray Crystal Structure* (1957).

[3] International Tables, II (1935), p. 556.

Diffraction by an Atom

If the atom contains n electrons, the average amplitude A_s in P is to a first approximation n times as large as that originating from one electron. More detailed examination shows that

$$A_s = f\,\frac{1}{R}\,\frac{e^2}{mc^2}\sqrt{\frac{1+\cos^2 2\theta}{2}}\,A_p$$

in which expression f, called the atomic factor (atomic scattering factor), depends on θ and the wavelength λ (Fig. 78).

Harmonic Waves and Oscillations

A progressive harmonic wave is described by

$$u = A\cos 2\pi\left(\frac{t}{T}-\frac{R}{\lambda}\right)$$

in which expression

$u =$ in a material wave the displacement, in an electromagnetic wave the electrical field strength

$T =$ time of vibration

$\lambda =$ wavelength

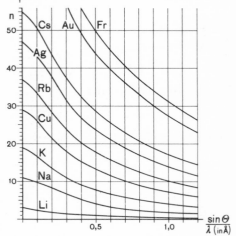

FIG. 78.   Some values of atomic factors f; n is the atomic number.

The equation describes the situation for all values of R at one moment — that is, when t is given a fixed value. When we assign to R a given value, the equation describes the situation (harmonic vibration) at the point P for all values of t.

The energy at the point at distance R, and so the intensity of the vibration, are proportional to A^2; $I \propto A^2$. Henceforth we take $I = A^2$; in doing so, we do not diminish the generality of the results.

The concepts u and I are very important in what follows.

We add an imaginary part to the expression for u and demonstrate that the square of the absolute value of the new quantity Q is equal to I:[1]

[1] $z = a + bi$
$Re\ z = a$
absolute value $|z| = \sqrt{a^2+b^2}$
$|z|^2 = a^2 + b^2$

$$Q = A \cos 2\pi \left(\frac{t}{T} - \frac{R}{\lambda}\right) + i\, A \sin 2\pi \left(\frac{t}{T} - \frac{R}{\lambda}\right)$$

$$I = \left[A \cos 2\pi \left(\frac{t}{T} - \frac{R}{\lambda}\right)\right]^2 + \left[A \sin 2\pi \left(\frac{t}{T} - \frac{R}{\lambda}\right)\right]^2 = A^2$$

It is also possible to find I by multiplying Q by the conjugate complex of Q, the quantity we obtain by giving the opposite sign to the terms with i in the expression for Q.

We can write

$$\left[A \cos 2\pi \left(\frac{t}{T} - \frac{R}{\lambda}\right) + i\, A \sin 2\pi \left(\frac{t}{T} - \frac{R}{\lambda}\right)\right]$$
$$\times \left[A \cos 2\pi \left(\frac{t}{T} - \frac{R}{\lambda}\right) - i\, A \sin 2\pi \left(\frac{t}{T} - \frac{R}{\lambda}\right)\right] = A^2$$

It is often written that

$$Q = A\, e^{2\pi i\left(\frac{t}{T} - \frac{R}{\lambda}\right)} \quad [1]$$

and, in a simpler way, it is found that

$$I = |Q|^2 = A\, e^{2\pi i\left(\frac{t}{T} - \frac{R}{\lambda}\right)} \times A\, e^{-2\pi i\left(\frac{t}{T} - \frac{R}{\lambda}\right)} = A^2$$

imaginary axis

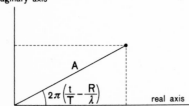

FIG. 79.   Graphic representation of a complex number by a point.

The graphic representation (Fig. 79) is also often used.

If on the line OP waves of the same wavelength start from two points O and O', the phases at P are, in general, different; the total displacement at P is the sum of the two displacements u_1 and u_2 (principle of superposition).

$$u = u_1 + u_2 = A_1 \cos 2\pi \left(\frac{t}{T} - \frac{R_1}{\lambda}\right) + A_2 \cos 2\pi \left(\frac{t}{T} - \frac{R_2}{\lambda}\right)$$

In order to calculate I at P, we demonstrate that P performs a harmonic vibration — in other words, that the composition of two harmonic vibrations is again a harmonic vibration. To this end we apply the formula

[1] $e^{i\varphi} = \cos \varphi + i \sin \varphi$
$e^{-i\varphi} = \cos \varphi - i \sin \varphi$
$2 \cos \varphi = e^{i\varphi} + e^{-i\varphi}$
$2i \sin \varphi = e^{i\varphi} - e^{-i\varphi}$

$$\cos(\alpha - \beta) = \cos \alpha \cos \beta + \sin \alpha \sin \beta$$

$$u = A_1 \cos 2\pi \frac{t}{T} \cos 2\pi \frac{R_1}{\lambda} + A_1 \sin 2\pi \frac{t}{T} \sin 2\pi \frac{R_1}{\lambda}$$

$$+ A_2 \cos 2\pi \frac{t}{T} \cos 2\pi \frac{R_2}{\lambda} + A_2 \sin 2\pi \frac{t}{T} \cos 2\pi \frac{R_2}{\lambda}$$

$$= \cos 2\pi \frac{t}{T} \left(A_1 \cos 2\pi \frac{R_1}{\lambda} + A_2 \cos 2\pi \frac{R_2}{\lambda} \right)$$

$$+ \sin 2\pi \frac{t}{T} \left(A_1 \sin 2\pi \frac{R_1}{\lambda} + A_2 \cos 2\pi \frac{R_2}{\lambda} \right)$$

We call

$$A_1 \cos 2\pi \frac{R_1}{\lambda} + A_2 \cos 2\pi \frac{R_2}{\lambda} \equiv A \cos 2\pi p$$

and

$$A_1 \sin 2\pi \frac{R_1}{\lambda} + A_2 \sin 2\pi \frac{R_2}{\lambda} \equiv A \sin 2\pi p$$

$$u = A \cos 2\pi \frac{t}{T} \cos 2\pi p + A \sin 2\pi \frac{t}{T} \sin 2\pi p = A \cos 2\pi \left(\frac{t}{T} - p \right)$$

$$I = A^2 = A^2 (\cos^2 2\pi p + \sin^2 2\pi p)$$

$$I = \left[A_1 \cos 2\pi \frac{R_1}{\lambda} + A_2 \cos 2\pi \frac{R_2}{\lambda} \right]^2 + \left[A_1 \sin 2\pi \frac{R_1}{\lambda} + A_2 \sin 2\pi \frac{R_2}{\lambda} \right]^2$$

If we add imaginary terms to u_1 and u_2 and call the sum S, then

$$S = A_1 e^{2\pi i \left(\frac{t}{T} - \frac{R_1}{\lambda} \right)} + A_2 e^{2\pi i \left(\frac{t}{T} - \frac{R_2}{\lambda} \right)}$$

and again the intensity appears as the square of the absolute value, found by multiplication with the conjugate complex:

$$I = |S|^2 = [A_1 e^{2\pi i \left(\frac{t}{T} - \frac{R_1}{\lambda} \right)} + A_2 e^{2\pi i \left(\frac{t}{T} - \frac{R_2}{\lambda} \right)}]$$

$$\times [A_1 e^{-2\pi i \left(\frac{t}{T} - \frac{R_1}{\lambda} \right)} + A_2 e^{-2\pi i \left(\frac{t}{T} - \frac{R_2}{\lambda} \right)}]$$

$$= A_1^2 + A_2^2 + 2 A_1 A_2 \cos 2\pi \frac{R_1 - R_2}{\lambda}$$

The result is the same as shown above.

The graphic representation shows that the radius vectors to the two points, representing the two complex terms of S, have to be composed vectorially in order to give the resultant point; from the radius vector to this resultant point the projection on the real axis is equal to $u_1 + u_2$, and the square is equal to I (Fig. 80).

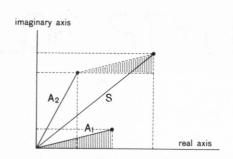

FIG. 80.   FIG. 81.

Diffraction by a Row (of Equal Points — for example, Atoms)

If the primary beam is normal to a row with M_1 atoms (therefore also with M_1 elementary cells), the vibration at P is described (Fig. 81) by

$$Q = A_s e^{2\pi i\left(\frac{t}{T} - \frac{R}{\lambda}\right)} + A_s e^{2\pi i\left(\frac{t}{T} - \frac{R}{\lambda} + w_1\right)}$$
$$+ A_s e^{2\pi i\left(\frac{t}{T} - \frac{R}{\lambda} + 2w_1\right)} + \ldots.$$

A_s is the amplitude of the secondary wave at P, originating from one atom.

$$Q = A_s e^{2\pi i\left(\frac{t}{T} - \frac{R}{\lambda}\right)} \cdot \left\{1 + e^{2\pi i w_1} + e^{2\pi i 2 w_1} + \ldots\right\}$$

The expression between braces is a geometrical series; so

$$Q = A_s e^{2\pi i\left(\frac{t}{T} - \frac{R}{\lambda}\right)} \cdot \frac{e^{2\pi i M_1 w_1} - 1}{e^{2\pi i w_1} - 1}$$

$$I = A_s e^{2\pi i\left(\frac{t}{T} - \frac{R}{\lambda}\right)} \cdot A_s e^{-2\pi i\left(\frac{t}{T} - \frac{R}{\lambda}\right)} \cdot \frac{e^{2\pi i M_1 w_1} - 1}{e^{2\pi i w_1} - 1} \cdot \frac{e^{-2\pi i M_1 w_1} - 1}{e^{-2\pi i w_1} - 1}$$

$$I = A_s^2 \frac{1 - e^{2\pi i M_1 w_1} - e^{-2\pi i M_1 w_1} + 1}{1 - e^{2\pi i w_1} - e^{-2\pi i w_1} + 1}$$

$$= A_s^2 \frac{2 - 2\cos 2\pi\, M_1 w_1}{2 - 2\cos 2\pi\, w_1} = A_s^2 \frac{\sin^2 \pi\, M_1 w_1}{\sin^2 \pi\, w_1}$$

This function of w_1 has principal maxima for $w_1 = h$ (h is a whole number), becomes zero for $w_1 = h \pm \dfrac{1}{M_1}$, and has also a number of auxiliary maxima, which, when M_1 is large, are negligible with respect to the principal maxima (Fig. 82).

If $w_1 = h$, then $I = \dfrac{0}{0}$; after numerator and denominator are twice differentiated, I appears to be equal to $M_1^2 A_s^2$.

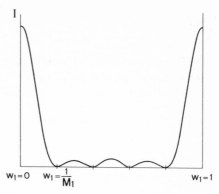

FIG. 82.   Graph of the function I for $M_1 = 5$.

If M_1 is large, the *energy* between $w_1 = h - \dfrac{1}{M_1}$ and $w_1 = h + \dfrac{1}{M_1}$ is

$$E_{\text{principal maximum}} = A_s^2 \int_{w_1 = h - 1/2}^{w_1 = h + 1/2} \frac{\sin^2 \pi M_1 w_1}{\sin^2 \pi w_1} \, dw_1 = A_s^2 M_1$$

and in the remainder of the integration area the intensity is negligible.

Therefore, at exactly $w_1 = h$, the intensity is proportional to the square of the number of atoms, but the total energy within and close to the direction $w_1 = h$, namely, between

$$w_1 = h - \frac{1}{M_1} \text{ and } w_1 = h + \frac{1}{M_1}$$

is proportional to the number of atoms and therefore also to the *number of cells* and the length of the row.

Diffraction by a Lattice (of Equal Points — for example, Atoms)

In an analogous way it might be shown that the intensity of the secondary beam at P, the direction of which is characterized by three numbers w_1, w_2, and w_3, is given by

$$I = A_s^2 \, \frac{\sin^2 \pi M_1 w_1}{\sin^2 \pi w_1} \cdot \frac{\sin^2 \pi M_2 w_2}{\sin^2 \pi w_2} \cdot \frac{\sin^2 \pi M_3 w_3}{\sin^2 \pi w_3}$$

In this expression w_1 means the number of wavelengths in the path difference of two secondary wavelets generated by two neighboring points along the A axis, w_2 the same along the B axis, and w_3 the same along the C axis. Principal maxima are present in the directions for which w_1, w_2, and w_3 are whole numbers. The intensity in such a direction is proportional to $(M_1 \times M_2 \times M_3)^2$; the total energy in and close to this direction is proportional to $(M_1 \times M_2 \times M_3)$ and therefore to the number of cells and to the volume of the exposed crystal.

The Directions of the Principal Maxima

We consider each of the six (seven) elementary Bravais lattices (p. 99) in three different ways: (1) as a collection of equal and parallel rows, according to Laue; (2) as a collection of equidistant nets, according to Bragg; (3) in polar form, according to Ewald.

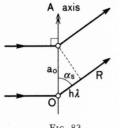

FIG. 83.

1. If a parallel beam of monochromatic X-rays with wavelength λ falls normal to a row, the directions of the principal maxima are conditioned (Fig. 83) by

$$a_0 \cos \alpha_s = h\lambda$$

in which α_s is the angle between the secondary ray and the row and h is a whole number (zero and negative numbers included).

The equation is satisfied if P is situated on the conical surface of the cone whose axis is the row and in which α_s is the internal cone half-angle.

If angle α_p between the primary beam and the row is not 90°, then (Fig. 84)

$$a_0 (\cos \alpha_s - \cos \alpha_p) = h\lambda$$

If there are many rows parallel to one another, the same condition applies to each, and therefore no new directions of principal maxima

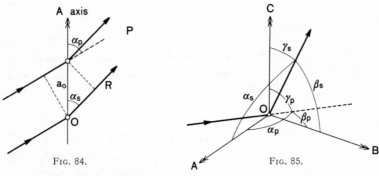

FIG. 84.   FIG. 85.

occur. If the rows are situated regularly, as in a three-dimensional Bravais lattice, the directions of the principal maxima have to satisfy three row conditions (Laue's equations) at the same time (Fig. 85):

$$a_0 \left(\cos \alpha_s - \cos \alpha_p\right) = h_{\text{Laue}} \; \lambda$$
$$b_0 \left(\cos \beta_s - \cos \beta_p\right) = k_{\text{Laue}} \; \lambda$$
$$c_0 \left(\cos \gamma_s - \cos \gamma_p\right) = l_{\text{Laue}} \; \lambda$$

If the crystal is stationary, only a few directions, at most, comply. If we let the crystal rotate — for example, round the third row as axis — the three conditions will be satisfied in many positions at the same time, and directions of principal maxima will fall along a number of generators of the cone round the third row. For these directions l is therefore constant, but h and k have many values.

2. Diffraction by lattice planes containing points.

When a primary beam falls on a lattice plane at an angle θ, we call the *direction of reflection* that direction which lies in the plane of the primary beam and of the normal to the lattice plane and which encloses with the plane an angle θ (Fig. 86). If q' is the direction of reflection of q, then, when there is reflection from the lattice plane, all paths between the flat planes Q and Q' are equal; the secondary waves, starting from all points of the lattice plane, have therefore the same phase in Q'. In other

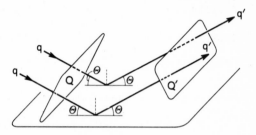

FIG. 86. $Q \perp q$ and $Q' \perp q'$.

words, there is always a principal maximum in the direction of reflection.

A lattice consists not, however, of one plane, but of a number of equidistant "reflecting" planes with spacings d_{hkl}. There will therefore be a principal maximum in the direction of reflection only if the path differences of the secondary rays originating from all planes comprise a whole number of wavelengths. This requirement is formulated in Bragg's *reflection equation* (see Fig. 87),

$$2d_{hkl} \sin \theta = n\lambda$$

in which n is an integer (number of order) and the angle θ is called the *glancing angle*. The angle between the primary and the secondary beam is 2θ.

The relation between the two ways of considering the phenomenon is that the Laue indices (these are the whole numbers h_{Laue}, k_{Laue}, and l_{Laue}) are equal to the Miller indices of the lattice plane (which have no common factor greater than 1) multiplied by the number of order n.

If the directions of the primary and secondary beam are described with the aid of Laue's formulas, then h, k, and l indicate that the primary beam is "reflected" from the lattice planes which are parallel to the crystal face $(h\,k\,l)$, provided Laue's indices h, k, and l have no common factor. If they have a common factor, this factor indicates the order of the reflection according to Bragg.

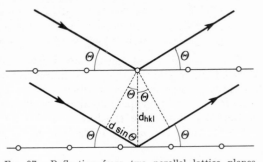

FIG. 87.   Reflection from two parallel lattice planes.

3. According to Ewald, the directions of the principal maxima may be constructed as follows (Fig. 88):

From the direct lattice the polar lattice in regard to a sphere with radius ρ, is constructed and round O a second sphere with radius $R = \dfrac{\rho^2}{\lambda}$ (*Ewald's sphere*) is drawn. The origin O^* of the polar lattice is not made to coincide with the origin O of the direct lattice, but is shifted to the point

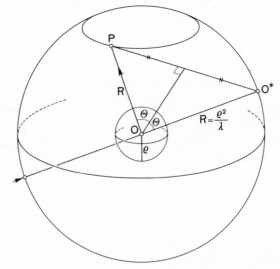

FIG. 88.   Construction sphere of radius ρ and Ewald's sphere R; these spheres coincide when $\rho = \lambda$.

where the primary ray leaves Ewald's sphere. If a point P of the polar lattice is situated on this sphere, there is a principal maximum in the direction from O to this point, for this direction satisfies Bragg's condition:

$$O^* P = \frac{\rho^2}{d_{nh\ nk\ nl}} \quad \text{(p. 54)}$$

And also

$$\tfrac{1}{2} O^* P = R \sin \theta$$

Hence

$$\frac{\rho^2}{d_{nh\ nk\ nl}} = 2 \frac{\rho^2}{\lambda} \sin \theta$$

$$\lambda = 2 d_{nh\ nk\ nl} \sin \theta$$

$$n\lambda = 2 d_{hkl} \sin \theta$$

When the number of order n is included in d_{hkl}, the formula is valid for all points of the polar lattice.

Experimental Methods [1]

With most methods, the secondary beams are registered photographically; in order to determine the intensities accurately, we use the Geiger-Müller counter. The registration apparatus can be either stationary or moving (Table 7).

TABLE 7

	stationary recorder	moving recorder
monochromatic X-ray beam	rotation photograph oscillation photograph circle photograph	Schiebold-Sauter photograph
		Weissenberg photograph
	Bragg method	
	powder photograph	retigram
"white" beam	Laue photograph	

Rotation (Circle, Oscillation) Photograph

The crystal is made to rotate round an edge (for example, the C axis), and the reflections are registered on a cylindrical film whose axis coincides with the rotation axis of the crystal. It follows from the considerations

[1] M. J. Buerger, *X-Ray Crystallography* (1942); D. McLachlan, *X-ray Crystal Structure* (1957).

on p. 110 that, if the crystal consists of one row parallel to the C axis, horizontal straight lines appear on the cylindrical film, but that, if there are many regularly arranged rows, only a few spots of these lines remain. When the film is opened out and developed, these spots, situated on lines normal to the rotation axis, form the so-called *layer lines* (Fig. 89).

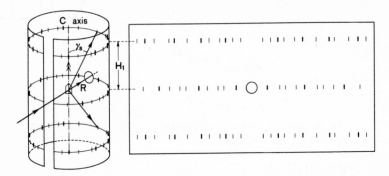

FIG. 89.   Rotation photograph showing the zero and positive and negative first layer lines: (left) during the exposure, (right) with the film flattened out.

The identity distance along the rotation axis, and in this case therefore the absolute axial length c_0, can be derived from the heights of the layer lines. If the primary beam falls normal to the rotation axis (Figs. 83, 89), then

$$\tan (90° - \gamma_s) = \frac{H_l}{R}$$

$$\cos \gamma_s = \frac{l\lambda}{c_0}$$

In our case l is constant for all the spots on one layer line; in other words, these spots are caused by reflections from *coplanar* [1] planes whose third index is constant and known; for the zero layer line $l = 0$, for the first $l = 1$, etc.

This follows also from the considerations on p. 112. If we place O^* at the point of intersection of the primary beam and the film (Fig. 90), all the reciprocal points $(h\,k\,l)$ with fixed l are situated in a horizontal plane, for A^* and B^* are normal to C. The intersection of this plane with Ewald's sphere, which we thus give a radius R, is a horizontal circle, and

[1] We call lattice planes (crystal faces) coplanar when their representative points in the indirect (polar) lattice are situated in a lattice plane. When this plane contains the origin O^*, the coplanar faces belong to a zone. The indices of each face of coplanar faces satisfy the equation $\lambda h + \mu k + \nu l =$ constant (λ, μ, and ν are integers).

the spots on the film are also situated on a horizontal circle. The height of this circle can be calculated with the aid of the polar lattice ($\rho^2 = R\lambda$).

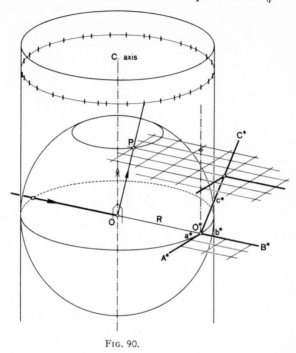

FIG. 90.

In making an *oscillation photograph*, we let the crystal oscillate through a small angle — for example, $10°$ or $15°$ — so that only some of the spots of a rotation photograph occur. We use this method chiefly in order to set the crystal edge accurately parallel to the rotation axis [1] or to photograph (weak) diffuse spots (p. 250).

If, instead of a cylindrical film round the crystal, a flat film normal to the rotation axis above the crystal is exposed, the layer lines become circles (*circle photograph*). As on p. 114, the value of c_0 can be derived from the diameters of the circles and the height of the film.

Bragg Method

The Bragg method is to record and measure the secondary beam in an ionization chamber or, nowadays, in a counter. The chamber or the counter

[1] C. W. Bunn, *Chemical Crystallography* (1946), p. 173; R. B. Roof, *Acta Cryst.* 8 (1955), 434.

is rotating round the same axis as the crystal; as a rule, only reflections of the zero layer line are recorded (Fig. 91).

The method is very suitable for measuring intensities, especially when a counting-rate meter registers automatically.

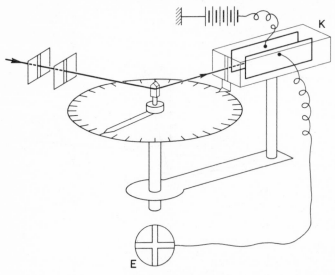

FIG. 91. Bragg spectrometer; the conductivity of the gas in the ionization chamber K, caused by the secondary X-ray beam, is measured by the electrometer E.

Powder Photograph [1]

For a powder photograph (Debije and Scherrer, Hull), many very small crystals, oriented in all directions, are put on a small glass rod, on a hair, or in a very thin-walled glass tube, in the axis of a cylindrical camera; the film is placed round the inside of the camera. Then lattice planes $(h\,k\,l)$, with a definite d_{hkl}, will be oriented in a number of the particles in such a way that the primary beam strikes at the — according to Bragg's formula — correct angle θ and therefore is reflected.

The secondary beams fall along generators of a cone with semi-angle 2θ and produce on the film a curved line, which is the line of intersection of the cone with the cylindrical film (Fig. 92).

With a cubic crystal, as a rule, it is easy to index the range of planes

---

[1] H. S. Peiser, H. P. Rooksby, and A. J. C. Wilson, *X-Ray Diffraction by Polycrystalline Materials* (1955); H. P. Klug and L. E. Alexander, *X-Ray Diffraction Procedures* (1954); L. V. Azároff and M. J. Buerger, *The Powder Method* (1958).

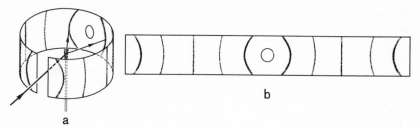

FIG. 92. Powder photograph: (*a*) during the exposure; (*b*) with the film flattened out.

from which a line originates, for 2θ, and therefore θ, can be read on the film. Then we have

$$\sin \theta = \frac{n\lambda}{2d} \text{ (Bragg)}$$

$$d^2 = \frac{a^2}{h^2 + k^2 + l^2}$$

$$\sin^2 \theta = \frac{\lambda^2}{4a_0^2} \{(nh)^2 + (nk)^2 + (nl)^2\}$$

Since the expression between braces is a whole number (Table 8), it is usually not difficult to derive the value of the constant $\frac{\lambda^2}{4a_0^2}$, and hence the length of a_0, from the values of $\sin^2 \theta$.

We note that, since $\sin^2 \theta$, at most, equals 1, the number of lines is limited.

It is often difficult or impossible to index the lines of a powder photo-

TABLE 8

nh	nk	nl	$(nh)^2 + (nk)^2 + (nl)^2$
1	0	0	1
1	1	0	2
1	1	1	3
2	0	0	4
2	1	0	5
2	1	1	6
2	2	0	8
	etc.		

graph of a less symmetric crystal unless the absolute axial lengths are known from other photographs.

Suppose that, for a cubic crystal, a_0 or, in general, a_0, b_0, c_0, α, β, and γ, are known not very accurately. Now $\sin^2 \theta$ can be calculated approximately for all (hkl), and from a powder photograph these angles can be measured accurately, especially if the powder of the crystal to be examined is mixed with the powder of NaCl, W, or another well-known standard material. The accurate values of the angles allow us to determine the absolute crystal elements accurately.

Powder photographs are also very suitable for identification and determination, for they are pre-eminently characteristic of the kind of crystalline material.[1]

If the camera is equipped for taking photographs at various temperatures, polymorphous transitions can be observed. This method has given important results, especially in the metallurgical examination of alloys. The expansion coefficients of crystals can be derived from the shifting of the lines.

Another application is the examination of stresses in metal objects, which usually consist of very small crystals. Stresses cause deformations of the crystals, therefore changes in the dimensions of the structure, and hence displacements of the powder lines. These displacements are largest for the lines of which $2\theta \sim 180°$ and therefore for those appearing on a *back-reflection photograph* (Fig. 93).

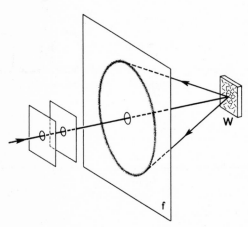

FIG. 93. Back-reflection photograph; powder lines appear on the film f in the form of concentric circles, originating from small crystals of the (metal) specimen W.

The average size of the powder particles may be derived from the broadening of the powder lines when this size is smaller than 0.1μ (p. 254).

Organic crystals, especially, often have large d_{hkl}'s, so that important

---

[1] Tables of the American Society for Testing Materials enable us to determine a crystalline compound by means of the strongest three lines on the powder photograph.

lines appear near to the undeviated beam. To detect and measure these lines, methods using highly monochromatic X-rays, produced by reflection from a crystal, have been developed.[1]

Photographs with Moving Film

When we take a rotation photograph, we do not know the moment at which a reflection of — for example — the first layer line is taken or the position of the crystal at that moment, and we thus lack one of the data that we need for indexing a spot.

If a powder photograph is taken with the same camera, and if its lines can be indexed, it is usually possible to determine on which line the spot falls, and then indexing is possible.

We can attain the goal better by making the film move with the rotation of the crystal. If the Schiebold-Sauter method is followed, the reflections are caught on a flat film that rotates once while the crystal is rotating once. The spots of a reciprocal lattice plane are distributed over the film in a rather complicated way.

By the Weissenberg method, which is oftener used, the cylindrical film shifts along its axis, during one rotation of the crystal, by, for example, 2π times the diameter of the cylinder (Fig. 94). When the film is flattened out, the spots on the axes in the zero C^* net plane (Fig. 95) are situated on straight lines, those on net lines parallel to the reciprocal axes on curved lines. It is not difficult to index the spots, especially graphically.

Nomograms have been constructed

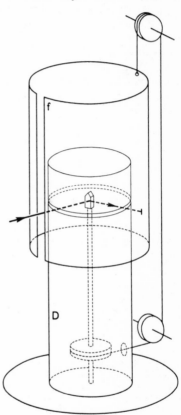

Fig. 94. Weissenberg photograph; the shifting of the film f is coupled to the rotation of the crystal; the slot in the screen D allows only the reflections of the zero layer line to pass.

[1] A. Guinier and G. Fournet, *Small Angle Scattering of X-Rays* (1955).

which can serve for the zero C^* net plane and for other net planes provided the photograph is taken in such a way that the primary and secondary rays for a net plane form the same angle with the rotation axis of the crystal and therefore also with the rotation axis of the film (*equi-inclination method*).

If a flat film is made to coincide with one of the polar net planes, and if the film is rotated round an axis through O^* parallel to the rotation axis of the crystal in the same sense and with the same velocity as the crystal, the net plane is photographed without any distortion. The apparatus with which this result is achieved is called a *retigraph* (net writer).[1] A nomogram is no longer needed for indexing; as soon as the polar axes have been determined, the indices are read as coordinates. Figs. 96 and 97 show the apparatus and a retigram.

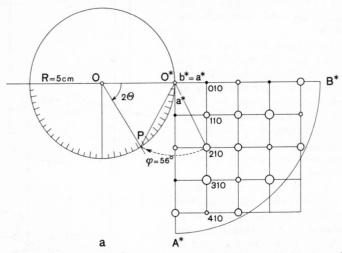

Fig. 95.   Explanation of a Weissenberg photograph of the zero C^* net plane of rutile (tetragonal TiO_2), photographed with monochromatic X-rays normally incident on the rotation axis C axis; the radius of the camera is 5 cm, the shifting of the film is $2/360 \cdot 2\pi \cdot 5$ cm $= 0.1745$ cm for each degree of rotation of the crystal.

(a) A quarter of the net plane with the planes recorded (small open circles), the coordinate lines, and also the intersection with Ewald's sphere, of which $R = 5$ cm.

(b) Some reflections of the zero layer line on the rotation photograph; for example, (210) reflects when the point 210 pierces the sphere in P. This happens after a rotation of $\varphi = 56°$ of the polar net plane round O^* and so of the crystal round O. The abscissa of the reflection is R bg $2\theta = 4.9$ cm.

(c) Part of the flattened film of the Weissenberg photograph with the coordinate lines of the polar net plane; the ordinate of (210) is $56 \cdot 2/360 \cdot 2\pi \cdot 5$ cm $= 9.76$ cm.

[1] J. Bouman and others, *Selected Topics in X-Ray Crystallography* (1951), p. 19.

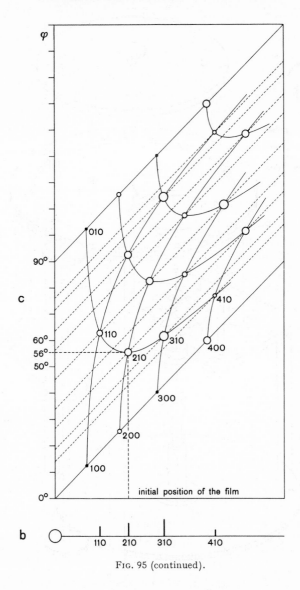

FIG. 95 (continued).

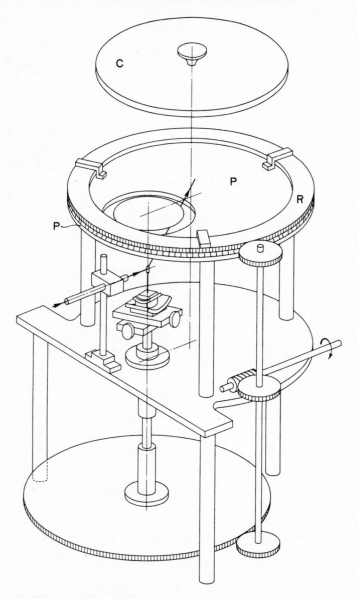

FIG. 96.   Retigraph. The filmholder C rotates in the ring R on ball bearings; the secondary beams pass through an adjustable annular slot in the plate P.

Buerger has designed a variation of the retigraph (*precession method*).[1] The direct crystal elements can be derived from the lengths of the polar axes and their angles (p. 53). A method of identifying crystals is founded on the fact that those elements are characteristic.[2]

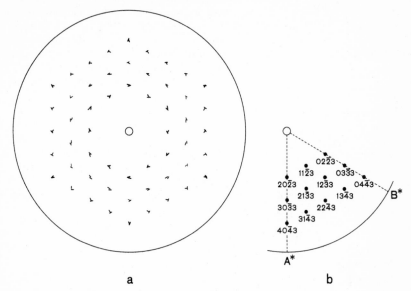

a   b

FIG. 97.   (a) Retigram of the third C^* net plane of quartz; (b) some of the reflections indexed.

Laue Photograph

The crystal is stationary, and the primary beam of white X-rays falls on a few ranges of lattice planes, each with its own spacing, at such an angle that the Bragg condition is satisfied for one wavelength for each range. Each spot on the photographic plate, which is normal to the primary beam behind the crystal, is therefore caused by X-rays of a single wavelength, which are, in general, of different wavelength for all the spots, each spot having its own "color."

By letting the primary beam fall along a symmetry element, we obtain symmetric photographs; the method may therefore serve for determination of the Laue group (cf. p. 192).

[1] M. J. Buerger, *The Photography of the Reciprocal Lattice* (Cambridge, Mass., 1944).
[2] J. D. H. Donnay and W. Nowacki, *Crystal Data* (1954).

Intensity of the Reflections (Diffraction by a Structure)

The intensity of a reflection (secondary beam) depends on distance R, on a number of physical factors that vary continuously with 2θ

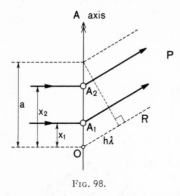

Fig. 98.

— absorption, primary and secondary extinction, polarization factor, heat factor, Lorentz factor L, and atomic factor f — and on the discontinuous crystallographic factors — structure factor F and multiplicity factor ν.

The *structure factor* F, which is determined by the kind of atoms and their arrangement in an elementary cell, is the amplitude of the secondary wave starting from an elementary cell — in other words, the vectorial compound of all A_s (p. 105) starting from such a cell.

If a one-dimensional cell contains one atom A_1 and one atom A_2 (Fig. 98), the vibration at P is (cf. p. 107)

$$Q = A_{s1} e^{2\pi i\left(\frac{t}{T} - \frac{R}{\lambda} + \frac{x_1}{a} h\right)} + A_{s2} e^{2\pi i\left(\frac{t}{T} - \frac{R}{\lambda} + \frac{x_2}{a} h\right)}$$

In general,

$$Q = e^{2\pi i\left(\frac{t}{T} - \frac{R}{\lambda}\right)} \cdot \Sigma A_s e^{2\pi i \frac{x}{a} h}$$

Three-dimensionally,

$$Q = e^{2\pi i\left(\frac{t}{T} - \frac{R}{\lambda}\right)} \cdot \Sigma A_s e^{2\pi i\left(\frac{x}{a} h + \frac{y}{b} k + \frac{z}{c} l\right)}$$

A_s is the amplitude of the secondary wavelet at P, starting from one atom, and is determined by the continuous factors and the quantity $\frac{e^2}{mc^2}$. Of these factors only the atomic factor f depends on the kind of atoms; the others are the same for all atoms. The total wave movement at P is therefore described by the expression

$$Q = \text{Const.} \times e^{2\pi i\left(\frac{t}{T} - \frac{R}{\lambda}\right)} \cdot \Sigma f\, e^{2\pi i\left(\frac{x}{a} h + \frac{y}{b} k + \frac{z}{c} l\right)}$$

The expression Σ is called the *structure factor* F or the complex amplitude.

The intensity at P is proportional to the square of the absolute value of Q and therefore also to that of F; hence

$$I \propto |F|^2 = \left[\Sigma f \cos 2\pi \left(\frac{x}{a}h + \frac{y}{b}k + \frac{z}{c}l\right)\right]^2$$
$$+ \left[\Sigma f \sin 2\pi \left(\frac{x}{a}h + \frac{y}{b}k + \frac{z}{c}l\right)\right]^2$$

The *multiplicity factor* ν indicates how many times the range of planes considered (with definite d_{hkl}) is present in the crystal, and this factor is therefore proportional to the number of faces of the form $\{h\,k\,l\}$, but in this case a face and the parallel opposite face are counted as one (cf. Friedel's law, p. 127).

The ratio of the intensities of the lines of a powder photograph on a cylindrical film becomes

$$I \propto \frac{1 + \cos^2 2\theta}{2} \cdot \frac{1}{\sin^2 \theta \cos \theta} \, \nu \, |F|^2$$

The first two factors are called the polarization factor and the Lorentz factor. For the intensities of the spots on a retigram and other photographs, see the literature.[1]

Fourier Analysis

The electron density of a crystal is periodic and can therefore be represented by a Fourier series (or Fourier integral).

Let this density, in a one-dimensional case, be a continuous function $\rho(x)$ of x; x is the distance to O (Fig. 99).

The function can be written in three ways:

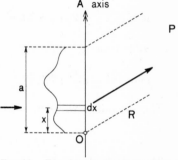

FIG. 99.   The electron density is plotted at the left of the A axis.

(1) $\rho(x) = A_0 + A_1 \cos 2\pi \dfrac{x}{a} + A_2 \cos 2\pi \dfrac{2x}{a} + \ldots + B_1 \sin 2\pi \dfrac{x}{a} + \ldots$

(2) If $\left.\begin{array}{l} A_0 \equiv C'_0 \\ A_h \equiv 2C'_h \cos \alpha_h \\ B_h \equiv 2C'_h \sin \alpha_h \end{array}\right\}$ (A_h, B_h and C_h are real)

then

$$\rho(x) = C'_0 + 2C'_1 \cos \left(2\pi \frac{x}{a} - \alpha_1\right) + 2C'_2 \cos \left(2\pi \frac{2x}{a} - \alpha_2\right) + \ldots$$

(3)   If we insert

$$2 \cos \varphi = e^{i\varphi} + e^{-i\varphi}$$

[1] Internationale Tabellen zur Bestimmung von Kristallstrukturen II (1935), 562; J. Bouman and others, *Selected Topics in X-Ray Crystallography* (1951), p. 27.

and call

$$C'_0 \equiv C_0$$
$$C'_h \, e^{-ia_h} \equiv C_h$$
$$C'_h \, e^{ia_h} \equiv C_{\bar{h}}$$

$\left.\right\}$ (C_h and $C_{\bar{h}}$ are therefore complex and conjugate)

then the expression becomes

$$\rho(x) = \ldots\ldots\ldots C_{\bar{1}} \, e^{-2\pi i \frac{x}{a}} + C_0 + C_1 \, e^{2\pi i \frac{x}{a}} + \ldots\ldots\ldots$$

If at $x = 0$ (that is, at O) there is an inversion point, there is also one at $x = \frac{1}{2}\, a$, and $\rho(x) = \rho(-x)$.

From this it follows that

(1) all $B_h = 0$

$$\rho(x) = A_0 + A_1 \cos 2\pi \frac{x}{a} + A_2 \cos 2\pi \frac{2x}{a} + \ldots\ldots\ldots$$

(2) $2C'_h \sin \alpha_h = 0$, hence $\alpha_h = 0$ or π, and $\cos \alpha_h = \pm 1$

$$\rho(x) = C'_0 \pm 2C'_1 \cos 2\pi \frac{x}{a} \pm \ldots\ldots$$

(3) $\alpha_h = 0$ or π, hence $e^{i\alpha_h}$ or $e^{-i\alpha_h} = \pm 1$, and $C_{\bar{h}} = C_h$ (real)

$$\rho(x) = C_0 \pm 2C_1 \cos 2\pi \frac{x}{a} \pm 2C_2 \cos 2\pi \frac{2x}{a} \pm \ldots\ldots$$

The secondary wavelet, starting from dx, is, at P

$$dQ = \rho(x) \, dx \, e^{2\pi i \left(\frac{t}{T} - \frac{R}{\lambda} + h \frac{x}{a} \right)}$$

The entire cell gives, at P,

$$Q = \int_0^a \rho(x) \, dx \, e^{2\pi i \left(\frac{t}{T} - \frac{R}{\lambda} + h \frac{x}{a} \right)} = e^{2\pi i \left(\frac{t}{T} - \frac{R}{\lambda} \right)} \int_0^a \rho(x) e^{2\pi i h \frac{x}{a}} \, dx$$

The integral is the structure factor F, indicated as F_h (h indicating its order).

If we insert for $\rho(x)$ the Fourier series, we obtain

$$F_h = \int_0^a \ldots\ldots\ldots + \int_0^a C_{\bar{h}} \, e^{-2\pi i h \frac{x}{a}} \cdot e^{2\pi i h \frac{x}{a}} \, dx + \int_0^a \ldots\ldots\ldots$$

All integrals have the value zero except the fully written one, which has the value $C_h a$. Therefore

$$F_h = C_{\bar{h}}a$$

$$C_{\bar{h}} = \frac{F_h}{a}$$

$$\rho(x) = \sum_{h=-\infty}^{h=+\infty} \frac{F_h}{a} e^{-2\pi i h \frac{x}{a}}$$

in which F_h is complex.

If there is an inversion point at O, then

$$\rho(x) = \frac{F_0}{a} + \sum_{h=1}^{h=\infty} \pm 2 \frac{F_h}{a} \cos 2\pi h \frac{x}{a}$$

in which F_h is real.

F_0 follows from the expression for Q and is $\int_0^a \rho(x)dx = \rho a$, the total number of electrons in a; therefore $\frac{F_0}{a}$ is the average density of the electrons.

Three-dimensionally, an inversion point at O gives

$$\rho(xyz) = \frac{1}{v_p} \sum_{h=-\infty}^{\infty} \sum_{k=-\infty}^{\infty} \sum_{l=-\infty}^{\infty} \pm F_{hkl} \cos 2\pi \left(\frac{x}{a} h + \frac{y}{b} k + \frac{z}{c} l \right)$$

F_{000} is again the total number of electrons per elementary cell. If in each term we take, for example, $z = c/2$, the series gives the course of density in a cut through the cell on the height $c/2$; if in each term we take $l = 0$, the series gives the projection of the density on the coordinate plane AB.

The absolute value of F_{hkl} is equal to the square root of that of the intensity (cf. p. 109) and can therefore be determined experimentally (but see p. 133).

From $C_{\bar{h}} = \frac{F_h}{a}$ we see that $C_{\bar{h}}$ is determined only by the amplitude of the secondary beam of the order h. From the fact that $C_{\bar{h}}$ and C_h are conjugate it follows that the strength of the secondary beam of the h^d and $\bar{h}^d$ order is the same; or, in other words, an X-ray diagram always shows an inversion point: there is always, as it were, an inversion point added to the symmetry of the crystal, so that only eleven classes can be distinguished by means of X-ray diffraction (*Friedel's law*).[1]

If for a structure with an inversion point a sufficient number of values of F are known, and if the sign for each term can be determined, then, by summing, we find $\rho(xyz)$ and therefore also the places of the atoms

---

[1] But see J. M. Bijvoet, Endeavour 14 (1955), 71.

in the cell. If we can arrive at an approximate structure — for example, by means of a Patterson diagram (see below) — the signs can be determined, and with their aid $\rho(xyz)$ can give the places of the atoms (cf. p. 133).

Since only a limited number of F's can be determined experimentally, we have to break off the series without the certainty that the missing terms are so small as to be negligible. In order to attain this smallness, we may introduce an *artificial temperature factor*.

At a higher temperature t, the F's decrease:

$$F^t = F^0\, e^{-B\left(\frac{\sin\theta}{\lambda}\right)^2} = F^0\, e^{-\frac{B}{4\,d^2}}$$

The value of B is known for different temperatures. If d is large and h, k, and l are therefore small, the factor $e^{-\frac{B}{4\,d^2}}$ is approximately 1 — rather strongly decreasing, however, with smaller d. If we assume that we take a photograph at high temperature, we have to multiply the F's, measured at room temperature, with factors decreasing to higher orders. Then we can choose the value of B, and hence the artificial temperature, so that the error involved in summation of the incomplete series is negligible. The result is, however, that details of the electron density are lost and that in the representation the atoms appear to be more diffuse.

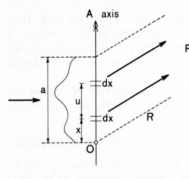

FIG. 100.

Patterson Diagram [1]

If in a one-dimensional crystal (Fig. 100) the electron density is

$$\rho(x) = \frac{1}{a} \Sigma\, F_h\, e^{-2\pi i \frac{x}{a} h}$$

and u is a parameter, we can consider the product

$$\rho(x)\, \rho(x + u)\, dx$$

and integrate this quantity over the whole cell:

$$P(u) = \int_0^a \rho(x)\, \rho(x + u)\, dx$$

$$= \frac{1}{a^2} \int_0^a \left(\Sigma\, F_h\, e^{-2\pi i h \frac{x}{a}}\right)\left(\Sigma\, F_{h'}\, e^{-2\pi i \frac{x+u}{a} h'}\right) dx$$

[1] C. W. Bunn, *Chemical Crystallography* (1946), p. 351.

We consider, when calculating this expression, the term

$$\frac{1}{a^2} \int_0^a F_h\, e^{-2\pi i h\frac{x}{a}} \cdot F_{\bar{h}}\, e^{2\pi i h\frac{x}{a}} \cdot e^{2\pi i \frac{u}{a} h} \cdot dx$$

The value of this is

$$\frac{1}{a}\,(F_h\,F_{\bar{h}})e^{2\pi i \frac{u}{a} h} = \frac{1}{a}\,|F_h|^2\,e^{2\pi i h\frac{u}{a}}$$

The integrals of all the other products are zero. Therefore

$$P\,(u) = \frac{1}{a}\,\Sigma\,|F_h|^2 \cdot e^{2\pi i h\frac{u}{a}}$$

Since $|F_h|^2$'s are proportional to the intensities of the secondary beams, $P(u)$ can be determined, and there is no uncertainty about the phase (the sign). If u is made to run from 0 to a and the values of $P(u)$ are plotted in a diagram, a peak indicates that this u is a distance on which the two values $\rho(x)$ and $\rho(x + u)$ are both large — that is, that two atoms, separated by a distance u, exist in the cell. Their places in the cell are not determined at this stage, but the diagram gives valuable indications regarding the correctness of the approximate structure mentioned on p. 128.

We choose as a one-dimensional example the projection on the A (or B) axis of an elementary cell of rutile (p. 156). From the symmetry of the space group it follows that the Ti ions are situated at fixed places and the O ions on the horizontal diagonals, but that the parameter p is undetermined (Fig. 101).

In order to determine p approximately, we start from five observed relative intensities of different order reflections on (100), and we draw a Patterson diagram (Table 9).

TABLE 9

h 00		observed intensity ($\propto F^2_{h00}$)
200 or	$\bar{2}$00	47
400	$\bar{4}$00	100
600	$\bar{6}$00	102
800	$\bar{8}$00	13
10 00	$\overline{10}$ 00	63

$$P(u) = \frac{1}{a}\,\sum_{h=-\infty}^{\infty} F^2_{h00} \cos 2\pi \frac{u}{a} h$$

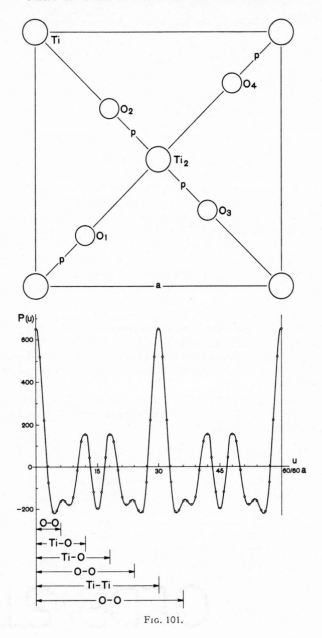

F𝙸𝙶. 101.

One takes, as a rule, the intervals of u equal to $1/60$ or $1/120$ a. The value of $P(u)$ at $u = 1/60$ a, for example, is

$$P(\tfrac{1}{60}a) = 63 \cos 2\pi \cdot \overline{10} \cdot \tfrac{1}{60} + 13 \cos 2\pi \cdot \overline{8} \cdot \tfrac{1}{60} + 102 \cos 2\pi \cdot \overline{6} \cdot \tfrac{1}{60}$$

$+\; 100 \cos 2\pi \cdot \overline{4} \cdot \tfrac{1}{60} + 47 \cos 2\pi \cdot \overline{2} \cdot \tfrac{1}{60} + F_{h00}^2 \cos 2\pi \cdot 0 \cdot \tfrac{1}{60}$ (the term which is constant for every u which we take to be zero) $+\; 47 \cos 2\pi \cdot 2 \cdot \tfrac{1}{60}$ $+\; 100 \cos 2\pi \cdot 4 \cdot \tfrac{1}{60} + 102 \cos 2\pi \cdot 6 \cdot \tfrac{1}{60} + 13 \cos 2\pi \cdot 8 \cdot \tfrac{1}{60} + 63 \cos 2\pi$ $\cdot\, 10 \cdot \tfrac{1}{60} = 520$

The complete Patterson diagram has been plotted in Fig. 101. At $u = 0$ a very large maximum appears, at $u = 6/60$ a a low one, at $u = 12/60$ a a medium one, etc. We ascribe the first to the zero distances: $(Ti_1 - Ti_1) + (O_1 - O_1) + (O_2 - O_2) + \ldots$; the second to the projected distances between ions with small refracting powers, hence $(O_1 - O_2) + (O_3 - O_4)$; the third to distances between average moderately refracting ions: $(Ti_1 - O_1) + (Ti_2 - O_2) + \ldots$; etc.

Assuming the projection of p to be $12/60$ a, we are sufficiently in accordance with the Patterson diagram, and we get a well-founded approximate structure.

Procedure of a Structure Analysis

1. From the *positions* of the reflections, or, better, from the angles 2θ, the elements of the elementary cell — that is, the shape and dimensions of the elementary Bravais lattice (of the pattern; see p. 99) — can be derived.

If we have a small crystal which can be oriented, the identity distances along the axes, and thus the absolute axial lengths, can be measured by means of rotation photographs, the crystal being rotated successively round the three crystallographic axes; the axial lengths follow from the heights of the layer lines (p. 114).

If only powder is available, it is usually possible, with cubic crystals, to determine, from the positions of the lines on a powder photograph, the length a_0 of the edge of the cell by means of the expression (see p. 117)

$$\sin^2 \theta = \frac{\lambda^2}{4a^2} \{(nh)^2 + (nk)^2 + (nl)^2\}$$

The expression between braces is always a whole number — for example, 1, 2, 3, 4, 5, 6, 8 ... (not 7); $\sin^2 \theta$ therefore forms an arithmetical series from which some terms are missing. The value of the difference and so of a_0 follows from the series, and the indices $h, k,$ and l can be determined; in other words, the lines can be indexed.

If the shape of the elementary cell has been derived (the angles between the axes are usually determined goniometrically), the number of atoms in the cell follows from the volume of the cell, the specific gravity, the chemical composition, and the absolute weight of each atom.

2. From the *intensities* of the reflections follow, in principle, (a) the kind of elementary Bravais lattice, (b) the space group, and (c) the positions of the atoms in the cell.

(a) The elementary Bravais lattice is P, I, F, A, B, C, or R (p. 99). In the presence of lattice P it follows from the intensity formula on p. 125 that none of the reflections has to be absent — in other words, that there is no *general extinction criterion*. Table 10 follows from the same considerations.

TABLE 10

lattice	general extinction criterion
P	none
I	$nh + nk + nl$, odd
F	nh, nk, nl, mixed odd and even
A	$nk + nl$, odd
B	$nh + nl$, odd
C	$nh + nk$, odd
R	$nh - nk + nl$, or $- nh + nk + nl$, not divisible by 3

(b) In general, the symmetry class is known or may be derived with the aid of etch figures, piezoelectrical properties, etc. (p. 87). The space group is determined by examination of the *special extinctions*. These extinctions occur if glide planes (*zonal extinctions*) or screw axes (*serial extinctions*), or both, are present. Nearly all space groups are characterized in this way by extinctions.[1]

(c) The positions of the atoms in the elementary cell (the motif; see p. 99) comply with the symmetry elements other than the translations. The various sets of equivalent positions, general and special, are given in published tables.[2]

If the space group is known, we can, on the basis of these tables, make an assumption about the atomic coordinates — having regard,

---

[1] A complete description will be found in the International Tables for X-Ray Crystallography I (1952); E. Brandenberger, *Angewandte Kristallstrukturlehre* (1938).

[2] International Tables I (1952); R. W. G. Wyckoff, *The Analytical Expression of the Results of the Theory of Space Groups* (1930).

of course, to the radii (pp. 140 and 176) and Pauling's rules (p. 165) —
and control these by comparing the calculated intensities of the reflections with those that have been observed.

Instead of applying this trial-and-error method,[1] we can try to derive
the electron density at all points of the cell from the F values (p. 125).
This direct method [1] would be preferable in all respects if there were
not the objection that, though the amplitude of a reflection can be
measured, its phase, in relation to that of the other reflections, cannot
be, so that α_h (p. 125) is not known in the terms of the Fourier series.
If the cell possesses an inversion point, $\alpha_h = 0$ or π, and therefore, with
the exception of the sign, F is known. It is often possible to derive this
sign from an approximately known structure or in a mathematical
way,[2] and then the electron density can be calculated at each point of
the cell by means of the Fourier series.

For this calculation, preferably, we project the content of the elementary cell on one of the sides and derive the atomic positions from two
or three of those projections. By projection — for example, $// C$ axis
on the plane of the A and B axes — we reduce the calculation to two-
dimensional Fourier series of the form

$$\rho\,(x\,y) = \frac{1}{a_0 b_0 \sin \gamma}\ \Sigma\ F_{hk0}\ e^{-2\pi i \left(\frac{x}{a}h + \frac{y}{b}k\right)}$$

If there is a J at O,

$$\rho(xy) = \frac{1}{v_p} \Sigma_h \Sigma_k F_{hk0} \cos 2\pi \left(\frac{x}{a}h + \frac{y}{b}k\right)$$

Applying

$$\cos(\alpha + \beta) = \cos \alpha \cos \beta - \sin \alpha \sin \beta$$

we get

$$\rho(xy) = \frac{1}{v_p} \Sigma_k \left[\Sigma_h F_{hk0} \cos 2\pi \frac{x}{a}h\right] \cos 2\pi \frac{y}{b}k$$

$$- \frac{1}{v_p} \Sigma_k \left[\Sigma_h F_{hk0} \sin 2\pi \frac{x}{a}h\right] \sin 2\pi \frac{y}{b}k$$

Since the calculations of the sine and cosine functions for different
values of x and y are tedious, methods of using calculating machines
on a large scale have been developed for this work.

The densities projected on a plane are plotted on a map by lines of
equal density; high density signifies the presence of an atom (Fig. 102).

---

[1] A complete description will be found in H. Lipson and W. Cochran, *The Crystalline
State*, III (1953), pp. 110 and 246.
[2] *Ibid.*, p. 250.

Methods of determining the atomic coordinates more *accurately* (F_0 synthesis, differential Fourier synthesis, least squares, steepest descents) and of testing their *reliability* have been developed.[1]

A two-dimensional Patterson diagram, designed in such a way, is often of much help in the setting up of an approximate structure. The series for a projection // C is

$$P(uv) = \frac{1}{ab \sin \gamma} \sum_{h=-\infty}^{\infty} \sum_{k=-\infty}^{\infty} |F_{hk0}|^2 \, e^{2\pi i \left(\frac{u}{a}h + \frac{v}{b}k\right)}$$

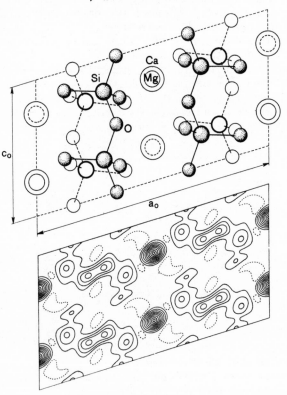

FIG. 102.   Projection of the elementary cell (four Si-O chains) of diopside (see p. 173): (above) with atoms; (below) with electron density derived from the Fourier analysis. [W. L. Bragg, Z. f. Krist. 70 (1929), 488.]

[1] H. Lipson and W. Cochran, *The Crystalline State*, III (1953), p. 277.

Part
III | Chemical Crystallography [1]

In this part we shall study the actual structure in which the "points" are occupied by atoms or ions, which, by their mutual forces, maintain the structure and determine its properties.

A. The Bonds

It is probable that all chemical bonds are of an electric nature (Desaguliers, 1742; Berzelius, 1819).

Four extreme types are distinguished:[2] (1) heteropolar (ionic) bond; (2) homopolar (covalent, atomic) bond; (3) metallic bond; (4) residual (Van der Waals) bond. The bond between two particles is often a combination of bond conditions (resonance bond).

We can get information on the kind of bond from (1) the distance between the particles; (2) the distribution of the electrons between the particles, which appears from the Fourier analysis (p. 125); (3) the nature of the particles, which is inferred from their behavior under the influence of infrared radiation (p. 250).

Heteropolar Bond

The particles are present as ions, their outer shells containing generally eight or eighteen electrons and each electron belonging to an ion. Between ions of opposite charges there are an attractive Coulomb force (inversely proportional to the square of the distance between the centers) and a repulsive Born force (inversely proportional to approximately the tenth power of the distance); when the ions are of the same charge, both of these forces are repulsive (p. 231).

The forces are *not oriented*, and the ions behave as small charged spheres. The arrangement of the surrounding oppositely charged ions is therefore a question of space (and of the size of the charges).

The smaller the distances between the centers of the ions and the

---

[1] R. C. Evans, *An Introduction to Crystal Chemistry* (1948); C. W. Stillwell, *Crystal Chemistry* (1938); C. W. Bunn, *Chemical Crystallography* (1946); W. Hückel, *Anorganische Strukturchemie* (1948); P. Groth, *Chemische Krystallographie*, 5 vols. (1906–19), description of all known crystals, no structures; *Strukturberichte*, 7 vols. (1913–43), description of all known structures; *Structure Reports*, 7 vols. (1951); R. W. G. Wyckoff, *Crystal Structures* (1948–53).

[2] Cf. J. A. A. Ketelaar, *Chemical Constitution* (New York, 1953).

larger their charges, the stronger are the bonds, and the greater, in general, is the hardness of the crystal (Table 11).

TABLE 11

	BeO	MgO	CaO	BaO	LiCl	SrO
ionic distance in A [1]	1.65	2.12	2.41	2.77	2.57	2.57
hardness on Mohs' scale [2]	9	6.5	4.5	3.5	3	3.5

From the melting point — the point at which the thermal movements become too great for the structural forces — it appears that the bond becomes weaker as the distance between the ions increases. The melting point also becomes higher when the charges increase (Table 12).

TABLE 12

	NaF	NaCl	NaBr	NaI	NaF	CaO
distance in A	2.31	2.82	2.99	3.24	2.31	2.41
melting point in °C	988	801	740	660	988	2,570

The electrons are all bound; the crystals are non-conducting or only very slightly conducting. Through the action of ultraviolet light or X-rays, however, electrons can be freed and conductivity can occur (p. 247).

The melt shows good ionic conductivity and is therefore decomposed by a transmitted current.

The refraction may be derived additively from the ion refractions (p. 252). (See p. 250 for the absorption of light rays and also for residual rays).[3]

Homopolar Bond

The outer shells of two particles are completed to a total of eight or eighteen by sharing pairs of electrons (Lewis, Kossel, 1926); for single bonds this is indicated by $:\ddot{C}l:\ddot{C}l:$ and for triple bonds by $:N:::N:$.

By this type of bond, therefore, an atom with seven valence electrons ($n = 7$) binds only one atom of the same kind, for then the outer shells

---

[1] 1 A = 1 Ångström unit = 10^{-8} cm.

[2] See p. 236.

[3] K. Fajans, Zeitschrift für Kristallographie 61 (1925), 18, and 66 (1928), 321, gives a survey of the properties.

are completed; and atoms with outer shells of less than four electrons cannot be bound to one another merely by homopolar bonds [the $(8 - n)$ rule].[1]

One particle cannot bind others in all directions, for the bonds are oriented. The NH_3 molecule is pyramidal; the H_2O molecule is not rectilinear, but the angle from O to H particles is 105°; single bonds between C particles are always oriented in tetrahedral directions, as in diamond, for example (p. 149). This kind of bond may be called "specifically chemical" and — in contrast to the ionic bond, which may be called "physical" — may be represented by a dash in the proper direction.

The electrons often being strongly bound, the crystals are insulators and, like the ionic structures, transparent. In molten state the conductivity is nil. The refractive index is often very high, the luster resinous.

The homopolar bond can be stronger than any other; diamond has hardness 10 (Mohs). The melting point is often high: C (diamond), about 3,500°; Si, 1,417°; Ge, 958° C.

Metallic Bond

All or many electrons of the outer shell form a mobile negative cloud, in which the positive "ions" lie (Drude, 1900).[2] The bond, therefore, is undirected. There is excellent conductivity without decomposition (electronic conduction). With light, especially ultraviolet light, electrons can be removed from the surface of a crystal (photoelectric effect). The bond is very variable in strength, and the hardness of the crystals therefore varies a great deal.

Residual Bond

This bond is the attraction between dipoles. It is proportional to the strength of the dipole and is inversely proportional to about the sixth power of the distance; it is weak at normal atomic distances. Three cases are distinguished: (1) permanent dipoles — for example, H_2O and NH_3 (orientation effect); (2) induced dipoles (induction effect); (3) dipoles generated by dynamic polarization, which may be explained by wave mechanics (dispersion effect). This last effect, as a rule, makes the greatest contribution to the bond, which is undirected. The particles, mostly molecules, are present in the structure in the same condition as in the liquid or in the vapor. The crystals are transparent and non-conducting.

[1] C. W. Stillwell, *Crystal Chemistry* (1938), p. 68.
[2] Cf. G. V. Raynor, *An Introduction to the Electron Theory of Metals* (1949).

The H Bond

Some atoms with a strong electron affinity — for example, O or F or N — may be bound by an H nucleus (proton), and then the distances are considerably smaller than usual. In O–H–O, for instance, the distance of the O ions is 2.55 A, whereas the radius of the O ion is normally 1.32 A. The bond occurs mainly in organic crystals and plays an important role in many polymerizations. It occurs also, however, in KH_2PO_4 and NH_4F. In the latter N and F form a structure of the wurtzite type (p. 153), and H nuclei connect each N with 4 F and each F with 4 N. In NH_4Cl, Cl has too small an electron affinity, and a coordination structure appears (p. 152).

Resonance Bond

The bond between two particles often has a mixed character. The

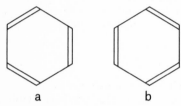

a   b

FIG. 103. The bond condition in the benzene ring is a resonance, chiefly of *a* and *b*.

bond condition in a benzene ring is mainly (formally) an average of the conditions indicated in Fig. 103; the distance C–C, which is 1.54 A for a single bond and 1.35 A for a double bond, becomes 1.39 in the entirely flat and regular C hexagon. This resonance can be fully explained in a quantum-mechanical way, and it occurs frequently with bonds which may be considered mixed ionic and atomic bonds. This is probably the cause of the rather great variability of the radii of the particles.

B. The Particles

The particles which occupy the "points" of the structure are atoms or ions. Strictly, we should speak of atoms only when the structure contains no other bonds than residual bonds, but in the case of homopolar and metallic bonds also we do speak of atoms.

It is assumed that in the crystals these particles can be considered small spheres and that they possess a fairly constant effective radius, the structure being a packing of small spheres touching one another (Barlow, 1897; Sollas, 1898; Bragg, 1920; Goldschmidt, 1926). This effective radius — or, briefly, radius — is not equal to the radius of the outer electron shell.

Structures in which the corresponding particles have the same or nearly the same radii are called *commensurable*. The atomic radii are calculated from the distances in the elements; for the ions we start from $O^{2-} = 1.32$ A and $F^- = 1.33$ A, which values were determined in another way by Wasastjerna (1923).

The nature of the particles in a structure can be determined from their radii, from the strength of X-ray diffraction (accurate Fourier analysis), or by means of residual rays (p. 250).

A number of atomic and ionic radii are mentioned in Table 13 [1] and in Fig. 104. In general, we see in a horizontal row of the periodic system — that is, among particles with the same number of electron shells — that the radius decreases with increasing charge of the nucleus; this effect is also clear in the row of the rare earths (lanthanide contraction). In a vertical column the radius becomes larger with increase of the number of shells; in the fourth and fifth rows, however, the radii are about the same. The radius of a particle increases as its positive charge decreases — for example,

Pb^{4+}	Pb^{2+}	Pb	Pb^{4-}
0.84	1.32	1.74	2.15

For a double, and still more for a triple, bond, the radius is less; for example, the distance $C-C$ is 1.54, $C=C$ is 1.35, and $C\equiv C$ is 1.20 A.

The radius of a particle depends more or less on the number of the nearest neighbors (that is, touching it); in other words, it depends on the *coordination number* (p. 144). The values for the coordination number 6 are indicated in Table 13. The radius changes approximately as follows: with coordination number 4 it decreases by 7%; with number 8 it increases by 3%; with number 12 it increases by 6%.

The most important decrease of the radius occurs with *polarization* of the particle. In an electric field, nucleus and electron shells shift with respect to one another, the particle becomes a dipole, and the atom shows, so to speak, a flattening at the side of the polarizing particle. The strength of the dipole, the moment **p**, is equal to the product of charge and shifting. The amount of shifting (polarizability) of each particle is approximately a constant, α; thus $\mathbf{p} = \alpha\mathbf{E}$ if **E** is the strength of the field. The polarizability is especially great for large negative ions (Table 14, in which many values are rather uncertain).

Experimentally, the polarizing force of an ion can be determined less well, and usually it is considered to be equal to the field strength at a distance equal to the effective radius (Table 15). Small positive ions, especially, polarize strongly, in particular the very small H^+ ion. Polari-

---

[1] Uranium and the elements beyond it are not placed in the correct columns.

TABLE 13 Effective Radii of the Atoms and Ions (in Å)

Period	I	II	IIIa	IVa	Va	VIa	VIIa	VIII	VIII	VIII	Ia	IIa	III	IV	V	VI	VII	O
1	H (1): 1− 1.27; 0 0.37; 1+ 0.0																	He (2): 0 0.93
2	Li (3): 0 1.52; 1+ 0.78	Be (4): 0 1.11; 2+ 0.34											B (5): 0 0.95; 3+ 0.2	C (6): 4− 2.6; 0 0.77; 4+ 0.2	N (7): 3− 1.7; 0 0.71; 5+ 0.1	O (8): 2− 1.32; 0 0.60; 6+ 0.1	F (9): 1− 1.33; 0 0.6; 7+ 0.1	Ne (10): 0 1.60
3	Na (11): 0 1.86; 1+ 0.98	Mg (12): 0 1.60; 2+ 0.78											Al (13): 0 1.43; 3+ 0.57	Si (14): 4− 1.98; 0 1.17; 4+ 0.39	P (15): 3− 2.12; 0 1.08; 5+ 0.3	S (16): 2− 1.74; 0 1.04; 6+ 0.3	Cl (17): 1− 1.81; 0 0.99; 7+ 0.3	Ar (18): 0 1.92
4	K (19): 0 2.31; 1+ 1.33	Ca (20): 0 1.97; 2+ 1.06	Sc (21): 0 1.51; 3+ 0.83	Ti (22): 0 1.49; 3+ 0.69; 4+ 0.64	V (23): 0 1.32; 2+ 0.72; 3+ 0.65; 4+ 0.61; 5+ 0.4	Cr (24): 0 1.25; 2+ 0.8; 3+ 0.65; 4+ 0.35; 6+ 0.35	Mn (25): 0 1.29; 2+ 0.91; 3+ 0.70; 4+ 0.52; 7+ 0.46	Fe (26): 0 1.26; 2+ 0.83; 3+ 0.67	Co (27): 0 1.26; 2+ 0.82	Ni (28): 0 1.24; 2+ 0.78	Cu (29): 0 1.27; 1+ 0.96	Zn (30): 0 1.33; 2+ 0.83	Ga (31): 0 1.22; 3+ 0.62	Ge (32): 4− 2.7; 0 1.22; 2+ 0.9; 4+ 0.44	As (33): 3− 2.22; 0 1.26; 3+ 0.69; 5+ 0.47	Se (34): 2− 1.91; 0 1.16; 6+ 0.4	Br (35): 1− 1.96; 0 1.19; 7+ 0.4	Kr (36): 0 2.01
5	Rb (37): 0 2.43; 1+ 1.49	Sr (38): 0 2.10; 2+ 1.27	Y (39): 0 1.81; 3+ 1.06	Zr (40): 0 1.62; 4+ 0.87	Nb (41): 0 1.43; 4+ 0.69; 5+ 0.69	Mo (42): 0 1.36; 4+ 0.68; 6+ 0.6	Tc (43): 0 1.36	Ru (44): 0 1.32; 4+ 0.65	Rh (45): 0 1.34; 3+ 0.69; 4+ 0.65	Pd (46): 0 1.37; 1+ 0.50	Ag (47): 0 1.44; 1+ 1.13	Cd (48): 0 1.49; 2+ 1.03	In (49): 0 1.62; 3+ 0.92	Sn (50): 4− 2.15; 0 1.40; 4+ 0.74	Sb (51): 3− 2.45; 0 1.40; 3+ 0.90; 5+ 0.5	Te (52): 2− 2.0; 0 1.43; 4+ 0.89; 6+ 0.5	I (53): 1− 2.20; 0 1.36; 7+ 0.5	Xe (54): 0 2.20
6	Cs (55): 0 2.62; 1+ 1.65	Ba (56): 0 2.17; 2+ 1.43	57 rare earths 71 — La (57): 0 1.86; 3+ 1.04; Ce (58): 0 1.83; 3+ 1.02; 4+ 1.02	Hf (72): 0 1.59; 4+ 0.84	Ta (73): 0 1.42; 4+ 0.69	W (74): 0 1.37; 4+ 0.68	Re (75): 0 1.37; 7+ 0.6	Os (76): 0 1.34; 4+ 0.67	Ir (77): 0 1.35; 4+ 0.66	Pt (78): 0 1.38; 1+ 0.55	Au (79): 0 1.44; 1+ 1.37	Hg (80): 0 1.49; 2+ 1.12	Tl (81): 0 1.71; 1+ 1.49; 3+ 1.05	Pb (82): 4− 2.15; 0 1.74; 2+ 1.32; 4+ 0.84	Bi (83): 0 1.55; 3+ 1.20; 5+ 0.7	Po (84)	At (85)	Rn (86)
7	Fr (87)	Ra (88): 2+ 1.52	Ac (89): 3+ 1.11	Th (90): 0 1.82; 4+ 0.95	Pa (91): 4+ 0.91	U (92): 0 1.38; 3+ 1.04; 4+ 0.89	Np (93): 0 1.50; 2+ 1.18; 3+ 1.02; 4+ 0.88	Pu (94): 2+ 1.16; 3+ 1.01; 4+ 0.86	Am (95): 2+ 1.16; 3+ 1.00; 4+ 0.85	Cm (96)	Bk (97)	Cf (98)	E (99)	Fm (100)	Mv (101)	No (102)		

NH_4^+ 1.50
OH^- 1.32
H_2O 1.38
$=CH_2$ 2.00

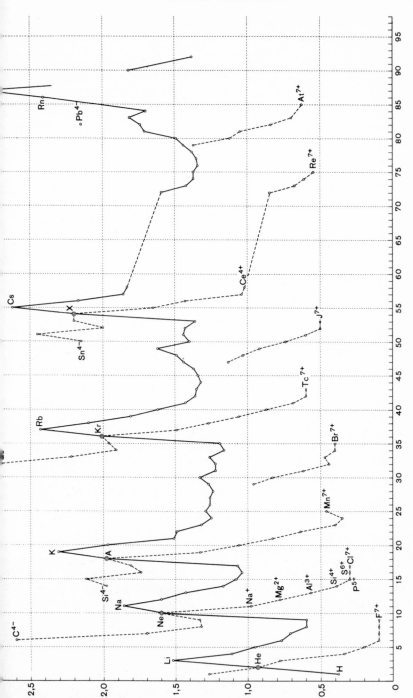

FIG. 104. Radii of some atoms and ions; the atomic numbers are indicated along the horizontal axis.

TABLE 14 **Polarizability ($\alpha \cdot 10^{24}$) of Some Ions**

	I	II	III	IV	V	VI	VII
2	Li^+ 0.075	Be^{2+} 0.028	B^{3+} 0.014			O^{2-} 3.1	F^- 0.99
3	Na^+ 0.21	Mg^{2+} 0.12	Al^{3+} 0.065	Si^{4+} 0.043		S^{2-} 7.25	Cl^- 3.05
4	K^+ 0.85	Ca^{2+} 0.57	Sc^{3+} 0.38	Ti^{4+} 0.27		Se^{2-} 6.4	Br^- 4.17
5	Rb^+ 1.81	Sr^{2+} 1.42	Y^{3+} 1.04			Te^{2-} 9.6	J^- 6.28
6	Cs^+ 2.79	Ba^{2+} 2.08	La^{3+} 1.56	Ce^{4+} 1.20			

zation occurs only slightly when the nearest neighbors of an atom are evenly arranged in space round it, as, for example, in a coordination structure (p. 144); strongly polarizable ions, therefore, often form other structures (radical and layer structures, p. 146).

The Particles (OH)⁻ and H_2O

• (OH)⁻ is in itself a "cylindrical" dipole, with one positive and one negative pole of unequal strength. Strong polarization can change it into a "tetrahedral" dipole, in which three vertices have a charge of $- \frac{1}{2} e$ and one a charge of $+ \frac{1}{2} e$. These tetrahedra can be placed in such a way that they attract one another: the layers in the structure of $Al(OH)_3$. These (OH)⁻ ions with four poles occur also in $B(OH)_3$ and form with B flat layers. Their effective radius is 1.35 A, whereas that of the "cylindrical" ion is 1.32 A.

H_2O forms what is almost a sphere with a radius of 1.38 A ($O-H = 0.958$ A, and the angle $H-O-H$ is 105°), which in itself is a quadrupole with two poles $+e$ and two poles $-e$, all at about the same tetrahedral angles. For this reason the environment of H_2O is nearly always tetrahedral; cf. the structures of ice (p. 157) and zeolites (p. 175).

TABLE 15 **Polarizing Force of Some Ions (Unit Undetermined)**

	I	II	III	IV	V	VI	VII
1							H^- 0.62
2	Li^+ 1.64	Be^{2+} 17.30				O^{2-} 1.15	F^- 0.57
3	Na^+ 1.04	Mg^{2+} 3.29	Al^{3+} 9.23	Si^{4+} 26.30		S^{6+} 51.90 S^{2-} 0.66	Cl^- 0.30
4	K^+ 0.57	Ca^{2+} 1.78 Zn^{2+} 2.90	Sc^{3+} 4.35 Ga^{3+} 7.80	Ti^{4+} 9.76 Ge^{4+} 20.66		Se^{2-} 0.55	Br^- 0.26
5	Rb^+ 0.45 Ag^+ 0.78	Sr^{2+} 1.24 Cd^{2+} 1.88	Y^{3+} 2.67 In^{3+} 3.54	Zr^{4+} 5.28 Sn^{4+} 7.30	Nb^{5+} 10.50	Te^{2-} 0.45	J^- 0.21
6	Cs^+ 0.37	Ba^{2+} 0.98 Hg^{2+} 1.59	La^{3+} 2.01 Tl^{3+} 2.72	Ce^{4+} 3.84 Pb^{4+} 5.67			
7				Th^{4+} 3.31			

C. The Structures

The bonds between the particles in a structure may be of one single type (*homodesmic* structures) or of more than one type (*heterodesmic*). In the latter case the particles may be bound by one type to finite or virtually infinite complexes (molecules, radicals, chains, layers, frameworks), and the structure may be formed by another type.

The structure-forming bond will be called the *structural bond*. If this bond is weak, the matter is soft, can easily be melted, and evaporates at a low temperature. The other bond is called the molecular bond, radical bond, etc.

The structure in which the particles possess a minimum of potential energy is stable (p. 231). We distinguish the types of structure exhibited in Table 16, but remark that not all structures can be classified in this way.

TABLE 16 **Types of Structure, with Examples**

kinds of atoms	structure		structural bond			
			ionic bond	atomic bond	metallic bond	residual bond
one	coordination layer chain molecule	neutral neutral neutral		C (diamond)	Cu	Ar C (graphite) Se S_8
two	coordination framework layer chain molecule	neutral neutral neutral neutral	NaCl	ZnS quartz Sb$_2$S$_3$	NiAs FeS$_2$	CdI$_2$ CO
more than two	coordination framework	$\{$ neutral charged	CaTiO$_3$ ortho-clase		CuFeS$_2$	cellulose
	layer	$\{$ neutral charged	mica group			
	chain	$\{$ neutral charged	pyroxene group			
	molecule radical	$\{$ neutral charged (radical) (complex)	CaCO$_3$		CoAsS	organic compounds

Coordination Structures

All the particles are surrounded by the adjacent particles more or less *evenly*, and the structure is homodesmic.

Each particle may therefore be imagined as situated at the center of a polyhedron, the corners of which are at the centers of gravity of the adjacent particles, the number of which determines the *coordination number*. Table 17 and Fig. 105 present the most important cases in which we may speak of evenly surrounded (central) particles.

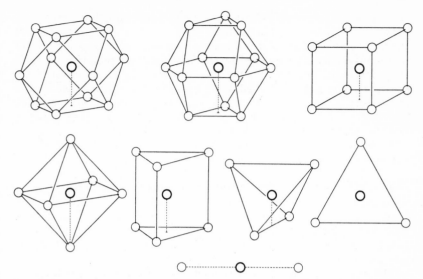

FIG. 105. The principal kinds of coordination: cubo-octahedron, disheptahedron, hexahedron, octahedron, trigonal prism, tetrahedron, triangle, and straight line.

TABLE 17

coordination number	polyhedron	$\dfrac{r_A}{r_X}$
12	cubo-octahedron and disheptahedron	1
8	hexahedron	1 — 0.73
6	octahedron and trigonal prism	0.73 — 0.41
4	tetrahedron	0.41 — 0.22
3	equilateral triangle	0.22 — 0.15
2	straight line	0.15 — ∞

With a homopolar bond, the coordination will depend on the oriented directions of the bonds (diamond and sphalerite, see p. 153). Ionic and metallic bonds are not oriented; the structure may be considered as a packing of small charged spheres, and the coordination is principally dependent on the ratio of the magnitudes and the ratios of the charges of the spheres. The residual bond appears in coordination structures in the crystals of the inert gases.

In structures with only one kind of atoms and with a metallic bond, the environment is cubo-octahedral (Cu) or, if the bond is slightly homopolar, disheptahedral (Mg) or hexahedral (W) or, if the bond is still more homopolar, octahedral (white Sn).

In ionic structures with two or more kinds of particles, the environment depends on the ratio of the numbers (and therefore of the charges) and the magnitudes and the states of polarization of the ions. The dependence on the magnitudes is expressed by the fact that the structure is unstable if an ion is too small to fill the hole at the center of the surrounding, oppositely charged ions, which are in contact with each other. But, if an ion is larger than the hole, the structure is quite stable. So, in general, the (large) negative ions touch one another entirely or nearly entirely, and the (small) positive ions do not.

Table 17 gives critical values, the radius of the positive ions being r_A and that of the negative ions r_X.

Molecular, Radical, Chain, Layer, and Framework Structures

In these structures not all particles are evenly coordinated. *Complexes* occur, which may be neutral or charged; chains may be called one-dimensional infinite radicals, etc. As a rule, the structures are hetero-desmic, the bonds in the complexes often being stronger than the structural bond.

The irregularity in the environment is caused by polarization of ions, by predominance in number or magnitude of the particles of one kind, or by homopolar bonds.

In this way, CdI_2 becomes a layer structure because of the strong polarizability of I; S_8 forms a molecular structure by the homopolar bonding of eight S atoms among themselves; CCl_4 has a molecular structure as a consequence of the large number of Cl particles, four of which surround each C particle ("enwrapped" compounds, Van Laar, 1916).

The excellent cleavage of layer and chain structures, which leaves the layers and chains intact, can be explained, especially when the complexes are neutral and the structural bond is therefore a residual bond.

In molecular structures, the stronger bond within the molecules becomes manifest in the fact that the molecules are still present in the melt, as in S_8 and organic compounds; after melting and crystallization, organic isomers are again the same isomers.

In radical structures, the complexes are charged; in Table 23 (p. 168) a few such radicals are described. Doubly charged ions around the central ion mostly form tetrahedral radicals, and singly charged ions preferably form octahedral radicals. In hypophosphite the radical is $(H_2PO_2)^-$, a tetrahedron, and NaH_2PO_2 is therefore, not an acid salt, but a normal salt, for it does not contain H bound to O.

If neutral molecules are strong dipoles (NH_3) or quadrupoles (H_2O), they may form, with an ion, a strongly bound complex radical; as a rule, the radical is then positive: $[Co(NH_3)_6]^{2+} Cl_2$; $[Na (H_2O)_4]_3^+ PO_4$. In aqueous solution the forces of hydration usually are not able to dissociate radicals or complexes.

D. Description of the Structures [1]

One Kind of Atom [2]

We divide the elements into four classes (Table 18): I, metals; II, sub-metals; III, sub-metalloids; IV, metalloids.

Class I (Metals)
Normal homopolar bonding, on account of the $(8 - n)$ rule (p. 137), is not possible with these elements. The metallic bond may be considered

TABLE 18

H₂ ○																	He ○
Li ⊡	Be ○											B	C	N	O	F	Ne □
Na ⊡	Mg ○					transition metals						Al □	Si	P	S	Cl	Ar □
K ⊡	Ca □	Sc ○	Ti ○	V ⊡	Cr ⊡	Mn	Fe ⊡	Co ○	Ni □	Cu □	Zn* ○	Ga	Ge	As	Se ○	Br	Kr □
Rb ⊡	Sr □	Y ○	Zr ○	Nb ⊡	Mo ⊡	Tc ○	Ru ○	Rh □	Pd □	Ag □	Cd* ○	In	Sn	Sb	Te ○	I	Xe □
Cs ⊡	Ba ⊡	R.E.§ □	Hf ○	Ta ⊡	W ⊡	Re ○	Os ○	Ir □	Pt □	Au □	Hg* ○	Tl ○	Pb □	Bi	Po	At	Rn
Fr	Ra	Ac	Th □	Pa	U												

I*a* light metals	I*b* metals									II sub-metals	III sub-met-alloids	IV metal-loids

§ not all   □ cubic close packing (Γ_c')
* not entirely   ⊡ structure with centered cubes (Γ_c'')
                         ○ hexagonal close packing

[1] Strukturberichte 1–7 (1913–43) and Structure Reports 8–15 (1951–57); R. W. G. Wyckoff, *The Structure of Crystals*, I, II (1931, 1934); R. W. G. Wyckoff, *Crystal Structures*, I, II, III (1948–53); W. L. Bragg, *Atomic Structure of Minerals* (1937).

[2] Henceforth the stable modification at the lowest temperature is indicated by α.

an extreme homopolar one; all atoms have a large number of valence electrons in common. This bond is not oriented. The structure is usually a close or very close packing of spheres.

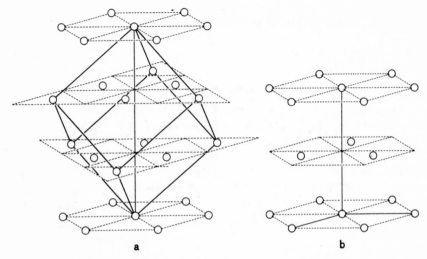

FIG. 106. The relative positions of the centers of gravity of equal spheres in (a) cubic and (b) hexagonal close packing. The arrangement in the layers indicated is always the same; the stacking is (a) 1—2—3—1... or (b) 1—2—1... Theoretically, there is an infinite number of stackings, all giving the same close packing; some of these are nearly realized in structures (O and F in topaz: 1—2—1—3—1—2—1—3...).

Two *close packings* occur here, the cubic (Cu, etc.) and the hexagonal (Mg, etc.), in which $c_0 : a_0 = 1.67$ (Fig. 106); in both the coordination number is 12, and the coordinations are, respectively, that of a cubo-octahedron and that of a disheptahedron (Fig. 105); the interstices occupy 25.95% of the space.

There is also a regular, somewhat less close packing, with coordination number 8 (W, etc.); the volume of the interstices is 32% (Fig. 107).

The structures are indicated in Tables 18 and 19. Many metals, however, crystallize in other structures as well and are therefore *allotropic* (Fe in four modifications).

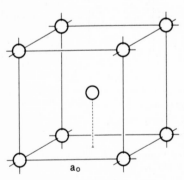

FIG. 107. The structure of W, etc.

TABLE 19

cubic close packing $(Fm3m-O_h^5)$	Al	Ar	Ni	Cu	Ag	Pt	Au	Pb
a_0	4.04	5.43	3.52	3.61	4.09	3.92	4.08	4.95
$\Gamma_c''(Im3m-O_h^9)$	Na	K	V	Cr	Fe	Mo	Ta	W
a_0	4.29	5.21	3.04	2.88	2.87	3.14	3.30	3.16
hexagonal close packing $(P6_3/mmc-D_{6h}^4)$	Be	Mg	Ti	Zn	Cd			
a_0	2.28	3.20	2.95	2.66	2.96			
c_0	3.57	5.20	4.73	4.94	5.56			

Class II (Sub-metals)

The homopolar character of the bond is stronger here. Zn $(P6_3/mmc-D_{6h}^4)$ and Hg $(R\,3m-D_{3d}^5)$ are still hexagonal but deviate somewhat from the close packing. Allotropism often occurs, and then a definitely homopolar bond occurs in one of the phases — for example, with Sn, which forms in the gray modification a structure of the diamond type (Fig. 112). The bond in white tin $(I4_1/amd-D_{4h}^{19})$ is preponderantly metallic, and the coordination number is 6 (nearly octahedral).

Class III (Sub-metalloids)

These elements have preponderantly homopolar and residual bonding. Diamond has only the first $(Fd3m-O_h^7)$ (Fig. 112), and its bonds are oriented tetrahedrally; the distance C-C is 1.54 A, as in aliphatic compounds; $a_0 = 3.57$ A; the atoms fill only 33.8% of the space.

In graphite $(P6_3/mmc-D_{6h}^4)$ the bond within the layers is a resonance bond, like that in benzene; C-C = 1.42 A. Between the layers, the distance between which is 3.40 A, residual bonding may perhaps be assumed (Fig. 108), and the electronic conductivity parallel to the layers is 10,000 times as strong as that normal to the layers. One half of the atoms are mutually equivalent, and so are the other half. If foreign matter can come in between the layers, these may separate as much as 8 A without destroying the coherence of the crystal.

Residual bonding may also be assumed between the layers in the layer structures of As, Sb, and Bi $(R\bar{3}m-D_{3d}^5)$.

Selenium and tellurium possess rings or chain structures $(P3_121-D_3^4)$ with chains of spiral form:

$$: Se : Se : Se :$$

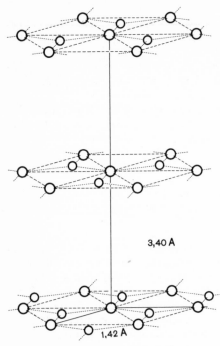

FIG. 108. The structure of graphite; the two structurally different kinds of C atoms are differently indicated.

Class IV (Metalloids)

These elements have molecular structures, homopolar bonds within the molecules, and residual bonds between the molecules. The molecules are not spherical, and the structure cannot be considered a packing of spheres. If the molecules are large, they do not easily fit into a structure; they hook into one another and show a tendency to the vitreous state (sulphur and selenium).

The sulphur structure ($Fddd-D_{2h}^{24}$) has ring-shaped molecules, S_8 (Fig. 109), of which there are sixteen in an elementary cell, all lying

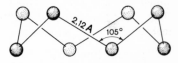

FIG. 109. S_8 molecule.

parallel to the C axis (orthorhombic sulphur). The crystal shows strong birefringence (p. 201).[1] At 110° the melt is a mobile liquid; at 200° it is very viscous; the rings are then broken and hook into one another.[2]

The crystal structures of the inert gases, owing to the pure residual bond, show a close packing of spheres.

In the hydrogen structure the H_2 molecules rotate, probably even at 0° K; thus their sphere of action is sphere-symmetrical, and the molecules are arranged in hexagonal close packing.

The halogens also form structures with molecules consisting of two atoms: Cl_2, Br_2, and I_2 are orthorhombic ($Cmca-D_{2h}^{18}$), with layer structures, the smallest distance between the atoms being 2.02, 2.27, and 2.70 A, respectively.

[1] C. W. Bunn, Chemical Crystallography (1946), p. 282.
[2] But see J. Bouman and others, Selected Topics in X-Ray Crystallography (1951), p. 206.

The centers of gravity of N_2 molecules nearly form a Γ_c' lattice ($P2_13$–T^4; cf. p. 155, CO type).

Two Kinds of Atoms

Table 20 gives representatives of a few types; in the description $A, B, \ldots$ are metals (also NH_4), and $X, Y, \ldots$ are metalloids (also radicals, OH etc.).

TABLE 20

	heteropolar bond	homopolar bond	metallic bond	residual bond
coordination structures	NaCl CsCl CaF_2 TiO_2 SiO_2 Al_2O_3	α-ZnS (sphalerite) β-ZnS (wurtzite) Cu_2O	NiAs NaTl mixed crystals	
layer structures (neutral layers)			MoS_2	$CdCl_2$ CdI_2
chain structures (neutral chains)		Sb_2S_3		
molecular structures		Sb_2O_3	FeS_2 CaC_2	CO

NaCl type (halite)

Cubic, $Fm3m$–O_h^5; coordination structure (Fig. 110). Two interpenetrating F lattices (Γ_c'), A at $[[000]]$ and X at $[[\frac{1}{2}\frac{1}{2}\frac{1}{2}]]$. For both kinds of particles the coordination number is 6. A third of all compounds AX examined crystallize according to this type; also a number of mixed crystals are based on this type (p. 162).

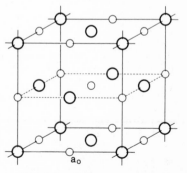

Fig. 110. The structure of NaCl: Na $\bigcirc$, Cl $\circ$.

	F	Cl	Br	I
Li	$a_0 =$ 4.03	5.14	5.50	6.01
Na	4.62	5.64	5.97	6.47
K	5.34	6.28	6.59	7.07
Rb	5.64	6.54	6.87	7.34
Cs	6.02	β 6.94		
NH$_4$		β 6.55	β 6.91	β 7.26
Ag	4.93	5.56	5.78	

	S	Se	Te
Mg	5.20	5.46	
Ca	5.70	5.92	6.36
Sr	6.01	6.24	6.47
Ba	6.38	6.59	7.00
Sn		6.30	
Pb	5.93	6.14	6.45
Mn	5.21	5.45	

	Mg	Ca	Sr	Ba	Cd	Ti	Mn	Fe	Co	Ni
O	4.24	4.81	5.15	5.54	4.71	4.24	4.45	4.29	4.25	4.17

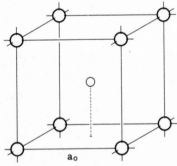

CsCl type

Cubic, $Pm3m-O_h^1$; coordination structure (Fig. 111). Two interpenetrating P lattices (Γ_c), A at [[000]], X at [[$^1/_2$ $^1/_2$ $^1/_2$]]; the coordination number for both kinds is 8; $d =$ the smallest distance A–X.

FIG. 111.   The structure of CsCl: Cs ◯, Cl ○.

	αCsCl	CsBr	CsI	TlCl	TlBr	α-NH$_4$Cl	α-NH$_4$Br
a_0	4.11	4.29	4.56	3.84	3.98	3.88	4.05
d	3.57	3.71	3.95	3.32	3.45	3.36	3.51

There are also a number of alloys (p. 161).

α-ZnS type [1] (sphalerite)

Cubic, $F\bar{4}3m$–T_d^2; coordination structure (Fig. 112). The packing is not close, the bonds are oriented, and the structure is typical, with homopolar structural bonds. This type often occurs when one component lies as far to one side of the fourth column of the periodic system as the other lies to the other side. Similar to the diamond type. A at [[000]], X at [[$^1/_4$ $^1/_4$ $^1/_4$]]. For both kinds of atoms, the coordination number is 4.

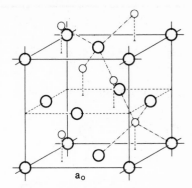

FIG. 112. The structure of α-ZnS (sphalerite): Zn ◯, S ○. This is also the structure of diamond, but then all the rings represent carbon atoms.

	S	Se	Te
Be	$a_0 = 4.87$	5.14	5.63
Zn	α 5.43	5.67	6.10
Cd	α 5.83	6.05	6.48
Hg	5.85	6.08	6.45

	Cu	Ag
F	$a_0 = 4.26$	
Cl	5.42	
Br	5.69	
I	6.06	β 6.47

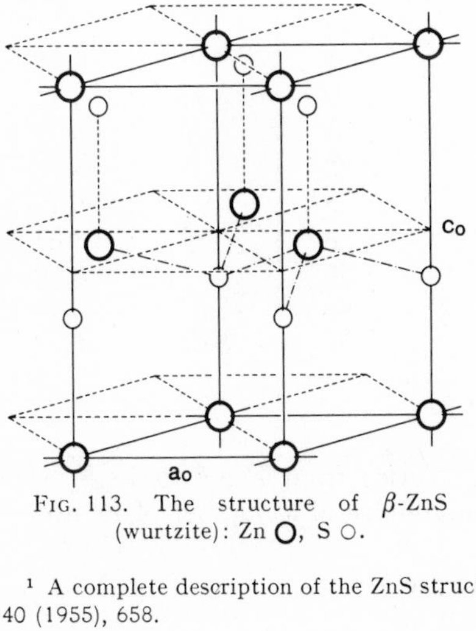

β-ZnS type [1] (wurtzite)

Hexagonal, $P6_3mc$–C_{6v}^4; coordination structure (Fig. 113). The coordination is the same as for sphalerite; the structural bond is homopolar. The structure can be described as sphalerite atomically twinned with a three-fold axis as twinning axis; in energy the two types are nearly equivalent.

FIG. 113. The structure of β-ZnS (wurtzite): Zn ◯, S ○.

---

[1] A complete description of the ZnS structures will be found in F. G. Smith, Am. Min. 40 (1955), 658.

	NH$_4$F	α AgI	BeO	ZnO	β-ZnS	β-CdS	CdSe
a_0	4.39	4.58	2.69	3.24	3.81	4.13	4.30
c_0	7.02	7.49	4.37	5.18	6.23	6.69	7.01

c_0/a_0 is approximately 1.63.

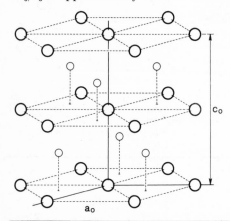

NiAs type (niccolite)
Hexagonal, $P6_3/mmc$–D_{6h}^4; coordination structure (Fig. 114). For both kinds of atoms the coordination number is 6, A in octahedra, X in trigonal prisms.

FIG. 114.   The structure of NiAs (niccolite): Ni ◯, As ○.

		S	Se	Te	As	Sb
Cr	a_0	3.44	3.59	3.98		4.11
	c_0	5.67	5.80	6.21		5.47
Mn	a_0			4.12	3.72	4.12
	c_0			6.69	5.70	5.79
Fe	a_0	3.43 [1]	3.61	3.80		4.06
	c_0	5.68	5.87	5.65		5.13
Co	a_0	3.37	3.59	3.88		3.87
	c_0	5.16	5.27	5.36		5.19
Ni	a_0	3.42	3.66	3.96	3.61	3.94
	c_0	5.30	5.33	5.35	5.03	5.14

c_0/a_0 varies from 1.4 to 1.6.

The composition of iron sulphide varies from FeS [2] to Fe$_6$S$_7$. The deviation from FeS is caused by the absence of a number of Fe atoms.

[1] But see M. J. Buerger, Am. Min. 32 (1947), 411.
[2] E. F. Bertaut, Bull. Min. et Crist. 79 (1956), 276.

The phenomenon of unoccupied sites occurs quite frequently; such structures are called *defect structures* (p. 227).

NaTl type

Cubic, $Fd3m-O_h^7$; coordination structure (Fig. 115). The coordination number of both kinds is 8, but each atom is surrounded by four atoms of the same and four of the other kind of atom (in α-CsCl by eight of the other kind).

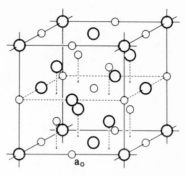

Fig. 115. The structure of NaTl: Na ⬡, Tl ○.

	Al	Zn	Ga	Cd	In	Tl
Li	$a_0 = 6.37$	6.22	6.21	6.70	6.80	
Na					7.31	7.49

CO type

Cubic, $P2_13-T^4$; molecular structure. Molecules CO; distance C-O = 1.05 A. The centers of gravity of the molecules nearly form a lattice Γ''_c; the atoms are situated nearly as the S atoms in pyrite are (p. 160); $a_0 = 5.64$ A. N_2 also crystallizes in this type of structure; N-N = 1.065A; $a_0 = 5.67$ A.

CaF₂ type (fluorite)

Cubic, $Fm3m-O_h^5$; coordination structure (Fig. 116). The coordination number of A is 8; that of X is 4. Three

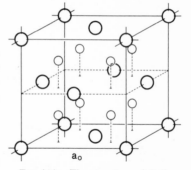

Fig. 116. The structure of CaF₂ (fluorite): Ca ⬡, F ○.

interpenetrating F lattices (Γ''_c), A at [[000]], X at [[$^1/_4$ $^1/_4$ $^1/_4$]] and [[$^3/_4$ $^3/_4$ $^3/_4$]]. Li₂O etc. form a so-called anti-fluorite structure.

	F₂	Cl₂	O₂	Li₂	Cu₂
Ca	$a_0 = 5.46$				
Sr	5.79	6.99			
Ba	6.19				
Zr			5.08		
U			5.47		
O				4.63	
S				5.72	5.57

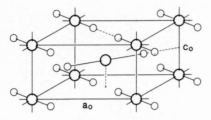

FIG. 117. The structure of TiO_2
(rutile): Ti $\bigcirc$, O $\circ$.

TiO_2 type (rutile)

Tetragonal, $P4_2/mnm-D_{4h}^{14}$; coordination structure (Fig. 117). Six interpenetrating lattices Γ_q. Round each X there are three A in a triangle and round each A six X in an octahedron.

	Mg	Zn	Ti	Sn	Pb	W	Mn	Fe	Ge
F_2 a_0	4.62	4.72					4.87	4.83	
c_0	3.05	3.14					3.31	3.36	
O_2 a_0			4.59	4.72	4.96	4.86	4.38		4.39
c_0			2.96	3.16	3.39	2.77	2.86		2.86

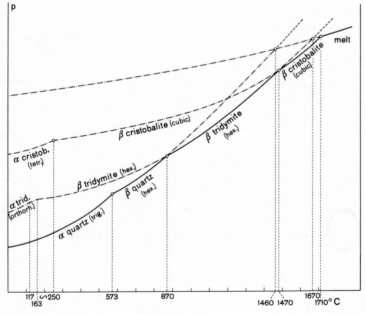

FIG. 118. Equilibrium diagram of SiO_2; $\alpha \rightleftarrows \beta$ at an external pressure of 1 bar at 572.3°, 1,000 megabars at 595°, and 9,000 megabars at 820° C. [See C. W. Correns, *Einführung in die Mineralogie* (1949), p. 158; R. B. Sosman, "New and Old Phases of Silica," Brit. Cer. Soc. 54 (1955), 655.]

Modifications of SiO_2

The equilibrium diagram is given in Fig. 118.

In all silicates and also in the SiO_2 modifications, Si is surrounded by 4 O in a tetrahedron; the distance Si-O ∞ 1.62 A. In the modifications the tetrahedra are *linked* in a coordination structure or a framework in such a way that each O belongs to two tetrahedra, each O being entirely or nearly symmetrically surrounded by 2 Si.

α-cristobalite, $P4_12_12–D_4^4$, tetragonal-trapezohedral.

β-cristobalite, $Fd3m–O_h^7$, possesses the highest symmetry;[1] the centers

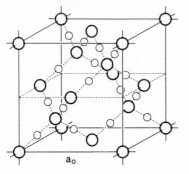

of gravity of the tetrahedra form a diamond structure; $a_0 = 7.12$ A (Fig. 119).

α-tridymite, orthorhombic, pseudo-hexagonal.

β-tridymite, $P6_3/mmc–D_{6h}^4$, hexagonal. The centers of gravity of the tetrahedra form a wurtzite structure. γ-Ice [2] shows a structure of the same type.

α-quartz, $P3_121–D_3^4$ and $P3_221–D_3^6$, trigonal-trapezohedral.

β-quartz, $P6_222–D_6^4$ and $P6_422–D_6^5$, hexagonal-trapezohedral.

FIG. 119. The structure of β-cristobalite: Si $\bigcirc$, O $\circ$.

In quartz, the tetrahedra are ranged in the form of a screw round the threefold axes; Fig. 120 gives the Si particles of three layers of tetrahedra in a vertical projection. It has

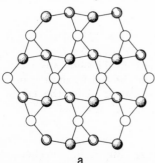
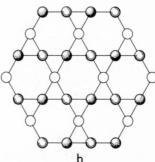

a   b

FIG. 120. Projection along the C axis of the Si ions in (a) α-quartz and (b) β-quartz. Ions shown in the same shading are at the same height [W. L. Bragg, *Atomic Structure of Minerals* (1937)].

[1] Perhaps orthorhombic, pseudo-cubic.
[2] R. C. Evans, *An Introduction to Crystal Chemistry* (1948), p. 298.

been ascertained that in α-quartz the bond is half heteropolar and half homopolar.[1] For α-quartz $a_0 = 4.90$ A and $c_0 = 5.39$ A.

α-Al$_2$O$_3$ type (corundum)

Hexagonal, $R\bar{3}c-D_{3d}^6$; coordination structure. The O ions are situated according to hexagonal close packing; Al ions are situated in two-thirds of the octahedral interspaces. γ-Al$_2$O$_3$, which above 900° changes quickly into corundum, belongs to the spinel type (p. 166), in which O lies in cubic close packing; Al fills twenty-one and two-thirds of the twenty-four interspaces which are occupied in spinel (defect structure; cf. p. 227).

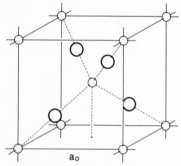

FIG. 121.   The structure of Cu$_2$O (cuprite): Cu ◯, O ○.

Cu$_2$O type (cuprite)

Cubic, $Pn3m-O_h^4$; coordination structure (Fig. 121). The coordination number of Cu is 2, and that of O is 4; $a_0 = 4.26$ A.

MoS$_2$ type (molybdenite)

Hexagonal, $P6_3/mmc-D_{6h}^4$; layer structure. The layers consist of Mo surrounded on both sides by S sheets. Each Mo atom has 6 as coordination number (trigonal prism). Excellent cleavage planes run between the layers; $a_0 = 3.85$ A, and $c_0 = 17.46$ A.

CdCl$_2$ type

Hexagonal, $R\bar{3}m-D_{3d}^5$; layer structure [2] (Fig. 122). The coordination number of Cd is 6. A layer consists of a Cd sheet surrounded on each side by a sheet of Cl. These layers are built in the same way as those of CdI$_2$, but the stacking is different in that the fourth sheet comes right above the first one. The cleavage is excellent along the layers. The primitive cell is rhombohedral. Cl is strongly polarized.

CdI$_2$ type

Hexagonal, $P\bar{3}m1-D_{3d}^3$; layer structure (Fig. 123). The coordination number of A is 6 (coordination nearly octahedral). A layer consists of

[1] R. Brill, C. Hermann, and C. Peters, Annalen der Physik V, 41 (1942), 233.

[2] An examination of the stacking of the layers in layer structures will be found in J. M. Bijvoet, N. H. Kolkmeyer, and C. H. MacGillavry, X-Ray Analysis of Crystals (1951), pp. 164, 274.

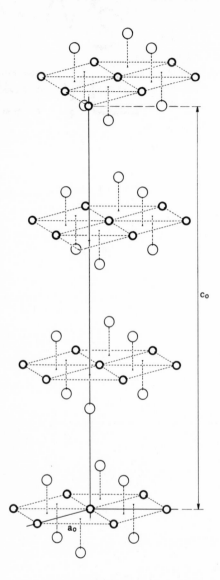

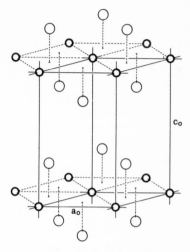

FIG. 123. The structure of CdI_2:
Cd $\bigcirc$, I $\circ$.

an A sheet surrounded at each side by an X sheet (similar to $CdCl_2$). X is strongly polarized. The layers are placed in such a way that the second layer lies right above the first one (cf. hexagonal and cubic close packing, p. 148).

The layers may also be shifted sideways, however, and then the sequence is less regular (*averaged structure*). In some kinds of mica (p. 174) the stacking of the layers is such that not until the twentieth layer is reached do we find a layer lying right above the first one[1] (for an explanation see p. 257).

[1] See note on p. 158 and H. Strunz, *Mineralogische Tabellen* (1957), p. 306.

FIG. 122.   The structure of $CdCl_2$: Cd $\bigcirc$, Cl $\circ$.

		Ag$_2$	I$_2$	S$_2$	(OH)$_2$
F	a_0	2.99			
	c_0	5.71			
Mg	a_0		4.14		3.12
	c_0		6.88		4.73
Ca	a_0		4.48		3.64
	c_0		6.96		4.85
Cd	a_0		4.24		3.47
	c_0		6.84		4.64
Fe	a_0		4.04		3.24
	c_0		6.75		4.47
Ti	a_0			3.40	
	c_0			5.69	

FeS$_2$ type (pyrite)

Cubic, $Pa3-T_h^6$; "molecular" structure (Fig. 124). X_2 forms "molecules." The centers of gravity of these molecules and those of the A atoms form a structure of the halite type; in pyrite the distance S-S = 2.10 Å.

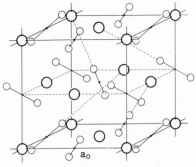

FIG. 124.   The structure of FeS$_2$ (pyrite): Fe ◯, S ○.

	Mn	Fe	Co	Ni	Ru	Pt	O	C
S$_2$	$a_0 = 6.11$	5.42	5.53	5.74	5.59			
Se$_2$			5.86	5.96	5.93			
As$_2$						5.97		
Sb$_2$						6.44		
N$_2$							5.72	
O$_2$								5.63

CaC$_2$ type

Tetragonal, $I4/mmm-D_{4h}^{17}$; molecular structure. This type is one of the so-called X_2 structures, to which the pyrite type also can be said to belong. The centers of gravity of the X_2 molecules form with those of the A atoms a somewhat tetragonally deformed halite structure.

Sb_2S_3 type (stibnite)

Orthorhombic, $Pnma-D_{2h}^{16}$; chain structure. Chains $(Sb_2S_3)_\infty$ in the direction of the C axis. Bi_2S_3 has the same structure.

Sb_2O_3 type (senarmontite)

Cubic, $Fd3m-O_h^7$; molecular structure. The centers of gravity of the molecules As_4O_6 form a diamond structure; $a_0 = 11.08$ A. An inorganic molecular structure is rare (cf. S_8).

Solid Solutions (Interstitial Structures) [1]

Small ($< \infty 0.6$ A) particles, H, B, C, N, and O, are, as it were, included in the structures of metals. The compounds are still metallic and often very hard; Ti and Zr, for example, may contain up to several tens percent O and are then very brittle.[2] With Fe_4N the filling-in N atoms in the $\varGamma'_c$ lattice of Fe are in the cavities $[[^1/_2\,^1/_2\,^1/_2]]$; with PdH the H atoms in the $\varGamma'_c$ lattice of Pd are situated in such a way that a sphalerite structure (somewhat deformed orthorhombically) occurs. The filling of sites may also be partial (cf. defect structures, p. 227).

Binary Alloys

The components of a binary alloy are two elements of the classes I, II, and III (p. 147). The alloys can arise from melting together, from sintering, or from simultaneous electrolytic deposition.

The structural bond is entirely (class I) or chiefly (classes II and III) the metallic bond. The notion of valence virtually disappears. There is often no trace of a stoichiometric compound, and the structures are characterized by a great adaptability; that is, they permit much replacement without essential structural change. In pure metal crystals gliding (p. 238) generally takes place easily; in alloys the gliding planes are, as a rule, less "smooth," and gliding becomes more difficult, so that an alloy is often hard and sometimes brittle (only 0.1% Bi in Au is required to make the alloy brittle). The color of an alloy is still unpredictable, but sometimes very striking; some gold-iron crystals are blue.

Table 21 gives a survey of features that may appear:

---

[1] We identify solid solutions with interstitial structures. In mixed crystals (or alloys) some atoms (ions) are replaced by foreign atoms either in an ordered or in an unordered way (substitutional structures).

[2] See the tables by G. Becker, Physikalische Zeitschrift 34 (1933), 185.

TABLE 21

	Ia alkali metals, alkaline- earth metals	Ib transition metals and Cu, Ag, Au	II sub-metals	III sub- metalloids
Ia	slightly miscible	poorly known	structures; types $\begin{cases} NaCl \\ CsCl \end{cases}$ often chiefly ionic bonding	structures; types $\begin{cases} NaCl \\ CaF_2 \end{cases}$
Ib		mixed crystals and overstruc- tures	electron compounds	structures; types $\begin{cases} NiAs \\ FeS_2 \\ MoS_2 \end{cases}$
II			often mixed crystals	structures; ZnS type
III				structures; NaCl type

1. There is no mixing; the crystals of the components remain beside one another. If miscibility occurred at high temperature, this diminishes with a fall of temperature, one of the components or a compound separates, and the hardness of the whole, as a rule, increases; for example, steel is iron with the finely divided and separated compound Fe_3C.

2. *Mixed crystals* are formed. Mixed crystals do not fulfill the condition (p. 95) that the environments of equal atoms are the same unless one imagines atoms of one kind to be replaced by atoms of the other kind. The following conditions are favorable to the formation of mixed crystals: (a) the radii of the atoms differ by no more than about 10%; (b) there is not much difference in electropositivity; (c) the structures of the components are of the same type, preferably Γ'_c.

Vegard's rule applies here very approximately; that is, the dimensions of the cell depend linearly on the composition.

The melting point of a mixed crystal lies, for many compositions, below that of each of the components, and the conductivity is less than that of either component. The structural sites are often occupied at random (statistical distribution), but sometimes with a certain regularity, and there are transitions from arbitrary occupation (disorder) to entirely regular order (the structure complies with the condition on p. 98).

We may distinguish "long-distance order" and "short-distance order." If, for example, the two components are each represented by the same number of atoms, and if these are placed alternately, there will be, one-dimensionally, absolute order. If the arrangement, for example, is of the following type,

$$\overset{\text{O . O . . O . . O . O O . O}}{\underset{\text{1 2 3 4 5 6 7 8 9 10 11 12 13 14}}{}}$$

there is not much long-distance order, for atom 1 has the right partners at places 2, 3, 4, 8, 9, 10, and 11, but the wrong ones at 5, 6, 7, 12, 13, and 14. The short-distance order, however, is considerable, for 1 has one right neighbor, 2 has two, 3 has two, 4 has one, etc. The better the order, the greater the ductility (gliding) of the crystal.

3. Normal, stoichiometric structures are formed, in which equal atoms occupy crystallographically equivalent places. In some cases over-structures are formed (see below).

As the components approach class II or III, the bond becomes more homopolar, and normal structures are preferred to mixed crystals. These structures, those of the so-called *intermediate compounds*, generally deviate in type from those of the components.

The *electron compounds* form a group of intermediate compounds, in which the ratio of the number of atoms to the number of valence electrons is fixed (Hume-Rothery, 1926, Table 22).

TABLE 22. **Some Representatives of the Three Types of Hume-Rothery Alloys**

phase	number		ratio
	atoms	electrons	atoms/electrons
$AgCd$	2	$1 + 2$	2/3
$CuZn$	2	$1 + 2$	2/3
Ag_5Cd_8	13	$5 + 16$	13/21
Cu_9Al_4	13	$9 + 12$	13/21
Ag_5Al_3	8	$5 + 9$	4/7

In the system Ag-Cd (Fig. 125) α is cubic ($\varGamma''_c$); β has approximately the CsCl type; γ is cubic, with fifty-two atoms per elementary cell; ε is hexagonal (close packing); η is hexagonal, deviating somewhat from ε.

Over-structures (Super-lattices) [1]

If the structures of the alloy components are entirely or nearly of the same type, if mixed crystals occur over a wide range, and if the

[1] Cf. N. F. M. Henry, H. Lipson, and W. A. Wooster, *The Interpretation of X-Ray Diffraction Photographs* (1951), p. 211.

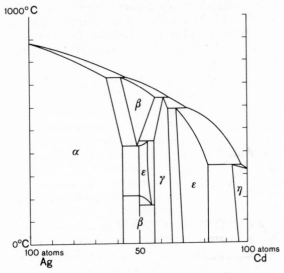

FIG. 125.   Equilibrium diagram of Ag-Cd alloys.

atoms differ somewhat in magnitude, then, for some ratios of the numbers, the distribution of the atoms is still statistical on rapid cooling, but not on slow cooling, and a structure is formed, of the type of the com-

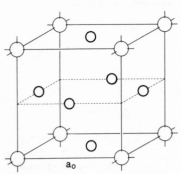

FIG. 126.   The structure of AuCu₃:
Au ◯, Cu ⊙.

ponents, in which some of the original atoms have been replaced systematically, so that often a larger cell and a slightly deformed structure occur (*over-structures*).

In this way Au and Cu form a continuous series of mixed crystals, in which both components possess a structure Γ_c' and the radii of the atoms are 1.44 A and 1.27 A respectively. At the composition AuCu there occurs, with slow cooling, a tetragonal structure which scarcely deviates from a regular one (c_0/a_0 = 0.932), and at the composition AuCu₃ a cubic structure occurs (Fig. 126); in both the elementary cell is nearly equal to that of the original structures, but some of the original atoms have been replaced in a systematic way.

More than Two Kinds of Atoms [1]

To ionic structures Pauling's rules generally apply; for structures with two kinds of ions they are not of much use, but for those with more kinds of ions they may be of great importance.

1. Each positive ion is often surrounded by an entirely or nearly regular polyhedron of negative ions (this environment is determined by the charges and the ratio of magnitudes; see p. 145).

2. If we call the value of the ratio

$$\frac{\text{valence of positive ion}}{\text{number of surrounding negative ions}}$$

the strength of the bond between positive and negative ion, then the sum of all strengths exercised on a negative ion is equal to its valence (Fig. 127).

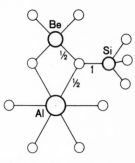

FIG. 127. The small circles are O ions; the total strength of the bonds on the central O ion is equal to its valence.

3. As a rule, the polyhedra have only corners in common, not edges or faces.

4. If there are different positive ions, those with a great charge and a small coordination number tend to have few corners of their polyhedra in common.

The rules are applied, for example, in the designing or checking of silicate structures, the polyhedra of which are tetrahedra (Si and Al), octahedra (Al, Fe, and Mg), or the polyhedra with fourteen faces mentioned on p. 145 (Ca, Na, and K.)

$CaTiO_3$ type (perovskite)

Cubic, $Pm3m-O_h^1$, coordination structure (Fig. 128). The coordination number of Ca is 12, of Ti is 6, and of O is 2. A very accurate examination indicates that perovskite, at room temperature, is not cubic, but triclinic. $BaTiO_3$ is polymorphous[2]; the tetragonal phase has $a_0 = 3.99$ and $c_0 = 4.04$ A.

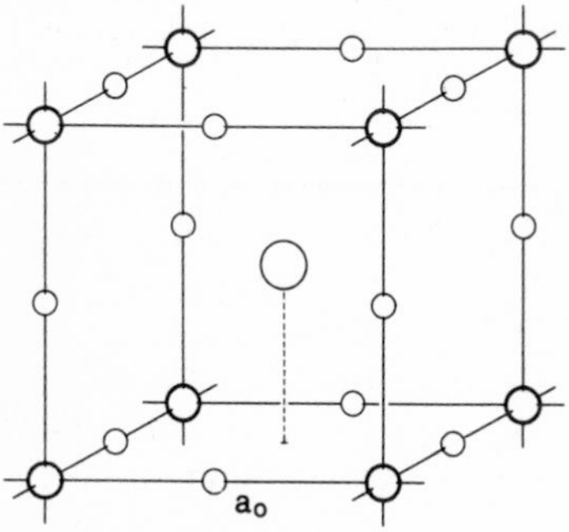

FIG. 128. The structure of $CaTiO_3$ (perovskite): Ca ◯, Ti ◉, O ○.

[1] See Table 16, p. 144.
[2] H. D. Megaw, *Ferroelectricity in Crystals* (1957), p. 58.

	KMg	KZn	CsCd	KI	CaTi	LaAl	NaW	BaTi
F_3	$a_0 = 4.01$	4.06						
Cl_3			5.21					
O_3				4.47	3.81	3.79	3.83	4.00

$MgAl_2O_4$ type (spinel)

Cubic, $Fd3m$–O_h^7 (Fig. 129). The elementary cell contains thirty-two O ions, lying in cubic close packing. Eight of the sixty-four tetrahedral interstices are occupied by Mg, and sixteen of the thirty-two octahedral interstices are occupied by Al, the Mg ions thus forming a structure of the diamond type.

Some structures have to be written $B(AB)O_4$ because the tervalent metal ions occupy the places of the bivalent ions, and the latter, statistically divided, occupy half of the places of the tervalent ions.

The structure allows large defects (see p. 227).

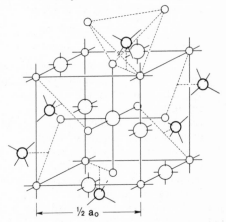

FIG. 129. The structure of $MgAl_2O_4$ (spinel): Mg ⬡, Al ◯, O ○. An eighth of the elementary cell is shown.

	MoAg₂	TiMg₂	Fe₃	MgAl₂	Co₃	Ni₃	ZnK₂
O_4	$a_0 = 9.28$	8.44	8.41	8.11	8.11		
S_4					9.42	9.48	
$(CN)_4$							12.57

$CuFeS_2$ type (chalcopyrite)

Tetragonal, $I\bar{4}2d$–D_{2d}^{12}; nearly a coordination structure (Fig. 130). A somewhat deformed α-ZnS type; 4 Zn are replaced by 2 Cu and 2 Fe.

$$a_0 = 5.24 \text{ A}; \quad c_0 = 10.30 \text{ A}.$$

CoAsS type (cobaltite)

Cubic, $P2_13-T^4$; molecular structure. Pyrite type, in which 1 S has been replaced, so that the symmetry decreases.

CoAsS	NiAsS	NiSbS
$a_0 = 5.60$	5.71	5.91

Mixed Crystals [1]

Two groups may be distinguished: the atoms "replacing" one another (*diadochic* atoms) may be of equal (isovalent mixed crystals) or of unequal valence (anisovalent mixed crystals). (Na, K)Br belongs to the first group; to the second group belong the spinels of the AlMgAlO$_4$ type (p. 166) and also, in a certain sense, Li_2TiO_3, which has the halite type of structure and in which Li^+ and Ti^{4+}, sta-

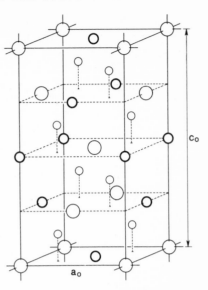

FIG. 130.   The structure of CuFeS$_2$ (chalcopyrite): Cu $\bigcirc$, Fe $\mathbf{O}$, S $\circ$.

tistically distributed, occupy the A places. Li_2TiO_3 and MgO, in all ratios, give mixed crystals of the same type of structure.

Vegard's rule is generally applicable: the dimensions of the cell vary linearly with the composition.

Radical Structures

A radical is a charged, finite complex of ions or atoms, often, for the greatest part, homopolarly bound, which, as a structural component, can participate as a whole in an infrared vibration of the structure (p. 251) and which usually exists also in solution. The structure of a radical is generally such that a number of negative ions are grouped evenly round a central, strongly positive, small ion.

If the surrounding particles are compound ions or molecules, one speaks of *complex radicals*.

In some structures, especially at temperatures not far below the melting point, the radicals rotate, a phenomenon by which the symmetry of the crystal is often increased. In the NaNO$_3$ crystal, whose melting point is 315° C, a few NO$_3$ radicals rotate at 150° C and all NO$_3$ radicals rotate at 275° C. NH$_4$ rotates in NH$_4$I at room temperature.

A few types of radicals are presented in Table 23.

[1] See p. 161.

TABLE 23

| shape | radical | |
	composition	distance [1]
octahedral	$(PtCl_6)^{2-}$	2.33 A
	$(SiF_6)^{2-}$	1.72
	$[Al(OH)_6]^{3-}$	
	$[Ir(NO_2)_6]^{3-}$	
	$[Mn(NH_3)_6]^{2+}$	
	$[Al(H_2O)_6]^{3+}$	
tetrahedral	$(SO_4)^{2-}$	1.49
	$(ClO_4)^{-}$	1.46
	$(PO_4)^{3-}$	1.64
	$(WO_4)^{2-}$	1.73
	$(CrO_4)^{2-}$	1.58
	$(SiO_4)^{4-}$	1.62
	$(BeF_4)^{2-}$	1.61
	$[Cu(CN)_4]^{3-}$	
pyramidal	$(SO_3)^{2-}$	1.39
	$(ClO_3)^{-}$	1.38
flat	$(CO_3)^{2-}$	1.24
	$(NO_3)^{-}$	1.27
	$(PtCl_4)^{2-}$	2.32
angular	$(NO_2)^{-}$	1.13
rectilinear	$(CN)^{-}$	1.06 [2]
	$(SCN)^{-}$	2.96 [2]
annular	$[Si_6O_{18}]^{12-}$	

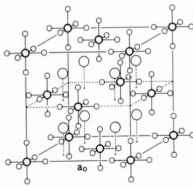

FIG. 131.   The structure of K_2PtCl_6:
K◯, Pt ⵔ, Cl ○.

K_2PtCl_6 type

Cubic, $Fm3m$–O_h^5; radical structure (Fig. 131). Pt is octahedrally surrounded by 6 Cl; the centers of gravity of these small octahedra form, together with the K ions, a structure of the fluorite type.

[1] From the central ion to the surrounding ions.

[2] Distance S–N; N has a free valence.

	$PtCl_6$	$TiCl_6$	SiF_6	$SnCl_6$	$PdBr_6$	$Co(NH_3)_6$
K_2	$a_0 = 9.74$			9.98		
$(NH_4)_2$	9.85		8.40			
Rb_2		9.94			10.04	
Cl_2						10.12

$BaSO_4$ type (barite)

Orthorhombic, $Pnma$–D_{2h}^{16}; radical structure (Fig. 132). The structure of $CaSO_4$, anhydrite, differs somewhat from that of barite.

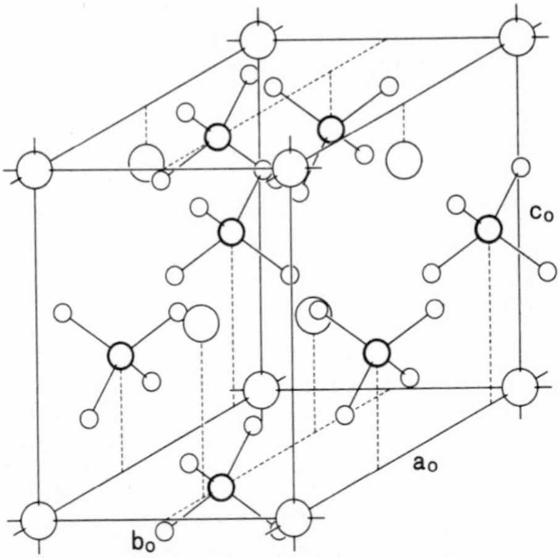

FIG. 132. The structure of $BaSO_4$ (barite): Ba ◯, S ⬤, O ○.

	$SrSO_4$	$BaSO_4$	$PbSO_4$	$KClO_4$
a_0	8.36	8.85	8.45	8.85
b_0	5.36	5.44	5.38	5.66
c_0	6.84	7.13	6.93	7.24

$CaWO_4$ type (scheelite)

Tetragonal, $I4_1/a$–C_{4h}^6; radical structure (Fig. 133). The surrounding of W by O is nearly tetrahedral.

		IO_4	MoO_4	WO_4
Na	a_0	5.32		
	c_0	11.93		
K	a_0	5.75		
	c_0	12.63		
Ca	a_0		5.23	5.26
	c_0		11.44	11.35
Ba	a_0		5.56	5.64
	c_0		12.76	12.70
Pb	a_0		5.41	5.44
	c_0		12.08	12.01

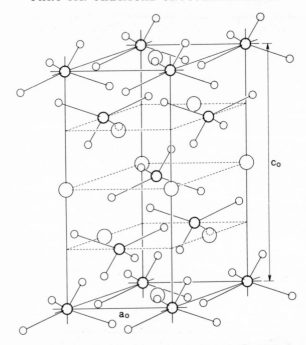

FIG. 133.   The structure of CaWO₄ (scheelite): Ca ◯, W 🔵, O ○.

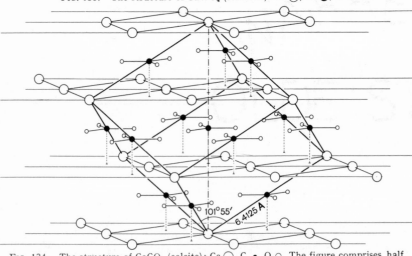

FIG. 134.   The structure of CaCO₃ (calcite): Ca ◯, C •, O ○. The figure comprises half of the height of the primitive rhombohedral cell.

$CaCO_3$ type (calcite)

Ditrigonal-scalenohedral, $R\bar{3}c-D_{3d}^6$; radical structure (Fig. 134).
C is surrounded by 3 O, all four lying in one plane, normal to the principal axis. The primitive cell is rhombohedral. The smallest "cleavage rhombohedron" is doubly ·primitive. The centers of gravity of CO_3 form with the Ca ions a structure which can be considered a compressed structure along a threefold axis of the NaCl type. The table gives the elements of the rhombohedral primitive cell.

		Mg	Ca	Zn	Mn	Fe	Na	Li
CO_3	a_0	5.61	6.36	5.67	5.84	5.75		
	α	48°12′	46°7′	48°26′	47°20′	47°25′		
NO_3	a_0						6.33	5.74
	α						47°17′	48°3′

In the dimorphous orthorhombic aragonite the radicals are the same and are also situated in parallel planes.

Complex Radicals [1] *and Hydrates*

The H_2O and NH_3 molecules are strongly polarizable and therefore able to form complex radicals. $[Mn(NH_3)_6]Cl_2$ is of the CaF_2 type, with $a_0 = 10.22$ A; also cubic, but of another type, are $Ca_3[Al(OH)_6]_2$ and $K_3[Ir(NO_2)_6]$; $[Al(H_2O)_6]Cl_3$ and $K_3[Cu(CN)_4]$ are hexagonal.

In other hydrates, too, six H_2O molecules often surround the metal ions, as in $Ni(H_2O)_6 SO_4 \cdot H_2O$, which is usually written $NiSO_4 \cdot 7H_2O$.

In gypsum, $CaSO_4 \cdot 2H_2O$, each Ca is surrounded by 6 O and 2 H_2O, and each H_2O is surrounded by 1 Ca and 2 O. The tetrahedral environment of H_2O is less pronounced here than in the zeolites (p. 175). In $CuSO_4 \cdot 5H_2O$, each Cu is surrounded by 4 H_2O, and a better way of writing may be $[Cu(H_2O)_4] SO_4 \cdot H_6O$. Alum may be written $[K(H_2O)_6] [Al(H_2O)_6] (SO_4)_2$.

Silicates [2]

After Berzelius the oxygen-containing silicon compounds (*silicates*) were considered salts, derived from acids which comply with the general formula $mSiO_2 \cdot nH_2O$. As a free acid, however, probably only H_4SiO_4 is known, the others being hypothetical.

From studies by Machatschki and determinations of structure,

[1] See Linus Pauling, *General Chemistry*, 2nd ed. (1953), p. 471.
[2] A survey of important compounds in ceramic products was made by G. R. Rigby, Transact. British Ceramic Soc. 48 (1949), 1.

especially by W. L. Bragg and his school, it appeared about 1927 that most of the silicates certainly cannot be considered salts, for acids with infinitely large acid radicals do not exist.

In all silicates the Si ion is tetrahedrally surrounded by four oxygen ions at about 1.62 A. These tetrahedra, with edges of 2.64 A, may be present as such in the structure, or they may occur *linked*; that is, two tetrahedra may have one oxygen ion, but not more, in common (cf. p. 165). Si^{4+}, however, may be replaced by Al^{3+} and in some cases O^{2-} by $(OH)^-$ or F^-, which are of about the same size.

The linkage can lead to finite or infinite complexes; nowadays the classification of the silicates is based on the type of these complexes.

Because Al may act as a substitute for Si and then has an environment of 4 O, but also occurs as an ion with an environment of 6 O, and since O may or may not form part of complexes, it was formerly not possible, on chemical grounds, without knowledge of the structures, to reach a satisfactory classification of the silicates.

I. Radicals. Small replacement of Si by Al.

    A. 1. Radicals $[SiO_4]^{4-}$, hence no linkage (Fig. 135). Zircon group, olivine group, garnet group, disthene group, topaz, titanite.
       2. Radicals $[Si_2O_7]^{6-}$ (Fig. 135). Calamine, melilite group.
       3. Radicals $[Si_5O_{16}]^{12-}$ (Fig. 136). Zunyite.
       4. Radicals $[SiO_4]$ and $[Si_2O_7]$ both. Vesuvianite.

    B. 1. Rings of three; $[Si_3O_9]^{6-}$ (Fig. 137). Benitoite.
       2. Rings of four; $[Si_4O_{12}]^{8-}$. Axinite.
       3. Hexagonal rings of six; $[Si_6O_{18}]^{12-}$ (Fig. 137). Beryl.
       4. Ditrigonal rings of six; $[Si_6O_{18}]^{12-}$. Tourmaline.

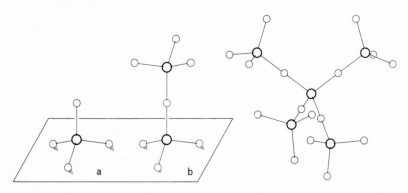

FIG. 135. The radicals (a) $[SiO_4]$ and (b) $[Si_2O_7]$.   FIG. 136.   The radical $[Si_5O_{16}]$

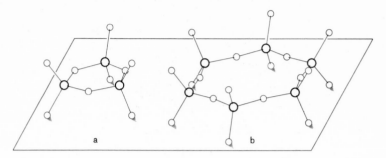

FIG. 137. The rings (*a*) [Si$_3$O$_9$] and (*b*) [Si$_6$O$_{18}$].

II. Charged chains. As much as a fourth of the Si may be replaced by Al. The cleavage is such that the chains are not broken, and so it is often fibrous (p. 235).

A. Single chains; [SiO$_3$] (Fig. 138). Pyroxene group.

B. 1. Chains of rings of four; [Si$_2$O$_5$] (Fig. 139). Sillimanite.

2. Chains of rings of six; [Si$_4$O$_{11}$] (Fig. 140). Amphibole group, serpentine group.

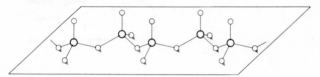

FIG. 138. The chain [SiO$_3$].

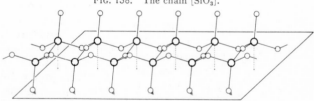

FIG. 139. The chain of rings of four [Si$_2$O$_5$].

FIG. 140. The chain of rings of six [Si$_4$O$_{11}$].

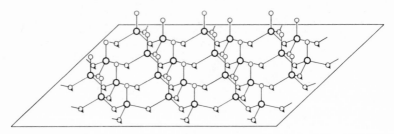

FIG. 141.   The layer [Si_4O_{10}].

III. Charged layers. Between a fourth and a half of the Si may be replaced by Al. The cleavage planes, which are always well developed, run between the layers.

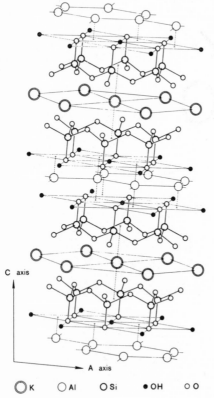

C axis

A axis

◎ K   ○ Al   ○ Si   ● OH   ○○ O

FIG. 142.   The structure of muscovite.

1. Layers of rings of four and eight; [Si_8O_{20}]. Apophyllite.
2. Layers of rings of six; [Si_4O_{10}] (Fig. 141). The negative layers, in themselves hexagonal, always contain (OH) and have the composition [(Si, Al)$_4O_{10}$](OH)$_2$. These layers, bound together, as a rule, by metal ions or metal hydroxydes, are shifted somewhat obliquely against one another in the structure, thereby producing a monoclinic whole. A number of these structures allow the penetration of foreign metal ions or molecules, if they are not too large, between the layers, thereby increasing the layer distance. The clay mineral montmorillonite may allow as much as a fourfold sheet of H_2O between the layers; the molecules of this H_2O are arranged hexagonally and

actually form a narrow sheet of ice with somewhat enlarged distances between the molecules. The ions or molecules which have penetrated can be driven out or exchanged (*base exchange*). These properties largely determine the fertility of the clay. Catalytically, also, the layer structures are important; they possess, as it were, a very large "internal surface," on which a catalyst may be applied and thus very finely divided.

Kaolin group, talc group, mica group (Fig. 142).

IV. Charged frameworks. The tetrahedra are linked in such a way that they form a three-dimensional infinite complex, which we may call a framework. Two tetrahedra have one O in common, and the composition of the framework is therefore $[(Si,Al)O_2]$. Without replacement of Si by Al this framework is neutral, and the structure is that of one of the SiO_2 modifications (p. 157). If replacement occurs, and it may involve as much as half of the Si, the framework becomes negative, and the charge must be compensated by positive ions such as Na, K, and Ca. Cavities often occur in the framework (porous frameworks), and they may be occupied by replaceable or irreplaceable molecules.

1. Compact frameworks. Feldspar group, nepheline, leucite, cordierite.
2. Porous frameworks.
   a. With salt molecules: sodalite group, cancrinite group, scapolite group.
   b. With water molecules: zeolite group; the water may be removed from the cavities and brought back into them without effect on the structure. The environment of each H_2O is approximately tetrahedral.

Organic Compounds

A molecular structure, with a residual bond as the structural bond, is usually present, but organic acids, bases, and salts and mixed organic-inorganic compounds often have ionic bonds.

Small molecules — CH_4, for example — may often be considered as spheres, and then the structure is a close packing of spheres; but for most molecules this view is not admissible. As the shape of these molecules is preserved, we can guess the structure of a crystal by packing its molecules into the volume of the cell, which is known beforehand.

On account of the homopolar bonds in a molecule the distances between the atoms in different compounds are fairly constant; often, however, the atoms are better thought of, not as true spheres touching one another, but as flattened spheres (Stuart, or calotte, models).[1] Table 24 gives some inter-atomic distances.[2]

TABLE 24

	distance in A	example
C — C [3]	1.54	aliphatic compounds; diamond
C = C [3]	1.35	ethylene
C ≡ C [3]	1.20	acetylene
C ⋯ C [3]	1.39	benzene ring; graphite
C — O	1.49	
C = O	1.14	
C — N	1.37	
C = S	1.64	
C — Cl	1.86	

The resonance bond of the benzene ring occurs also in oxalic acid, which forms a flat molecule.

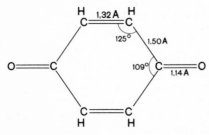

FIG. 143.   Molecule of benzochinone.

The angle between the valence directions of a C atom is nearly always 109°28′, especially in chains; it varies somewhat in rings (Fig. 143).

Of the aliphatic compounds, those with fairly long chains (length at least ten times the thickness) were examined first. These chains (paraffins, ketones, fatty acids, salts of fatty acids) always possess a zigzag shape (Fig. 144) and are placed in a structure with the long axes parallel; the chains are not parallel breadthwise, however, and therefore, if we look

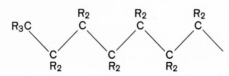

FIG. 144.   Chain in aliphatic compounds.

[1] Fortschritte der chemischen Forschung 1 (1950), 642; Nature 166 (1950), 59.

[2] More detail is given by R. C. Evans, *An Introduction to Crystal Chemistry* (1948), p. 313; for distances and angles in gaseous molecules and also in inorganic molecules, see Acta Cryst. 3 (1950), 46.

[3] Diagrams of the electron density around the two carbon nuclei will be found in J. M. Robertson, Journ. Chem. Soc. (1945), 249.

in the direction of the long axes, the arrangement shown in Fig. 148 often occurs.

Close to the melting point, the chains often rotate about the long axis. The width of the cell is independent of the length of the chain, but the length increases by 1.26 A when the chain is lengthened by one C. Paraffins are not always orthorhombic; the chains may also slope, the cell thereby becoming monoclinic. If the chains are polar — for example, on account of the presence of an alcohol, acid, or aldehyde group (ketones are never folded chains) — they form double layers in such a way that the active sides of two layers are placed against one another (Fig. 145).

We also find these double layers when soap — for example, sodium stearate, $C_{17}H_{35}COONa$ — slowly crystallizes as a thin sheet on a clean glass plate. We obtain single layers by letting a fatty acid spread out on a water surface; the

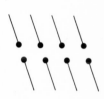

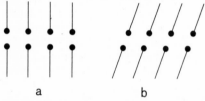

a   b

FIG. 145. Common arrangements of long polar chains of aliphatic compounds in their crystals.

FIG. 146. Relative positions of molecules of $C_{18}H_{37}NH_3Cl$ in the crystal.

hydrophilic groups —COOH are then turned towards the water; the chains, with difficulty, glide sidewise along one another, and the mobility of the water surface is considerably decreased (calming the sea by throwing oil on the waves).

With $C_{18}H_{37}NH_3Cl$ the situation in the structure is that shown in Fig. 146.

In aliphatic compounds with ring-shaped molecules these are puckered; the symmetry of the ring in hexamethylene, for example, is threefold and not sixfold (Fig. 147).

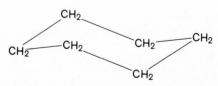

FIG. 147. Molecule of hexamethylene.

The benzene ring, on the other hand, is flat and has a sixfold axis; the cell of the benzene crystal is orthorhombic (Fig. 148).

In naphthalene ($C_{10}H_8$) and anthracene ($C_{14}H_{10}$), also, as in diphenyl

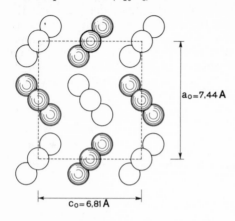

$a_0 = 7.44 A$

$c_0 = 6.81 A$

Fig. 148.   Projection along the B axis of the elementary cell of benzene. Of the four molecules of C_6H_6, only the C atoms are indicated; the shaded ones are at half the height.

and such compounds, all atoms of the multiple rings are situated in one plane. In 1,3,5-triphenyl-benzene, however, the outer rings have tilted approximately 25°.

The deformation which the nitro group causes in the benzene ring is remarkable (Fig. 149).

Some structures have closed cavities in which atoms or molecules may be enclosed without being chemically bound to the structure (cf. p. 175, IV, 2). If hydroquinone, for example, is crystallized out of a solution under a pressure of 40 atmospheres of argon,

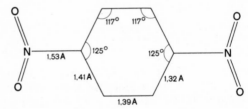

Fig. 149.   Molecule of dinitrobenzene.

each cavity encloses an atom of argon. The crystals are entirely stable; when they are dissolved, the argon is freed (*clathrate* crystals). [1]

Fibers [2]

These important compounds have very long molecules, the length of which is often variable (polymers) or not known.

[1] H. M. Powell, "Molecular Compounds," Endeavour 9 (1950), 154.

[2] The crystallographic definition of fiber reads: a fiber consists of a large number of long, parallel crystals, all having one and the same crystallographic axis in the longitudinal direction, the other two crystallographic axes lying at random.

Cellulose (Cotton, Flax, Ramie, Rayon)

A molecule (chain) is built up of a great number of glucose residues, which form double rings with composition $C_{12}H_{20}O_{10}$ and a length of 10.3 A (Fig. 150).

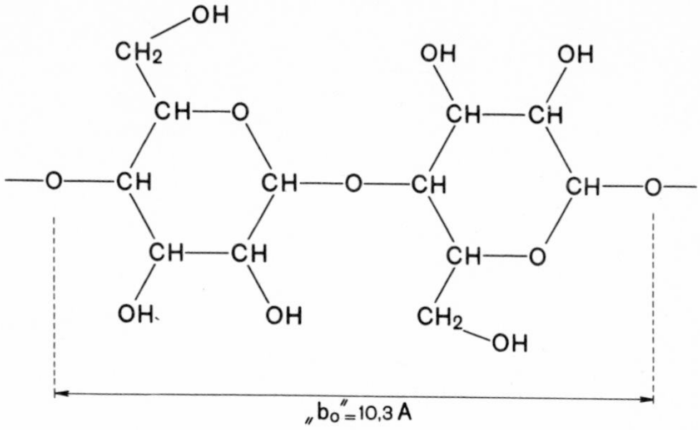

FIG. 150.   Two glucose residues in a cellulose chain: pseudo repeat distance.

The chains in the monoclinic cell are parallel to the *B* axis:

$$a_0 = 8.3 \text{ A}$$
$$b_0 \quad \text{unknown}$$
$$c_0 = 7.9 \text{ A}$$
$$\beta = 96°$$

The pseudo cell (its $b_0 = 10.3$ A) contains four glucose residues (Fig. 151).

The molecules often lie irregularly near one another, are sometimes twisted spirally (wood at the lower side of branches), or lie at an angle with one another (cotton);[1] so we cannot properly speak of crystal and cell. The periodicity 10.3 A, however, can always be clearly indicated experimentally.

Good parallelism of the chains gives strong fibers (ramie, flax). Cellulose is not elastic; the chains shift under strain, and the deformation is lasting.

Fibroin (Silk)

The chains are built up of units consisting of a glycine and an alanine molecule, connected, with loss of H_2O, by what is called the peptide bond:

$$- \text{C} - \text{N} -$$
$$\quad \| \quad \ \ |$$
$$\quad \text{O} \quad \text{H}$$

peptide bond

---

[1] W. T. Astbury, *The Fundamentals of Fibre Structure* (1933).

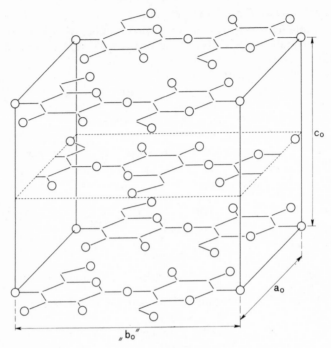

Fig. 151.   Orthorhombic pseudo cell of cellulose: four glucose residues, the O atoms of which are indicated.

The periodicity along the fiber axis is 7.0 A; the length of the molecules is said to be 120 times as great as their width.

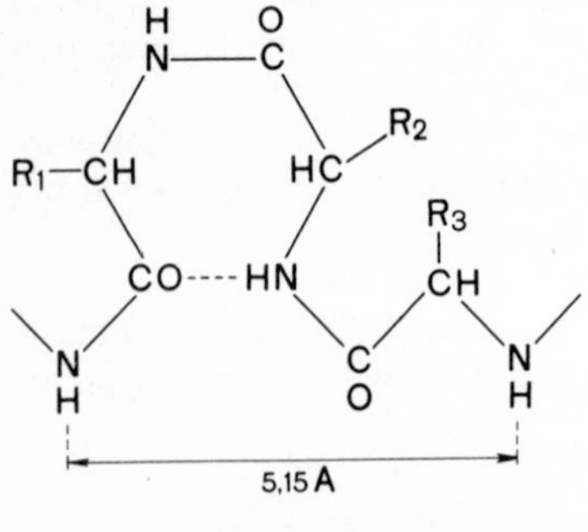

α-Keratin (*Wool, Hair, Horn, Whalebone*)

This also is essentially a polypeptide. The short periodicity distance of 5.15 A indicates that the chain is twisted, probably on account of a weak bond between N and C, as indicated in Fig. 152 by a broken line.

When pulled out, or strained, in hot water, the twisted (and spiral) chain stretches and may become twice as long as before; it then resembles

Fig. 152.   Pseudo repeat distance in an α-keratin chain; R_1, R_2, and R_3 are univalent groups.

the chain of silk or a relaxed muscle fiber. The contracted muscle corresponds to the unstretched, unstrained chain. The molecules of strained wool are somewhat different from those of unstrained wool, for weak bonds have been removed. Strained wool is called β-keratin, and the periodicity distance is 3.5 A (Fig. 153).

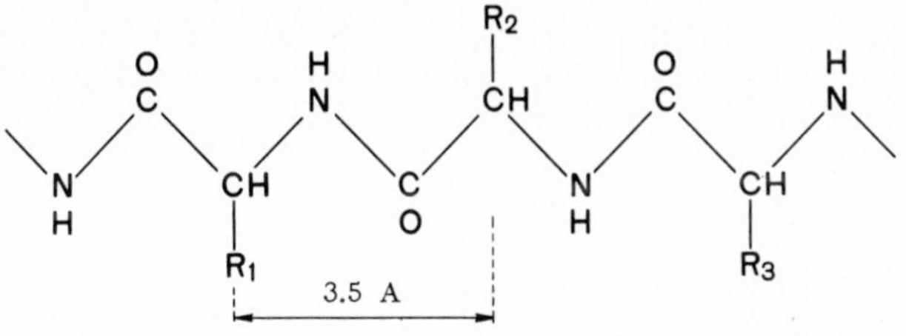

FIG. 153. Pseudo repeat distance in a β-keratin chain.

The strain is entirely reversible but is accompanied by changes in structure and therefore differs essentially from the normal elastic strain. The reversibility is lost if the fiber is held in a weak alkaline solution or in steam; this property is applied in the "permanent wave."

Globular Proteins

These are polypeptides in which long chains also probably occur. The examination by X-rays of the monoclinic hemoglobin, whose molecule contains a good 8,000 atoms, has been going on for years.[1]

Rubber

Non-vulcanized rubber consists of long chains of polymerized isoprene; a double bond moves with the polymerization (Fig. 154).

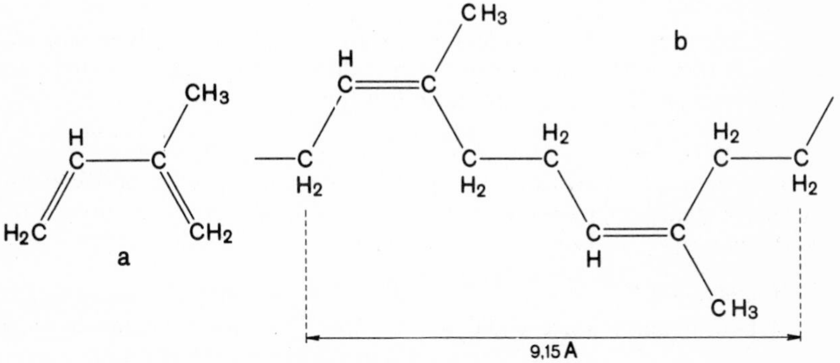

FIG. 154. (a) Isoprene and (b) calculated repeat distance in a rubber chain.

[1] W. L. Bragg, "Giant Molecules," Nature 164 (1949), 7.

When rubber is in normal condition, the chains are somewhat coiled up, are lying irregularly, and sidewise are weakly bound by residual bonds. When rubber is vulcanized, bridges of sulphur are formed between the chains.

As a result of cooling, strain, or pressure, the chains group themselves with partial regularity, and some crystallization occurs. The monoclinic pseudo cell now contains four isoprene residuals. The observed periodicity of the chains is 8.10 A, whereas the calculated periodicity is 9.15 A; so it may be assumed that the chains are somewhat twisted.

$$a_0 = 12.46 \text{ A}$$
$$b_0 = 8.89 \text{ A}$$
$$c_0 = 8.10 \text{ A}$$
$$\beta = 92°$$

The crystallization is of great importance for the properties of the rubber; it does not occur, as a rule, in artificial products, which therefore have less tensile strength, especially at higher temperature. Non-vulcanized rubber begins to crystallize at a strain of 80%; in vulcanized rubber the sulphur bridges hinder the chains from ordering themselves, and crystallization occurs only at a strain of 250%; if the rubber has been strongly vulcanized, there is no crystallization at all. Release from strain causes the crystals to disappear. From 30 to 40%, at most, crystallizes; the remainder continues to be amorphous.[1]

The striking elasticity of rubber is ascribed to the tendency of the chains to twist under the influence of the mutual affinity of the hydrogen particles at the outside of the chains.

E. Some Remarks

Isotypism

If the structures of two compounds are entirely or nearly equal, and if the ratios of the dimensions do not differ much, the structures are called isotypic. NaCl and PbS form isotypic structures.

Anti-isotypism

Two structures are anti-isotypic if, by changing the positive and negative charges in one of them, we obtain isotypic structures. Li_2O and ThO_2 are anti-isotypic (fluorite type).

Homotypism

If two structures are equal in principle but differ too much to be

[1] C. W. Bunn, Proc. R. Soc. London A 180 (1942), 40; C. W. Bunn, *Chemical Crystallography* (1946), p. 318; J. M. Goppel, Diss. Delft (1946); J. J. Arlman and J. M. Goppel, Appl. Sc. Res. A2 (1949), 1.

called isotypic, we call them homotypic. NaCl and Hg_2Cl_2 are homotypic though the structural points of the latter are occupied by "double atoms." CuO and NaCl are also called homotypic, although the former is triclinic and the latter cubic. Also diamond and sphalerite, even diamond and rutile, are sometimes called homotypic.

Isomorphism [1]

Originally (1819) Mitscherlich called two crystals isomorphous if the composing elements were closely related chemically and if the symmetry and shape of the crystals were entirely or nearly similar.

Nowadays the requirement of close chemical relationship is less important, and analogy of structure and the possibility of formation of mixed crystals are of importance. Albite and anorthite, for example, are called isomorphous; both are triclinic, with practically the same structure, although the cell of one of them is twice as large as that of the other; they form a continuous range of mixed crystals [2] (plagioclases); but chemically $NaSi_3AlO_8$ and $CaSi_2Al_2O_8$ are rather different. On account of the equality of volume and charge of $(NaSi)^{5+}$ and $(CaAl)^{5+}$, these groups can replace each other. A general rule is that, the larger the molecule, the more likely is replacement to occur, even by less closely related elements; but the deviation in radius of the replacing part may not be greater than about 15%.

Isomorphous compounds often form an uninterrupted range of mixed crystals and crystallize round one another as mantles (for example, the alums); and, as a rule, each causes crystallization in a super-saturated solution of the other.

Camouflage of Elements

A number of rare, usually heavy elements are hard to trace because their atoms often replace a small percentage of the atoms of frequently occurring and chemically related elements. Examples of such camouflage are: Hf in Zr compounds (1 atom of Hf to 100–150 of Zr); Ga in bauxite $(Al_2O_3 \cdot H_2O)$; Sc replaces Al in pyroxenes and biotite; Ca is replaced by Y in apatite, by Nd in violet apatite.

Polymorphism

This phenomenon, in elements, is also called *allotropism*. A polymorphous compound shows more than one crystalline modification (phase) — that is, type of structure. The phenomenon is general and

---

[1] T. Retgers, Jahrbuch für Mineralogie I (1891), 132; A. Arzruni, Physikalische Chemie der Kristalle (1893); B. Gossner, Zeitschrift für Kristallographie 44 (1907), 417.

[2] There is now known to be a structural break in the middle of the series.

occurs especially with structures which are not highly symmetrical; often these structures change at higher temperatures into more highly symmetrical ones. The terms "dimorphism," "trimorphism," etc. indicate that two, three, etc. modifications are known.

Morphotropism

If a change of structure that occurs by replacement becomes so great that we no longer want to use the term "isomorphism," we speak of morphotropism.[1]

A morphotropic range of compounds is one in which the replacing atoms differ gradually in one property — for example, in size or polarizability (Table 25).

TABLE 25

	SiO_2	TiO_2	ZrO_2	CeO_2	ThO_2
radius of the + ion	0.39	0.64	0.87	1.02	1.10
$\dfrac{r_A}{r_X}$	0.30	0.49	0.66	0.78	0.83
type	SiO_2	rutile	(mono-clinic)	fluorite	fluorite
coordination number	2 & 4	3 & 6	4 & 8	4 & 8	4 & 8

Fig. 155 shows how, in the range of compounds AX_2, the structural

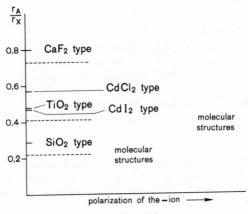

FIG. 155.

[1] V. M. Goldschmidt, *Geochemische Verteilungsgesetze*, VII (1926), p. 91.

type is a function of $\dfrac{r_A}{r_X}$ and the polarization. As polarization increases, enwrapment of the positive ion by negative ions (p. 146) is accomplished earlier, and molecular structures occur earlier. In layer structures, which may be regarded as intermediate between coordination structures and molecular structures, the layer as a whole forms, as it were, an infinite two-dimensional molecule.

Model Structures

A model structure (or a model crystal) is an ionic structure which is isotypic with and similar to another ionic structure and in which all bonds and polarization states are proportionally weaker or stronger. The properties of the model are weaker or stronger than, but otherwise entirely comparable to, those of the original.

Some of the properties of silicate crystals, which are difficult to prepare, can be derived to a good approximation from those of beryllium fluorides. A "weakened" model of SiO_2 glass is BeF_2 glass, the refractive index of which is even smaller than that of water (1.33). A "weakened" model of the orthorhombic Zn_2SiO_4 is Li_2BeF_4; Table 26 gives a comparison of the properties.

TABLE 26

	Zn_2SiO_4	Li_2BeF_4
c_0/a_0.	0.670	0.673
cleavage parallel to $\{10\bar{1}0\}$ and $\{0001\}$.	slight	clear
double refraction	0.02	0.006
refractive index.	1.7	1.3
hardness	5.5	3.8
melting point.	1,510°	470°
solubility.	insoluble	easily soluble

"Strengthened" models have higher melting points and greater hardness (p. 136).

Chemical Reactions in Structures [1]

The atoms or ions in a structure are not absolutely restricted to their

---

[1] J. A. Hedvall, *Reaktionsfähigkeit fester Stoffe* (1938); J. A. Hedvall, *Einführung in die Festkörperchemie* (1952); G. Tammann, Nachrichten der Göttinger Gesellschaft der Wissenschaften, mathematisch-physikalische Klasse (1930), 227; G. von Hevesy, Sitzungsberichte der Akademie für Wissenschaften, Wien, Abteilung IIa, 129 (1920), 549; K. Hauffe, *Reaktionen in und an festen Stoffen* (1955).

sites; besides executing thermal vibrations, they may also exchange sites with others, especially at temperatures not much below the melting point or when changing into another modification (active condition of the structure).

An example of this site exchange is the diffusion of metals (p. 243).

Pure site exchange — that is, without freeing of chemical energy — occurs with molecules (which may be regarded as very limited "structures") of $PbCl_2$ and $Pb(NO_3)_2$ which are dissolved in an organic liquid. This is proved by the fact that, if we start with a radioactive $PbCl_2$ and a non-radioactive $Pb(NO_3)_2$, the latter also is radioactive after crystallization.

At about 345°, in a mixture of powdered BaO and $CaCO_3$, the exothermic reaction occurs by which $BaCO_3$ and CaO come into being. This kind of reaction occurs between many pairs of compounds, even when the absence of any gaseous product of decomposition is fairly certain.

An example of an active structure is formed at 160° by $AgNO_3$, which at that temperature changes into another modification and then reacts with BaO.

The empirical rule of Tammann says that site exchange, recrystallization (p. 265), and aggression (growth at the expense of other crystals, p. 265) with noticeable velocity begin for metals at $0.33\,T_S$, for salts at $0.57\,T_S$, and for organic compounds at $0.90\,T_S$ (T_S being the absolute melting temperature).

For a site-exchange reaction, at a constant temperature, Jander's formula,

$$y = \sqrt{2kt}$$

in which

$y =$ thickness of reacting layer
$k =$ constant
$t =$ time

is valid.

Part

IV | Physical Crystallography [1]

The physical properties of crystals show differences from those of normal isotropic materials as soon as the phenomenon under consideration depends on direction (anisotropism). Entirely new phenomena often occur — piezoelectricity and gliding, for example.

We divide the discussion into two parts: phenomenological, or descriptive, and atomistic, or explanatory.

A. Phenomenological Part

The crystal is considered to be a homogeneous continuum.

The Quantities [2]

The quantities necessary for the description of a phenomenon are scalars, vectors, and the arrays of coefficients expressing the mutual dependence of the components of these quantities — the so-called affinors, or tensors, which may be of the second, third, and fourth rank, and which we denote as II-tensor, etc.

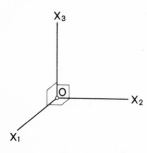

FIG. 156. Right-handed axial set.

A right-handed, rectangular, axial set is assumed (Fig. 156); for enantiomorphous crystals, sometimes, a left-handed set (p. 220). A new axial set — that is, one obtained by rotation of the old set while keeping the origin O — is denoted with accents; the direction cosines of the new axes are α_{ik}.

	X'_1	X'_2	X'_3
X_1	α_{11}	α_{12}	α_{13}
X_2	α_{21}	α_{22}	α_{23}
X_3	α_{31}	α_{32}	α_{33}

If we want to study a phenomenon in any particular direction, we rotate the axial set until X'_3 falls in that direction, and the formulas are transformed correspondingly. Then we have, for example,

$$x'_1 = \alpha_{11}x_1 + \alpha_{21}x_2 + \alpha_{31}x_3$$

[1] Many numerical data are mentioned in Landolt-Börnstein, *Physikalisch-chemische Tabellen;* International Critical Tables of Numerical Data (1926); *Tables annuelles de Constantes et Données numériques* (1912 et seq.).

[2] J. F. Nye, *Physical Properties of Crystals* (Oxford, 1957).

If we wish to indicate a *scalar* quantity at a point, one number is necessary. This indicates the number of units contained in this quantity, and it might also be called the component of the scalar. With transformation this number undergoes no change; the temperature θ is an example.

A *vector* $\mathbf{p}$ at a point is a quantity with direction and magnitude and may be indicated by an arrow.

We take three equal units $\mathbf{i}_1$, $\mathbf{i}_2$, $\mathbf{i}_3$ along the axes and consider the components of the vector along the axes; then

$$\mathbf{p} = p_1\mathbf{i}_1 + p_2\mathbf{i}_2 + p_3\mathbf{i}_3$$

which is also written as $\mathbf{p} = \Sigma\, p_i\mathbf{i}_i$ or, abbreviated, as $\mathbf{p} = p_i\mathbf{i}_i$.

The three numbers p_i are called the components of the vector; these three figures determine a vector.

The components of a vector in a new axial set are found from those in an old set by the following relations:

$$p'_1 = \alpha_{11}p_1 + \alpha_{21}p_2 + \alpha_{31}p_3$$
$$p'_2 = \alpha_{12}p_1 + \alpha_{22}p_2 + \alpha_{33}p_3$$
$$p'_3 = \alpha_{13}p_1 + \alpha_{23}p_2 + \alpha_{33}p_3$$
$$p'_i = \alpha_{ki}p_k$$

By the reverse transformation

$$p_1 = \alpha_{11}p'_1 + \alpha_{12}p'_2 + \alpha_{13}p'_3$$
$$p_2 = \alpha_{21}p'_1 + \alpha_{22}p'_2 + \alpha_{23}p'_3$$
$$p_3 = \alpha_{31}p'_1 + \alpha_{32}p'_2 + \alpha_{33}p'_3$$
$$p_i = \alpha_{ik}p'_k$$

All quantities transforming in this way are called vectors.

A *II-tensor* a_{ik} at a point is an array of nine numbers a_{ik}, called components, which transform in a typical way. They indicate how the components of two vectors $\mathbf{p}$ and $\mathbf{q}$ depend linearly on each other:

$$p_i = a_{ki}q_k$$

This may be written as

$$p_1 = a_{11}q_1 + a_{21}q_2 + a_{31}q_3, \text{ etc.}$$

By the reverse transformation

$$q_i = b_{ki}p_k$$

in which, for example,

$$b_{21} = \frac{-\begin{vmatrix} a_{21} & a_{31} \\ a_{23} & a_{33} \end{vmatrix}}{\begin{vmatrix} a_{11} & a_{21} & a_{31} \\ a_{12} & a_{22} & a_{32} \\ a_{13} & a_{23} & a_{33} \end{vmatrix}}$$

and also

$$a_{21} = \dfrac{-\begin{vmatrix} b_{21} & b_{31} \\ b_{23} & b_{33} \end{vmatrix}}{\begin{vmatrix} b_{11} & b_{21} & b_{31} \\ b_{12} & b_{22} & b_{32} \\ b_{13} & b_{23} & b_{33} \end{vmatrix}}$$

The transformation formulas are

$$a'_{ik} = \alpha_{li}\,\alpha_{mk}\,a_{lm}$$
$$a_{ik} = \alpha_{il}\,\alpha_{km}\,a'_{lm}$$

In the physics of crystals II-tensors are always symmetrical (that is, $a_{ik} = a_{ki}$), and there are, therefore, six different components. In a transformation we have, for example,

$$\begin{aligned}
a'_{33} &= \alpha_{13}\alpha_{13}a_{11} + \alpha_{13}\alpha_{23}a_{12} + \alpha_{13}\alpha_{33}a_{13} \\
&+ \alpha_{23}\alpha_{13}a_{21} + \alpha_{23}\alpha_{23}a_{22} + \alpha_{23}\alpha_{33}a_{23} \\
&+ \alpha_{33}\alpha_{13}a_{31} + \alpha_{33}\alpha_{23}a_{32} + \alpha_{33}\alpha_{33}a_{33} \\
&= \alpha_{13}^2 a_{11} + \alpha_{23}^2 a_{22} + \alpha_{33}^2 a_{23} \\
&+ 2\alpha_{13}\alpha_{23}a_{12} + 2\alpha_{13}\alpha_{33}a_{13} + 2\alpha_{23}\alpha_{33}a_{23}
\end{aligned}$$

For the direction X'_3, a'_{33} indicates in which way the component of $\mathbf{p}$ (p'_3) depends on that of $\mathbf{q}$ (q'_3); indeed,

$$p'_3 = a'_{13}q'_1 + a'_{23}q'_2 + a'_{33}q'_3$$

From an ellipsoid, the *tensor ellipsoid*, a'_{33} can be read.

If the ellipsoid

$$1 = a_{11}x_1^2 + a_{22}x_2^2 + a_{33}x_3^2 + 2a_{12}x_1x_2 + 2a_{23}x_2x_3 + 2a_{31}x_3x_1$$

is written in polar coordinates, the length r of a radius vector lying along the direction X'_3 is

$$\frac{1}{r^2} = a_{11}\alpha_{13}^2 + a_{22}\alpha_{23}^2 + a_{33}\alpha_{33}^2 + 2a_{12}\alpha_{13}\alpha_{23} + 2a_{23}\alpha_{23}\alpha_{33} + 2a_{31}\alpha_{33}\alpha_{13}$$

If we compare this expression with that of a'_{33}, it appears that this coefficient can be derived from the length of r according to the expression (see Fig. 157)

$$\frac{1}{r^2} = a'_{33} \quad \text{or} \quad r = \frac{1}{\sqrt{a'_{33}}}$$

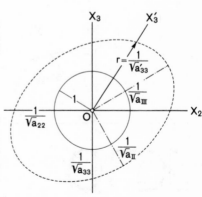

FIG. 157. Tensor ellipsoid with principal axes and unit circle.

An important transformation is from general axes to the principal axes of the ellipsoid. In this case $a'_{12} = a'_{13} = a'_{23} = 0$, and we write $a'_{11} \equiv a_I$, $a'_{22} \equiv a_{II}$, $a'_{33} = a_{III}$; the components become

$$p_1 = a_I \, q_1$$
$$p_2 = a_{II} \, q_2$$
$$p_3 = a_{III} \, q_3$$

and the equation of the ellipsoid is

$$a_I x_1^2 + a_{II} x_2^2 + a_{III} x_3^2 = 1$$

the lengths of the principal semi-axes being

$$\frac{1}{\sqrt{a_I}}, \quad \frac{1}{\sqrt{a_{II}}}, \quad \frac{1}{\sqrt{a_{III}}}$$

Then a_I, a_{II}, and a_{III} are the square roots S_1, S_2, and S_3 of the S equation:

$$\begin{vmatrix} a_{11}-S & a_{12} & a_{13} \\ a_{12} & a_{22}-S & a_{23} \\ a_{13} & a_{23} & a_{33}-S \end{vmatrix} = 0$$

and the directions of the principal axes — of X_I, for example — are

$$\alpha_{11} : \alpha_{21} : \alpha_{31} = \begin{vmatrix} a_{11}-S_1 & a_{12} & a_{13} \\ a_{12} & a_{22}-S_1 & a_{23} \end{vmatrix}$$

$$\equiv \begin{vmatrix} a_{12} & a_{13} \\ a_{22}-S_1 & a_{23} \end{vmatrix} : \begin{vmatrix} a_{13} & a_{11}-S_1 \\ a_{23} & a_{12} \end{vmatrix} : \begin{vmatrix} a_{11}-S_1 & a_{12} \\ a_{12} & a_{33}-S_1 \end{vmatrix}$$

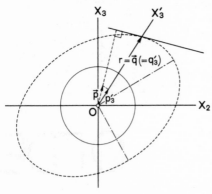

It can be demonstrated analytically that the direction and magnitude of **p** can also be derived from the tensor ellipsoid. If **q** is represented by r, **p** has the direction of the normal to the plane that is tangent to the ellipsoid at the point of intersection with r, and its magnitude is the reciprocal of the distance from the center to the tangent plane (Fig. 158).

As a result of symmetry, some a_{ik} may be equal or may become zero.

FIG. 158. Relation of direction and magnitude of **q** and **p** and of q'_3 and p'_3.

We have, for example,[1]

Class			
mmm	a_{11}	0	0
	0	a_{22}	0
	0	0	a_{33}
$3m,\ 4/mmm,\ 6/mmm$	a_{11}	0	0
	0	a_{11}	0
	0	0	a_{33}
$m3m,\ m3$	a_{11}	0	0
	0	a_{11}	0
	0	0	a_{11}

A *III-tensor* a_{ikl} at a point is characterized by twenty-seven components, which comply with typical transformation formulas. The twenty-seven numbers indicate in which way the components p_i of a vector depend linearly on the components a_{kl} of a II-tensor:

$$p_i = a_{kli}\, a_{kl}$$

One equation in full is

$$\begin{aligned}
p_2 =\ & a_{112}\, a_{11} + a_{212}\, a_{21} + a_{312}\, a_{31} \\
& + a_{122}\, a_{12} + a_{222}\, a_{22} + a_{322}\, a_{32} \\
& + a_{132}\, a_{13} + a_{232}\, a_{32} + a_{332}\, a_{33}
\end{aligned}$$

The transformation formulas are

$$\begin{aligned}
a'_{lik} &= \alpha_{ml}\, \alpha_{ni}\, \alpha_{ok}\, a_{mno} \\
a_{lik} &= \alpha_{lm}\, \alpha_{in}\, \alpha_{ko}\, a'_{mno}
\end{aligned}$$

A *IV-tensor* a_{ikpq} at a point is characterized by eighty-one components, which comply with typical transformation formulas. The eighty-one numbers indicate how the components a_{pq} of a II-tensor depend linearly on the components b_{ik} of another II-tensor:

$$a_{pq} = a_{ikpq}\, b_{ik}$$

An example is

$$\begin{aligned}
a_{33} =\ & a_{1133}\, b_{11} + a_{2133}\, b_{21} + a_{3133}\, b_{31} \\
& + a_{1233}\, b_{12} + a_{2233}\, b_{22} + a_{3233}\, b_{32} \\
& + a_{1333}\, b_{13} + a_{2333}\, b_{23} + a_{3333}\, b_{33}
\end{aligned}$$

[1] W. A. Wooster, *A Textbook on Crystal Physics* (1949), p. 7.

The transformation formulas are

$$a'_{ikpq} = \alpha_{mi}\,\alpha_{nk}\,\alpha_{op}\,\alpha_{rq}\,a_{mnor}$$
$$a_{ikpq} = \alpha_{im}\,\alpha_{kn}\,\alpha_{po}\,\alpha_{qr}\,a'_{mnor}$$

Many components of a III- or IV-tensor are equal or become zero in non-triclinic crystals.

If a physical property is centro-symmetrical, it complies with the symmetry of the crystal plus that of an inversion point, and only eleven classes can be distinguished (Friedel's classes, Laue groups, p. 127).

Friedel's class	comprises also		
$\bar{1}$	1		
$2/m$	2	m	
mmm	222	$mm2$	
$\bar{3}$	3		
$\bar{3}m$	$3m$	32	
$6/m$	6	$\bar{6}$	
$6/mmm$	$\bar{6}m2$	$6mm$	622
$4/m$	4	$\bar{4}$	
$4/mmm$	$4mm$	422	$\bar{4}2m$
$m3$	23		
$m3m$	$\bar{4}3m$	432	

The properties described by means of a II-tensor are centro-symmetrical; they have the symmetry of an ellipsoid (if there are also negative a_{ik}, there is another surface of the second order). For cubic crystals this is a sphere, for those with a principal axis, an ellipsoid of revolution. In orthorhombic crystals the axes of the ellipsoid coincide with the crystallographic axes; in monoclinic crystals one axis coincides with the B axis.

Of the scalar and vectorial quantities whose components depend linearly upon one another (the relation being therefore tensorial), those shown in Table 27 are discussed here.

TABLE 27

scalar	vector	II-tensor	III-tensor	IV-tensor
	position of a point **x** displacement of a point **u**, e.g. through heat dilatation position of a point **x**	⎱ deformation ⎰ coefficients γ ⎱ expansion ⎰ coefficients γ		⎫ strain constants ⎬ elasticity ⎭ moduli c
temp. θ	⎱ vectorial ⎰ pyroelec- polarization **P** ⎰ tricity	⎱ tensorial tensor. pol. ⎰ pyro- ⎰ electr.		
	direction **n** force **K**	⎱ stress compo- ⎰ nents σ	⎱ piezoelectrical ⎰ const. d	
	electr. field strength **E** electr. displacement **D**	⎱ dielectr. const. ε		
	magn. field strength **H** magn. induction **B**	⎱ permeability ⎰ constants μ		
	temp. gradient **τ** heat current **w**	⎱ heat conduction ⎰ constants k		
	electr. potential gradient **υ** electr. current **i**	⎱ electr. conduction ⎰ constants λ		

Homogeneous Deformation

After a homogeneous deformation the points, originally situated on
a straight line or in a flat plane, still lie on a straight line or in a flat
plane respectively. This definition is complied with when the components
of the displacement vector **u**
of any given point depend
linearly on those of the position vector **x** of that point
(Fig. 159).

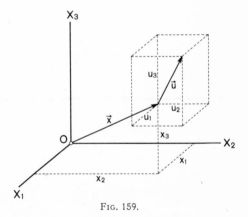

$$u_1 = \gamma_{11}x_1 + \gamma_{21}x_2 + \gamma_{31}x_3$$
$$u_2 = \gamma_{12}x_1 + \gamma_{22}x_2 + \gamma_{32}x_3$$
$$u_3 = \gamma_{13}x_1 + \gamma_{23}x_2 + \gamma_{33}x_3$$

In these expressions $\gamma_{ik} = \gamma_{ki}$.
If A is originally situated on
$x_1 = x_2 = x_3 = 1$, then A'
is situated on $x_1 + u_1$, etc.
(Fig. 160):

$$u_1 = \gamma_{11} + \gamma_{21} + \gamma_{31}$$

FIG. 159.

γ_{11} indicates the strain in the X_1 direction of a unit cube; γ_{21} the shear,
the tangent of the projected angle on the X_1X_2 plane of the movement
of X_2, etc.

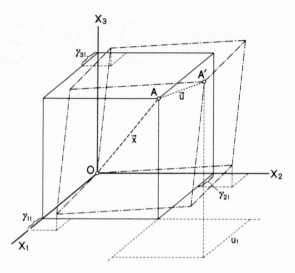

FIG. 160.   The first index of σ or γ denotes the direction of the plane considered, the second the direction of the force or displacement.

The points which originally lay on a sphere round O with a radius 1 are situated, after the deformation, on an ellipsoid:

$$x'_1 = x_1 + u_1 = x_1 + \gamma_{11}x_1 + \gamma_{21}x_2 + \gamma_{31}x_3$$
$$= (1 + \gamma_{11})x_1 + \gamma_{21}x_2 + \gamma_{31}x_3$$
$$x'_2 = \gamma_{12}x_1 + (1 + \gamma_{22})x_2 + \gamma_{32}x_3$$
$$x'_3 = \gamma_{13}x_1 + \gamma_{23}x_2 + (1 + \gamma_{33})x_3$$

TABLE 28 [1]

	γ_{I}	γ_{II}	γ_{III}
Cu	17.10^{-6}	17	17
Cd	21	21	52
NaCl	40	40	40
BeO	5.3	5.3	5.1
calcite	$- 5.66$	$- 5.66$	24.91
quartz	14	14	9

[1] Further values are given by W. A. Wooster, *Crystal Physics* (1949), p. 32; P. Niggli, *Lehrbuch der Mineralogie und Kristallchemie* (1942), p. 701; E. Schmid & W. Boas, *Kristallplastizität* (1935), p. 203.

If we solve these equations for x_1, x_2, and x_3 and insert the values in the equation of the sphere, this equation becomes that of another second-order surface, the ellipsoid, because the coefficients are positive.

We mention three cases in which homogeneous deformation of a crystal occurs: (1) application of hydrostatic pressure (p. 225); (2) secondary gliding (p. 242); (3) thermal dilatation (expansion on heating). We discuss the third case here.

Table 28 indicates for some crystals the linear expansion coefficients in the directions of the principal axes of the ellipsoids.

The simplest way of measuring is with X-rays; the change in the lattice dimensions can easily be derived from the displacement of the lines on a powder photograph [1] (p. 118).

We may inquire in which direction (at which angle φ with the principal axis) the expansion of calcite is nil — that is, how $\mathbf{x}$ (X'_3) has to be taken so that $\mathbf{u} = 0$. To find the answer, we transform to the axes of Fig. 161. Then the coefficient in the direction X'_3 becomes

$$a'_{33} = \alpha_{13}^2 \gamma_I + \alpha_{23}^2 \gamma_{II} + \alpha_{33}^2 \gamma_{III}$$
$$0 = \gamma_I \cos^2 (90° - \varphi) + 0 + \gamma_{III} \cos^2 \varphi$$

$$\tan^2 \varphi = - \frac{\gamma_{III}}{\gamma_I}$$

$$\varphi = 64°43'$$

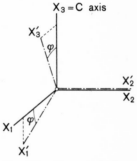

Fig. 161. The principal axes of the tensor ellipsoid lie along X_1, X_2, and X_3 (and X_2').

Because the thermal dilatation is a homogeneous deformation, the edges of a crystal remain straight, and the zone relation does not disappear; [2] the symmetry remains unless another modification occurs, but in general the relations of the axial lengths change with temperature continuously.

Stress

If we imagine a space element of a body, the stress at a point on the surface of the element is the outward force exerted per square centimeter of flat plane and is therefore the force divided by the surface.

[1] M. Straumanis & A. Jevins, *Die Präzisionsbestimmung von Gitterkonstanten nach der asymmetrischen Methode* (1940), p. 92. For interferometric determination with the aid of visible light see A. E. H. Tutton, *Crystallography and Practical Crystal Measurement* (1922), p. 1301.

[2] J. Grailich & V. von Lang, Sitzungsberichte der Wiener Akademie 33 (1858), 369.

If the stresses in three planes through a point are given, the stress in a plane with an arbitrary direction can be calculated. The direction of this plane is indicated by a unit vector **n** drawn normal to it. We now examine the small tetrahedron shown in Fig. 162: the stresses **X**, **Y**, and **Z** occur in the coordinate planes; in the fourth plane the stress is required.[1]

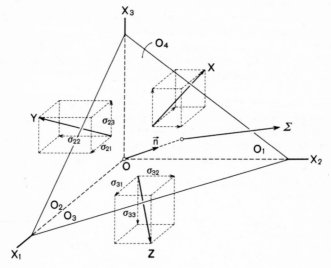

FIG. 162.   The vector **n** is perpendicular to the plane $X_1 X_2 X_3$.

From the fact that the small tetrahedron is in equilibrium it follows that the X_1 component of $\boldsymbol{\Sigma}$ equals the sum of the X_1 components of **X**, **Y**, and **Z**. Then

$$\Sigma_1 \, O_4 \mathbf{i}_1 = \sigma_{11} O_1 \mathbf{i}_1 + \sigma_{21} O_2 \mathbf{i}_1 + \sigma_{31} O_3 \mathbf{i}_1$$

Now $O_1 : O_4 = n_1 : 1$, etc.; therefore

$$\Sigma_1 = \sigma_{11} n_1 + \sigma_{21} n_2 + \sigma_{31} n_3$$

and, similarly,

$$\Sigma_2 = \sigma_{12} n_1 + \sigma_{22} n_2 + \sigma_{32} n_3$$
$$\Sigma_3 = \sigma_{13} n_1 + \sigma_{23} n_2 + \sigma_{33} n_3$$

It can be proved that $\sigma_{ik} = \sigma_{ki}$.

[1] With regard to what follows (p. 222), we do not write **σ**; the tensor components, however, are named σ_{ik}.

The tensor σ_{ik} does not depend on the material, but describes the state of stress at a point. If, therefore, forces are applied to a body, putting it into a state of stress, σ_{12} indicates that, on a unit plane normal to X_1, in the direction of X_2, there is a force of $\sigma_{12}i_2$ dynes.

If there is only a strain, the tensor ellipsoid degenerates into two parallel planes normal to the force; if the external forces are lying in one plane, the ellipsoid is the surface of an elliptic cylinder with the axis normal to that plane.

The Crystal as a Dielectric

In an electric field with a strength $\mathbf{E}$ the dipoles in an isotropic insulator are more or less directed: the body is polarized. The polarization $\mathbf{P}$ is proportional to $\mathbf{E}$ (κ = polarization factor):

$$\mathbf{P} = \kappa\mathbf{E}$$

The displacement $\mathbf{D}$ is determined by the original field plus the polarization (ε = dielectric constant):

$$\mathbf{D} = \mathbf{E} + 4\pi\mathbf{P} = \mathbf{E} + 4\pi\kappa\mathbf{E} = (1 + 4\pi\kappa)\mathbf{E} = \varepsilon\mathbf{E}$$

$\mathbf{P}$ is defined as the polarization per unit of volume. If, on the small end planes of a rectangular parallelepiped (Fig. 163), the charges are $+e$ and $-e$ per cm² and their distance is l, the moment is Oel, the volume Ol, and the (homogeneous) polarization $\mathbf{P} = e$; therefore, $\mathbf{P}$ indicates also the amount of charge on a flat plane of 1 cm² normal to $\mathbf{P}$, and $\mathbf{P}$ is independent of the length considered and therefore also of the length of the crystal.

In an insulating crystal, $\mathbf{D}$ does not generally lie in the same direction as $\mathbf{E}$; the relation is according to a II-tensor,

$$D_1 = \varepsilon_{11}E_1 + \varepsilon_{21}E_2 + \varepsilon_{31}E_3, \text{ etc.}$$

in which $\varepsilon_{ik} = \varepsilon_{ki}$.

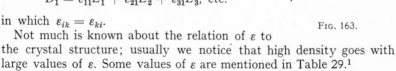

FIG. 163.

Not much is known about the relation of ε to the crystal structure; usually we notice that high density goes with large values of ε. Some values of ε are mentioned in Table 29.[1]

---

[1] Symposium Nederlandse Chemische Vereniging (1947). For the measurement of ε see W. A. Wooster, *Crystal Physics* (1949), p. 119.

TABLE 29

	ε_I	ε_{II}	ε_{III}
S	3.59	3.82	4.61
NaCl	5.85	5.85	5.85
quartz	4.49	4.49	4.55
calcite	8.48	8.48	8.03
$BaSO_4$	7.62	12.25	7.63

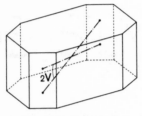

FIG. 164.   Crystal of
Rochelle salt.

Rochelle salt (sodium potassium tartrate, $NaKC_4H_4O_6 \cdot 4H_2O$) possesses very special dielectric properties (Fig. 164). It is orthorhombic-bisphenoidal, $222 - D_2$, and $a : b : c = 0.8317 : 1 : 0.4296$. The plane of the optical axes is $b(010)$ (p. 202). $Bx_a = n_g = A$ axis; $2V = 71°$. ε_A up to 60,000, ε_B and $\varepsilon_C \backsim 60$.

ε_A is not constant, but depends greatly on temperature and field strength. The crystal is called ferroelectric because it behaves towards the electric field more or less as iron does towards the magnetic field; it also shows hysteresis. On account of its piezoelectric properties it is applied on a large scale in phonograph pick-ups, etc., despite its fragility and low hardness [1] (p. 202). The other groups of technically useful ferroelectric crystals are phosphates such as ADP (ammonium dihydrophosphate), arsenates, and titanates ($BaTiO_3$).

Propagation of light [2]

General

In an *isotropic* (that is, not birefringent) medium an electric field **E** causes a displacement **D**; the directions of these vectors coincide, and **D** is proportional to **E** (**D** = ε**E**).

Change of **D** causes a magnetic field **H**, normal to **D**. With **H** occurs a magnetic induction **B**; **B** = μ**H** (p. 216).

---

[1] See also pp. 214 and 222; C. A. Beevers & W. Hughes, Proc. R. Soc. A 177 (1941), 251 (structure); W. G. Cady, *Piezoelectricity* (1946), Ch. 20.

[2] F. Pockels, *Lehrbuch der Kristalloptik* (1906); E. S. Dana & W. E. Ford, *A Textbook of Mineralogy* (1932), pp. 233–332; A. N. Winchell, *The Optical Properties of Organic Compounds* (1954); A. N. Winchell, *The Microscopic Characters of Inorganic Substances or Artificial Minerals* (1931).

D is propagated with the velocity v. According to the electromagnetic theory of light (c = velocity of light in a vacuum),

$$v = \frac{c}{\sqrt{\varepsilon\mu}}$$

In nearly all cases $\mu = 1$; hence the relation of v and the refractive index n is

$$v = \frac{c}{\sqrt{\varepsilon}} = \frac{c}{n}$$

At a point in a plane perpendicular to a beam of parallel light (plane wave front), the displacement **D** is subject to a harmonic change; this perturbation is propagated as a sine wave and is called a ray of light (Fig. 165).

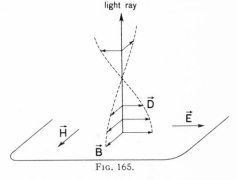

FIG. 165.

The electric displacement can take place in all directions normal to the ray; this means that the velocity does not depend on the vibration direction (polarization direction). Moreover, the velocity is independent of the direction of the ray; ε is the same in all directions, and n, therefore, is constant also.

It follows from Huygens' principle (Fig. 166) that the direction of propagation of a plane wave front, in a medium whose propagation velocity is the same in all directions, coincides with the wave normal.

In an *anisotropic* medium (non-cubic crystals) ε is not the same in all directions, but may be derived from an ellipsoid of which the principal semi-axes are (p. 189):

$$\frac{1}{\sqrt{\varepsilon_I}}, \quad \frac{1}{\sqrt{\varepsilon_{II}}}, \quad \frac{1}{\sqrt{\varepsilon_{III}}}$$

In general, **E** and **D** do not coincide. The following can be derived from the theory.

1. As an auxiliary figure we take the *indicatrix*, which is an ellipsoid with principal semi-axes $\sqrt{\varepsilon_I}$, $\sqrt{\varepsilon_{II}}$, and $\sqrt{\varepsilon_{III}}$, its equation being, therefore,

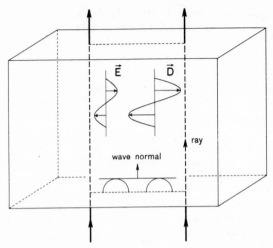

FIG. 166. Passage of an unpolarized beam of light through an isotropic parallel-sided plate; $\mathbf{E}$ and $\mathbf{D}$ are always parallel and always lie in the same direction, as do the front normal and the ray direction.

$$\frac{x_1^2}{\varepsilon_I} + \frac{x_2^2}{\varepsilon_{II}} + \frac{x_3^2}{\varepsilon_{III}} = 1$$

or, if we assume that $\varepsilon_I > \varepsilon_{II} > \varepsilon_{III}$,

$$\frac{x_1^2}{n_g^2} + \frac{x_2^2}{n_m^2} + \frac{x_2^2}{n_p^2} = 1$$

n_g, n_m, and n_p are the principal refractive indices ($g = grand$, $m = moyen$, $p = petit$).

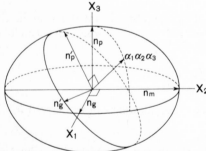

FIG. 167. n'_g and n'_p are the principal axes of the elliptical section whose plane is perpendicular to the direction $(\alpha_1, \alpha_2, \alpha_3)$.

2. In the plane normal to the arbitrary direction $(\alpha_1, \alpha_2, \alpha_3)$, a $\mathbf{D}$ can occur only in two directions, which are normal to each other and which fall along the principal axes of the *elliptical section* of the indicatrix and the plane constructed at its center normal to $(\alpha_1, \alpha_2, \alpha_3)$. There are, therefore, normal to $(\alpha_1, \alpha_2, \alpha_3)$, only two wave fronts, each formed by one of the $\mathbf{D}$'s.

The velocity in the direction $(\alpha_1, \alpha_2, \alpha_3)$ — that is, in the direction of the *wave normal* (the front normal) — is determined by the corresponding ε; or, what comes to the same thing: the refractive index is given by the length of the principal semi-axis of the elliptical section; the lengths of these semi-axes are called n'_g and n'_p (Fig. 167).

n'_g and n'_p are the square roots n of Fresnel's equation

$$\frac{\alpha_1^2}{\dfrac{1}{n^2} - \dfrac{1}{n_g^2}} + \frac{\alpha_2^2}{\dfrac{1}{n^2} - \dfrac{1}{n_m^2}} + \frac{\alpha_3^2}{\dfrac{1}{n^2} - \dfrac{1}{n_p^2}} = 0$$

3. The direction of propagation of the front — that is, the direction of the ray — is such that the **E** belonging to a **D** is normal to this direction and lies in the plane **D** — $(\alpha_1, \alpha_2, \alpha_3)$ (see Fig. 168).

In natural light vibrations occur in all directions transverse to the wave normal; in polarized light vibrations occur in only one such transverse direction. In an anisotropic crystal, therefore, mutually perpen-

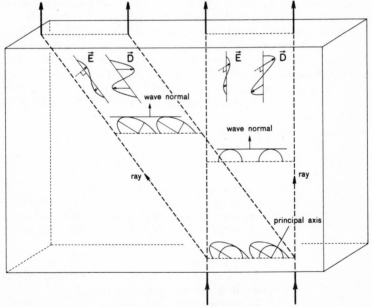

FIG. 168. Passage of an unpolarized beam of light through a birefringent parallel-sided plate (of a uniaxial negative crystal); in the plate, two wave fronts, each of polarized light, are propagated with unequal velocities; the (plane) fronts are the envelopes of the velocity figures — in this case the spheres and the ellipsoids, which, in a uniaxial crystal, coincide at the ends of the optic axis.

dicular plane vibrations are propagated, the velocities (and thus also the refractive indices) of the two being different (*birefringent* crystals).

For crystals with a principal axis the indicatrix is an ellipsoid of revolution, the axis of which coincides with the principal axis. For crystals of lower symmetry the indicatrix is a general (three-axial) ellipsoid.

In the important practical applications, a broad, plane wave front, passing through air or glass, falls vertically on the bottom of a thin, horizontal, plane-parallel crystal plate; it then, in the form of two horizontal fronts that are polarized normal to each other, passes through the plate at different velocities. The two horizontal fronts leave the top of the plate with a relative retardation and are studied with a microscope (Fig. 168). Sidewise shifting of the fronts is not noticeable, for the thickness of the plate is slight in proportion to its width.

Optic Axes

If the elliptical section is a circle, the two fronts have the same velocity (that is, there is no birefringence) and are not polarized; the direction of the front normal is then called the *optic axis*. For crystals having a principal axis there is only one circular section, and this is normal to the revolution axis of the indicatrix; for crystals of lower symmetry there are two circular sections (uniaxial and biaxial crystals). In the first case the optic axis coincides with the principal axis of the crystal; in the second the optic axes are situated in the plane of n_g and n_p, and the ellipsoid axes n_g and n_p are the bisectrices of the angles between the optic axes.

The angle of these axes, *measured over* n_g, is $2V$:

$$\tan V = \frac{n_g}{n_p} \sqrt{\frac{n_m^2 - n_p^2}{n_g^2 - n_m^2}}$$

$2V$, for a uniaxial crystal, is equal to $0°$ or $180°$.

n_m is called the optic normal; the bisectrix of the acute angle between the optic axes is called Bx_a, and that of the obtuse angle is called Bx_o (Fig. 169).

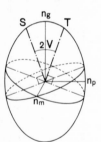

Optic Character

If $2V < 90°$, the crystal is called optically positive; if $2V > 90°$, negative (Fig. 170).

It follows from the formula for tan V that the optical character is indicated by the sign of

$$\frac{2}{n_m^2} - \frac{1}{n_g^2} - \frac{1}{n_p^2}$$

FIG. 169. The optic axes S and T are normal to the circular sections of the ellipsoid.

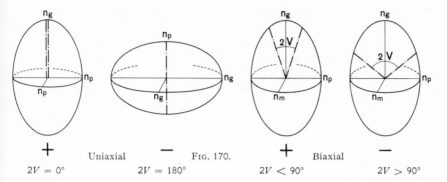

$$+$$
Uniaxial   Fig. 170. $$+$$ Biaxial $$-$$
$2V = 0°$ $2V = 180°$ $2V < 90°$ $2V > 90°$

Orientation of the Indicatrix

For orthorhombic crystals the indicatrix axes lie along the crystallo-graphic axes.

For monoclinic crystals, the plane of the optic axes coincides with

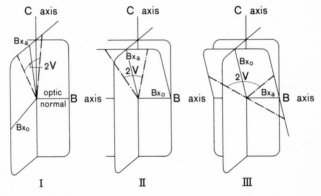

Fig. 171.   For monoclinic crystals the plane of the optic axes is ⊥ to or // to the B axis.

the symmetry plane or is normal to it; in the latter case Bx_a or Bx_o falls along the B axis (Fig. 171).

For triclinic crystals the orientation is arbitrary.

Dispersion of the Optic Axes

Since ε depends on the wavelength λ, there is a separate indicatrix, in principle, for each value of λ.

With biaxial crystals, 2V may sometimes differ considerably (disper-sion of the optic axes); if 2V is larger for red light than for violet light, we note that $\rho > v$. Occasionally the optic-axial angle for a certain λ is 0°, and the axial plane for red light is different from that for violet light (brookite, orthorhombic TiO_2, Fig. 172).

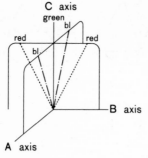

FIG. 172. Optic-axial planes in brookite (orthorhombic TiO_2).

Dispersion of the Indicatrix Axes

This dispersion is possible only with monoclinic and triclinic crystals and sometimes occurs distinctly. For monoclinic crystals three cases can be distinguished; these may be observed in sections normal to Bx_a (or nearly so):

1. B is the optical normal, and the inclination of Bx_a is different for red and for violet (inclined dispersion, Fig. 173–I).

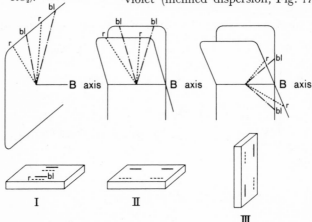

FIG. 173. Dispersion of the optic axes for monoclinic crystals: (above) perspective figures; (below) the points where the axes emerge from the sections, which are cut ⊥ to Bx_a; I inclined, II horizontal, III crossed dispersion.

2. B is Bx_o. For one color the axial plane is nearer to the horizontal plane than for the other (horizontal dispersion, Fig. 173–II).
3. B is Bx_a. The axial planes appear crossed (crossed dispersion, Fig. 173–III).

Polarization Microscope

A polarization microscope with rotating stage is generally used for optical examination. The polarized light is obtained by means of a polaroid or a nicol — that is, a calcite rhombohedron somewhat ground down and divided into two parts which are cemented together with Canada balsam. In the nicol the ordinary ray is totally reflected by the cement plane and then absorbed by the blackened side of the nicol

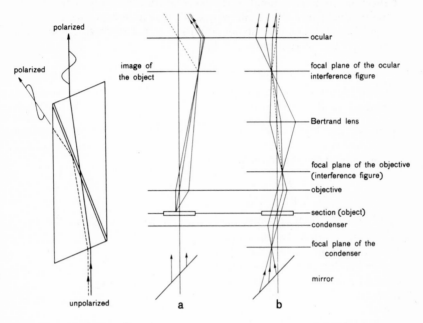

polarized

polarized

image of
the object

unpolarized

a   b

ocular

focal plane of the ocular
interference figure

Bertrand lens

focal plane of the objective
(interference figure)
objective

section (object)
condenser

focal plane of the
condenser

mirror

FIG. 174. Nicol; the ordinary ray, after total reflection, is absorbed on a black surface.

FIG. 175. Polarizing microscope (a) as a microscope and orthoscope and (b) as a conoscope.

(Fig. 174). In order to determine the vibration plane, we regard a shiny table through the nicol, which we rotate until the greatest extinction of the light occurs; the vibration plane of the light coming out of the nicol (**E**) intersects the table on a sagittal line.

The fixed nicol below the microscope stage serves as *polarizer*, the removable one above the stage as *analyzer*. Usually the nicols are crossed; that is, the vibration planes are perpendicular to each other, that of the polarizer being mostly sagittal.

The microscope may be used in three different ways:

1. As an orthoscope. The objective, as a rule, is weak, and hence the aperture angle is small. The observed rays are practically parallel (Fig. 175–a).

2. As a microscope. The objective is strong, and the analyzer is removed. The image of the crystal is at the focus of the ocular (Fig. 175–a).
3. As a conoscope. The objective is powerful, and the aperture angle is therefore large. The analyzer is in place, as are the Bertrand lens and the condenser. At a point of the focus of the ocular are concentrated all rays which in the section are parallel to a certain direction, and therefore each point in the field of vision corresponds with a direction through the section (Fig. 175–b).

Path and Phase Difference Between the Two Wave Fronts

If the plate is d cm thick, the faster front (monochromatic light, wavelength λ) passes through it at a velocity V_1 cm/sec, the slower at V_2 cm/sec; the first passes through the plate in $\dfrac{d}{V_1}$ and the second in $\dfrac{d}{V_2}$ seconds. The difference in time is

$$\frac{d}{V_2} - \frac{d}{V_1} = d\,(n'_g - n'_p)\,\frac{1}{c}\ \sec$$

in which $n'_g - n'_p$ is called the measure of birefringence in that direction. During this difference in time the faster front, after leaving the section, travels, in the air, $W = d(n'_g - n'_p)$ cm. ($W =$ the difference in path between the two fronts.)

If the elliptical section of the ellipsoid in the section examined in the orthoscope is situated as in Fig. 176, the vibration planes of the two fronts in the section are indicated by A_1 and A_2, and the components of the amplitude A are $A_1 = A \sin \alpha$ and $A_2 = A \cos \alpha$.

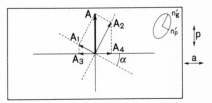

FIG. 176. p is the vibration plane of the polarizer, a that of the analyzer.

After passing the analyzer, the component of A_1 is

$$A_3 = A_1 \cos \alpha = A \sin \alpha \cos \alpha$$

and that of A_2 is

$$A_4 = A_2 \sin \alpha = A \cos \alpha \sin \alpha$$

The light intensities of the two fronts are therefore always equal: zero at $\alpha = 0°$, $90°$, $180°$, and $270°$ (extinction positions of the plate) and at a maximum at $\alpha = 45°$, $135°$, $225°$, and $315°$ (diagonal positions).

After leaving the analyzer, the vibration planes of the (coherent) fronts coincide in the frontal plane and interfere.

If there is no difference in velocity between the two fronts in the section, A_3 and A_4 are opposed, and the difference in phase is 180°, no light coming out of the analyzer. If the path difference is W cm, the phase difference when leaving the analyzer is

$$\delta = 180° + \frac{W}{\lambda} \, 360°$$

When the path difference is an even number of times $\lambda/2$, no light leaves at any value of α; when the path difference is an odd number of times $\lambda/2$, the light is at a maximum.

When white light is used, the phase differences and the intensities of the various λ are all different, and the result is that colored light leaves the analyzer (Newton's colors). If the path difference is 550 mμ, a yellow green is extinguished, and the color seen is red (*red of the first order*, red I). With a path difference of 1,100 $m\mu$ the result is red II, etc. (Fig. 177).

If d is known, the measure of birefringence can be determined from the interference color, for this determines the retardation.

In order to establish this retardation, we observe the subsequent

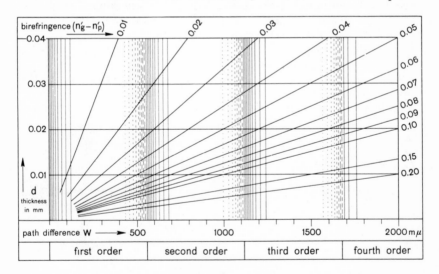

FIG. 177.   Relation of birefringence and thickness of a section to the color between crossed nicols (*scale of colors*).

orders on a sloping edge of the section or compensate the birefringence of the section by that of a quartz wedge.

Orientation of the Elliptical Section

In order to determine the orientation of the axes of the elliptical section of the ellipsoid in the crystal section and hence the angle α (Fig. 176), we rotate the stage with the section towards one of the extinction positions. In order to establish which axis is n'_g and which is n'_p, we put the section into a diagonal position and insert in the tube a test plate with known directions of n'_g and n'_p — for example, a plate of gypsum showing red I — also in diagonal position. If the color rises, the long axes of the ellipses of the section and the plate coincide (there is *addition*); if it falls, the two long axes are perpendicular to each other (there is *compensation*).

A section shows parallel extinction if n'_g or n'_p is parallel to the observed trace of a dominant crystal face or cleavage plane, and it shows symmetric extinction if n'_g or n'_p bisects the angle between two equivalent traces; in the other cases the section shows inclined extinction.

Sections of triclinic crystals show, in general, inclined extinction; those of monoclinic crystals parallel to the B axis always have, and crystals of higher symmetry cut parallel to a crystallonomic direction often have, parallel or symmetrical extinction.

Uniaxial Interference Figure

If we place a section of a uniaxial crystal, cut perpendicular to the principal axis, under the conoscope, and if we use monochromatic light, each point of the field of vision is illuminated by a beam of parallel

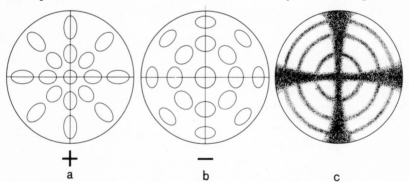

a b c

FIG. 178. Section of a uniaxial crystal, cut normal to the optic axis, under the conoscope in monochromatic light; some elliptical sections of (a) a positive and (b) a negative crystal; (c) rings of equal retardation (isophases) and the isogyre cross.

rays, the angle of which with the principal axis depends on the distance from the point to the center of the field of vision; each point of the field has its own elliptical section (Fig. 178).

At all points of a circle round the center the ellipses have the same shape, for the phase difference is the same; these circles are *isophases*. When the phase difference δ amounts to a whole number of times 360°, there is complete destructive interference and the circles appear as dark lines.

At the points where the axes of the ellipses are parallel to the vibration planes of polarizer and analyzer, extinction occurs; the dark cross resulting therefrom is formed by the *isogyres*.

When white light is used, the isophases are colored (Newton's colors).

If the plate is cut not quite normal to the optic axis, the center of the optical figure (the *interference figure*) does not coincide with the center of the field of vision, but the bars of the black cross remain parallel to the vibration planes of polarizer and analyzer.

If the plate is cut parallel to the optic axis, the isophases are equilateral hyperbolas; the isogyres are vague and disappear rapidly from the field of vision when the section is rotated, thereby giving the impression of belonging to a biaxial interference figure.

Biaxial Interference Figure

A section of a biaxial positive crystal, cut normal to Bx_a, gives under the conoscope a field of elliptical sections such as that sketched in Fig. 179.[1]

In extinction positions of the section the isogyres form a black cross,

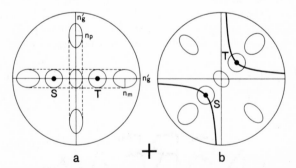

FIG. 179. Section of a (positive) biaxial crystal, cut $\perp$ to Bx_a, under the conoscope in monochromatic light; field of vision with a few elliptical sections and schematically indicated isogyres: (*a*) extinction position; (*b*) diagonal position.

[1] B. G. Escher, Verhandelingen van het Geologisch-Mijnbouwkundig Genootschap (1915), 337.

as with a uniaxial crystal. If the section is rotated to a diagonal position, they form an equilateral hyperbola with the vertices through the points of emergence of the optic axes S and T; the vibration directions of polarizer and analyzer are the asymptotes. Since the isophases are lemniscates, the interference figure is as depicted in Figs. 179 and 180–a. When white light is used, the lemniscates are in colors of Newton's scale.

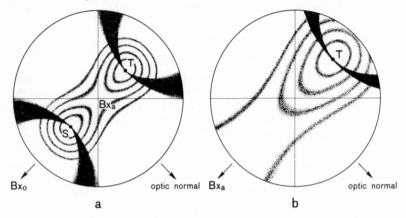

a   b

Fig. 180. Biaxial interference figure (*a*) with the points of emergence of both optic axes and (*b*) with that of one axis in the field of view.

If $2V$ is larger than about 60°, the axes fall outside the field of vision. This also occurs often when the sections are not normal to Bx_a. In many positions of the section only one axis falls within the field of vision, and only one arm of the hyperbola is visible; if the curvature can be observed, the nearest point of emergence of Bx_a lies on the convex side (Fig. 180–b).

Dispersions are often visible in interference figures; of special impor-

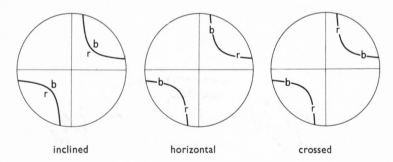

inclined   horizontal   crossed

Fig. 181. Dispersion with monoclinic crystals.

tance are cases I, II, and III in the monoclinic system (p. 204 and Fig. 181).

Determination of the Optic Character

This determination is carried out by means of the interference figure.

We examine a section of a uniaxial positive crystal with white light. If now a red I gypsum plate is inserted, also in diagonal position, a rising of color occurs in two opposite quadrants, a falling in the other two, and quite *near the axis* we observe the colors named in Fig. 182.

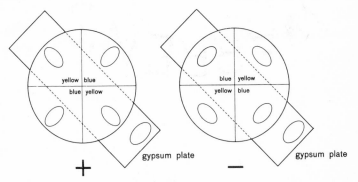

FIG. 182. Uniaxial crystal: determination of the optic character.

With a biaxial positive crystal in diagonal position, the colors indicated in Fig. 183 are observed *near the axes*.

If the points of emergence of the axes are not visible, determination of the character is generally not possible.

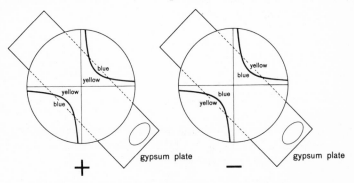

FIG. 183. Biaxial crystal: determination of the optic character.

Measurement of the Principal Refractive Indices

Under the polarization microscope, n'_g and n'_p of an arbitrarily oriented grain of crystal may be determined fairly accurately by the immersion method of Schroeder van der Kolk or Becke.[1] The largest and smallest values of these magnitudes, determined on many grains, may, as a rule, be considered equal to n_g and n_p of the crystal.

The easiest way to make a more accurate determination is to grind an oriented or arbitrary face and put it on the glass hemisphere, which has

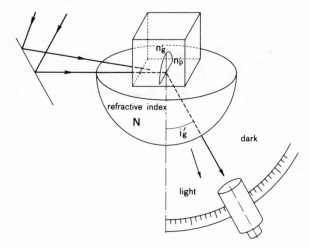

FIG. 184.   Principle of Abbe's refractometer.

a very high refractive index N, of Abbe's refractometer (Fig. 184). Light, entering the crystal horizontally and vibrating according to n'_g, is refracted and emerges at an angle i'_g:

$$\sin i'_g = \frac{n'_g}{N}$$

For light vibrating according to n'_p the angle of emergence is

$$\sin i'_p = \frac{n'_p}{N}$$

If, by rotation through a known angle about the vertical axis, we determine the refractive indices in two other positions, we can calculate the entire indicatrix from these six data.

[1] P. Niggli, *Lehrbuch der Mineralogie und Kristallchemie*, II (1942), p. 719; W. F. de Jong, *Tabellen zur Bestimmung der wichtigsten lichtdurchlässigen Mineralien* (1940).

Measurement of the Axial Angle $2V$

If the three principal refractive indices are known, $2V$ can be calculated (p. 202). Observation with Fedorov's stage or Liebisch's apparatus usually gives a more accurate result. The best way is to cut a small section approximately normal to Bx_a and to place this in a liquid with refractive index n_m, which is the refractive index of the crystal in the direction of the optic axes. The point of emergence of each of the two axes is subsequently brought into the center of the field of vision, and the angle of rotation is read.[1]

Rotation of the Vibration Plane

Some crystals [2] possess the property of rotating the vibration plane of a polarized beam of light through a certain angle; maximum rotation occurs along certain directions in the crystal. The rotation is proportional to the thickness of the section and approximately inversely proportional to the square of the wavelength; a section normal to the C axis of quartz 1 mm thick rotates the plane 21°44′ (Na light). The rotation, observed as one looks towards the source of light, is clockwise or anti-clockwise. Quartz with right trapezohedra (p. 41) rotates the plane clockwise. The phenomenon is observed in the orthoscope when extinction occurs, not with crossed nicols, but only after rotation of the analyzer (or polarizer) through the rotation angle. By inserting in the conoscope a $\lambda/4$ plate, we obtain a spiral interference figure which may be wound clockwise or anti-clockwise. If we put a clockwise- and an anti-clockwise-rotating plate one on top of the other, we may observe Airy's spirals (Fig. 185).

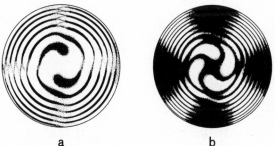

a   b

Fig. 185. (*a*) Section of anti-clockwise rotating quartz (left-handed) covered by a $\lambda/4$ plate under the conoscope; (*b*) section of a clockwise plus one of an anti-clockwise rotating quartz under the conoscope.

[1] J. Beckenkamp, *Statische und kinetische Kristalltheorien* II (1915), p. 217.
[2] W. A. Wooster, *Crystal Physics* (1949), p. 156.

Some biaxial crystals also rotate the vibration plane (Table 30). The phenomenon cannot occur in the classes with inversion point or in $3\,m$, $4\,mm$, $6\,mm$, $\bar{6}$, $\bar{6}m2$, and $\bar{4}3\,m$.

TABLE 30

	class	seen in the direction of	rotation angle per mm of path covered (Na light)
quartz (SiO₂)	$32 - D_3$	single optic axis	$21°44'$
cinnabar (HgS)	$32 - D_3$	single optic axis	$325°$ (red light)
NaClO₃	$23 - T$	threefold symm. axes	$3°8'$
Rochelle salt	$222 - D_2$	both optic axes	$-1.35°$
sugar	$2 - C_2$	both optic axes	$-1.6°$ and $+5.4°$

The rotation, in general, occurs to different degrees in all propagation directions; but a quartz section whose normal makes an angle of $56°10'$ with the principal axis has a rotation angle of $0°$.

Constructions

By means of the stereographic net the optical properties (ellipse orientation, interference figure) of a section with known orientation may be derived with sufficient accuracy.

If, for example, a tetragonal positive crystal has a cleavage $\{100\}$ and the section is cut parallel to a plane P whose position is $\varphi=60°$ and $\rho = 50°$, the normal projection is tilted $50°$ round pq (Fig. 186). The vibration plane of one wave front is situated in the principal plane — that is, the plane through the wave normal $\underline{P}$ and the optic axis $\underline{S}$; the vibration plane of the other front is normal to it. The trace of the cleavage plane (100) is normal to $\underline{P}-\underline{a}$, and the extinction angle

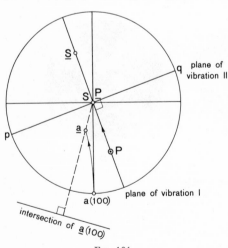

FIG. 186.

with regard to this can be read off.

For a biaxial crystal, the axes of the elliptical section may be found by Fresnel's construction: the planes are constructed through the direction of view P and each of the optic axes S and T, the bisectrix planes of which are the vibration planes (Fig. 187). If the direction of view lies in one of the symmetry planes of the indicatrix, we can also indicate which elliptical axis is the longest; if P lies outside such a plane, a calculation is usually necessary.

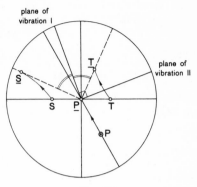

Fig. 187.

In order to ascertain whether the points of emergence of the optic axes will fall within the field of vision, we draw a circle of the size of this field round the center of the projection; the radius of this circle is usually about 30°.

Pleochroism

If absorption on passage through the crystal differs for different wavelengths, the crystal appears colored. The absorption depends on the direction of vibration. If the measure of absorption in all vibration directions is indicated by vectors from one point, all end points are situated on an ellipsoid which is characteristic for each wavelength and whose principal axes comply with conditions similar to those of the indicatrix (p. 199).

White light, vibrating along an axis of this ellipsoid, [1] appears after passage as a principal color. Uniaxial crystals may therefore show two principal colors, and biaxial crystals three principal colors; the former are dichroitic, the latter trichroitic. For the strongly trichroitic (orthorhombic) cordierite the color seen when light is vibrating parallel to the A axis is violet, that parallel to the B axis blue, and that parallel to the C axis yellow ("axial colors"). A cube having the axes as edges, seen in natural light, therefore shows in the A direction the mixed color of blue and yellow, in the B direction that of violet and yellow, in the C direction that of violet and blue ("face colors"). The unmixed colors are perceptible with polarized light (orthoscope).

Magnetic Induction

In a way that is analogous to the behavior of an insulator in an

---

[1] It is assumed here that all ellipsoids of the different λ's coincide.

electric field, elementary small magnets in a crystal are directed by a magnetic field $\mathbf{H}$, and the polarization $\mathbf{M}$ is proportional to $\mathbf{H}$ ($\chi =$ susceptibility factor):

$$\mathbf{M} = \chi\mathbf{H}$$

The total field in the body becomes ($\mu =$ permeability factor)

$$\mathbf{B} = \mathbf{H} + 4\pi\mathbf{M} = \mathbf{H} + 4\pi\chi\mathbf{H} = (1 + 4\pi\chi)\mathbf{H} = \mu\mathbf{H}$$

In a crystal, in general, $\mathbf{B}$ does not lie in the same direction as $\mathbf{H}$, the relation being according to a II-tensor:

$$B_1 = \mu_{11}H_1 + \mu_{21}H_2 + \mu_{31}H_3, \text{ etc.}$$

in which $\mu_{ik} = \mu_{ki}$.

The determination of μ or χ can be carried out even with microscopic crystals.[1]

If $\mu > 1$, the crystal (in that direction) is called paramagnetic; if $\mu < 1$, diamagnetic. For most crystals μ deviates from 1 only at the fifth or sixth decimal place. For ferromagnetic crystals, such as some iron and nickel compounds, the deviation may be much larger, and μ may even be as high as 3.000; it is then no longer constant, however, and depends upon the field strength and antecedents of the crystal.

The magnetic properties of organic crystals with carbon rings can be easily calculated. By means of such calculations in reverse, it has been possible to obtain very valuable data about the orientation of the molecules in these compounds.[2] We refer the reader to the literature for the quantum-theoretical explanation of the magnetism of metal and alloy crystals.[3]

If a crystal of a suitable compound is cooled in liquid helium in a strong magnetic field, the directed particles, after removal of the field, will range themselves at random and will thereby absorb so much energy that a further cooling down to some thousandths of a degree Kelvin can be achieved.

Thermal Conduction

If a body is in a steady state, and if the temperature θ is not everywhere the same, there will be at each point a temperature gradient $\boldsymbol{\tau}$. As a result of this gradient, heat flows, and amounts of heat are displaced. The flow of heat is indicated by $\mathbf{w}$; in isotropic bodies it occurs in the same direction as $\boldsymbol{\tau}$, but in general the dependency of

[1] W. A. Wooster, *Crystal Physics* (1949), p. 102.
[2] W. A. Wooster, *Crystal Physics* (1949), p. 112.
[3] G. V. Raynor, *An Introduction to the Electron Theory of Metals* (1949), p. 73.

w on **τ** is given by a II-tensor (k = thermal conduction constants):

$$w_1 = k_{11}\tau_1 + k_{21}\tau_2 + k_{31}\tau_3, \text{ etc.}$$

$k_{ik} = k_{ki}$; if this were not so, the flow of heat would follow a spiral (Stokes).

$$\tau_1 = \frac{\partial \theta}{\partial x_1}; \quad \tau_2 = \frac{\partial \theta}{\partial x_2}; \quad \tau_3 = \frac{\partial \theta}{\partial x_3}$$

In two cases the coefficients k are easy to determine in principle, but the practical difficulties are considerable.

1. A plane-parallel crystal plate is clamped horizontally between two flat copper plates, which are kept at different temperatures. The isothermal planes are horizontal when the body is in a steady state, and **τ** is therefore vertical (Fig. 188).

In general, the flow of heat is not vertical; but, when the thickness of the plate is small with respect to the other dimensions, only the vertical component is significant. If, therefore, the X'_3 axis is made vertical, this component is k'_{33}, and the flow of heat $k'_{33}\boldsymbol{\tau}$; this may be measured and k'_{33} determined.

In order to be able to calculate all the principal coefficients k, we need three measurements of differently oriented plates (p. 190):

$$k'_{33} = k_I \alpha_{13}^2 + k_{II} \alpha_{23}^2 + k_{III} \alpha_{33}^2$$

2. The conduction along a wire is determined. An objection here is that loss of heat on the boundary is difficult to avoid. The flow of heat **w** is directed along the axis of the wire; **τ**, in general, is not (Fig. 189).

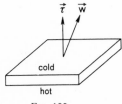

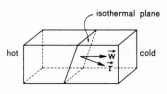

FIG. 188.   FIG. 189.

The Isothermal Surface in a Crystal

If a point within the crystal is kept at a different temperature from the surface, and if the body is in a steady state, then, for a crystal element whose side faces are parallel to the coordinate planes, as much heat is entering as leaving; hence

$$\frac{\partial w_1}{\partial x_1} + \frac{\partial w_2}{\partial x_2} + \frac{\partial w_3}{\partial x_3} = 0$$

With respect to the principal axes, we have

$$w_1 = k_I \tau_1 = k_I \frac{\partial \theta}{\partial x_1}$$

Therefore

$$k_I \frac{\partial^2 \theta}{\partial x_1^2} + k_{II} \frac{\partial^2 \theta}{\partial x_2^2} + k_{III} \frac{\partial^2 \theta}{\partial x_3^2} = 0$$

Away from the origin, this equation is satisfied by

$$\frac{x_1^2}{k_I} + \frac{x_2^2}{k_{II}} + \frac{x_3^2}{k_{III}} = \frac{\text{const.}}{\theta^2}$$

For an isothermal surface θ is constant, this surface being, therefore, an ellipsoid.

In an analogous manner we find that the isothermal lines on a flat crystal plate of which one point is heated are generally ellipses. In the demonstration the surface is covered with a layer of elaidic acid, which melts at $45°$, and this shows the $45°$ isotherm clearly.

A few numerical values of k are given in Table 31,[1] where we see, for example, that in copper, when the gradient in temperature is $1°$ C per cm, 43 calories pass per minute through 1 cm^2 normal to the direction of the flow.

TABLE 31

	k_I	k_{II}	k_{III}
Cu	43	43	43
NaCl	0.8	0.8	0.8
calcite	0.472	0.472	0.576
quartz	0.957	0.957	1.576

Electronic Conduction

In conducting crystals — of metals, for example — the flow $\mathbf{i}$ is related to the potential gradient $\mathbf{v}$ by a II-tensor (λ = conductivity coefficient):

$$i_1 = \lambda_{11} v_1 + \lambda_{21} v_2 + \lambda_{31} v_3, \text{ etc.}$$

and vice versa (r = resistance):

$$v_1 = r_{11} i_1 + r_{21} i_2 + r_{31} i_3, \text{ etc.}$$

[1] W. A. Wooster, *Crystal Physics* (1949), p. 85; E. Schmid & W. Boas, *Kristallplastizität* (1935), p. 202 (metal crystals).

It is not known for certain whether this relation is valid for semi-conductors also (p. 247), but for hematite, hexagonal Fe_2O_3, its validity is ascertained, r depending greatly on the temperature (Table 32).

TABLE 32

		r_I	r_{II}	r_{III}
Fe_2O_3	0° C	40.8 × 10⁷	40.8	80.8
	17°	35.1	35.1	68.7
	100°	18.3	18.3	33.1

Pyroelectricity

If a tourmaline crystal (ditrigonal pyramidal silicate) is strongly heated or cooled, electric charges appear at the ends of the polar axis; upon heating, a positive charge (analogous pole) appears at the often acute upper end, a negative one (antilogous pole) at the lower end. If the temperature is kept constant, the charges disappear after some time by conduction or neutralization. This behavior of tourmaline has been known for ages and has given it the name of ash-drawer: upon being heated, it attracts ashes. The phenomenon is ascribed to deformation of the structure, whereby the whole of positive ions is displaced in relation to the negative whole, thereby changing the electric moment.

When pyroelectricity occurs in crystals of the seven pyramidal classes and classes 2, m, and 1, as in sugar (monoclinic-sphenoidal), calamine (orthorhombic-pyramidal silicate), and tourmaline, the generated polarity is proportional to the change in temperature, and we speak of vectorial pyroelectricity.

If pyroelectricity occurs in other crystals without center, positive and negative charges occur at various places on the surface, and the phenomenon is described by a II-tensor (tensorial pyroelectricity).

Since change in temperature is always associated with deformation, it is difficult to ascertain how much the electric effect depends on the first change (true pyroelectricity) and how much on the second (false pyroelectricity). At any rate, part of the vectorial pyroelectricity seems to be true pyroelectricity.

The absence of a center may always be inferred from the occurrence of pyroelectricity.

Quantitatively, not much is known. Qualitatively, the charges are demonstrated with Kundt's test, in which a mixture of sulphur and red-lead powders passes through a fine sieve of muslin so that the sulphur particles become negatively charged and the red-lead particles positively charged. The particles adhere to the positive and negative parts, respectively, of the crystal. Hull [1] describes a better powder (carmine, sulphur, and blue lycopodium). A smoke of MgO or ice particles can also be made to adhere to the crystals.

Piezoelectricity [2]

In 1880 J. and P. Curie discovered that some crystals, when subjected to strain or pressure, show electric charges on the faces (piezoelectricity). It became apparent later that this property may occur in all crystals without inversion point except those of the class 432. Examples are tourmaline, quartz, sodium chlorate, Rochelle salt, and potassium dihydrogen phosphate.[3]

The components of the polarization $\mathbf{P}$ (p. 197) depend linearly, according to a III-tensor, on those of the II-tensor which describes the stress (d = piezoelectric modulus):

$$P_i = d_{kli}\sigma_{kl}$$

As an example we can write the following equation:

$$\begin{aligned}
P_1 = {} & d_{111}\sigma_{11} + d_{211}\sigma_{21} + d_{311}\sigma_{31} \\
& + d_{121}\sigma_{12} + d_{221}\sigma_{22} + d_{321}\sigma_{32} \\
& + d_{131}\sigma_{31} + d_{231}\sigma_{23} + d_{331}\sigma_{33}
\end{aligned}$$

in which $\sigma_{12} = \sigma_{21}$ etc. and $d_{121} = d_{211}$ etc.; there are, therefore, eighteen different components d_{kli}.

Sometimes the polarization components are expressed as dependent on the deformation components:

$$P_i = e_{kli}\gamma_{kl}$$

Symmetry of crystals causes some components to be equal or zero. Thus for quartz (class 32), in which X_1 is taken along a twofold axis and X_3 vertically,[4]

(P_1)	d_{111}	0	0	0	$-d_{111}$	d_{321}	0	d_{321}	0
(P_2)	0	$-d_{111}$	$-d_{321}$	$-d_{111}$	0	0	$-d_{321}$	0	0
(P_3)	0	0	0	0	0	0	0	0	0

[1] H. H. Hull, Journal of Applied Physics 20 (1949), 1157.

[2] W. G. Cady, *Piezoelectricity* (1946); W. P. Mason, *Piezoelectric Crystals and Their Application to Ultrasonics* (1950).

[3] S. Zerfoss & L. R. Johnson, Am. Min. 34 (1949), 61 (relation between composition and piezoelectricity).

[4] In the electrotechnique which uses the piezoelectricity of quartz, it is usual to take X_1 along a twofold axis and to apply a left-handed axial set for left-handed crystals. Cf. W. G. Cady, *Piezoelectricity* (1946), p. 407.

Hence

$$P_1 = d_{111}\sigma_{11} - d_{111}\sigma_{22} + 2\,d_{321}\sigma_{23}$$
$$P_2 = -\,2\,d_{111}\sigma_{12} - 2\,d_{321}\sigma_{13}$$
$$P_3 = 0$$

In order to determine the two components d_{111} and d_{321}, we cut a small rectangular body out of a quartz crystal, as indicated in Fig. 190. The front and back faces are covered with silver so that the charges occurring there can be measured when pressure is applied successively to each pair of opposite faces.

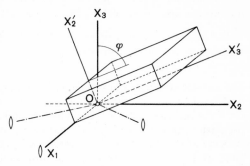

FIG. 190.

If the pressure is applied parallel to X_1, only the tension component $-\,\sigma_{11}$ is present (minus sign because strains are taken as positive), and the expression for P_1 becomes, therefore, in this case,

$$P_1 = d_{111} \times -\,\sigma_{11}$$

If the pressure is applied parallel to X'_3 (and the charges on front and back faces are measured), then

$$P'_1 = d'_{331} \times -\,\sigma'_{33}$$

In order to express d'_{331} in d_{kli}, we transform to the new axes:

	X'_1	X'_2	X'_3
X_1	$\alpha_{11} = 1$	$\alpha_{12} = 0$	$\alpha_{13} = 0$
X_2	$\alpha_{21} = 0$	$\alpha_{22} = -\cos\varphi$	$\alpha_{23} = \sin\varphi$
X_3	$\alpha_{31} = 0$	$\alpha_{32} = \sin\varphi$	$\alpha_{33} = \cos\varphi$

Then we obtain (p. 191)

$$d'_{331} = \alpha_{13}\alpha_{13}\alpha_{11}d_{111} + \ldots\ldots\ldots + \alpha_{23}\alpha_{23}\alpha_{11}d_{221}$$
$$+ \alpha_{33}\alpha_{33}\alpha_{11}d_{331} + \alpha_{33}\alpha_{23}\alpha_{11}d_{321} + \alpha_{23}\alpha_{33}\alpha_{11}d_{231}$$

Of the twenty-seven terms, only the last four mentioned differ from zero. For quartz, furthermore, $d_{331} = 0$, $d_{221} = -\,d_{111}$, and $d_{321} = d_{231}$, so that

$$d'_{331} = -\sin^2\varphi\,d_{111} + 2\sin\varphi\cos\varphi\,d_{321}$$

For quartz it is found that

$$d_{111} = -6.4 \times 10^{-8} \text{ cgsesu}$$
$$d_{321} = 0.72 \times 10^{-8} \text{ cgsesu}$$

The value of d_{111} remains fairly constant with increase of temperature, but declines greatly above 500° C and becomes zero at the transition into hexagonal quartz. Since d_{321} does not disappear at the transition, β-quartz is also piezoelectric, but in another way than α-quartz.

The d_{231} of Rochelle salt at temperatures between $-16°$ C and $+22°$ C is abnormally large — for example, 25.000 $\times$ 10^{-8} — and varies from crystal to crystal.

A crystal or crystal powder can be qualitatively examined for piezoelectric behavior by the method of Giebe and Scheibe. The material is put between the plates of a condenser, and the capacity of the electric oscillation circuit to which the condenser is connected is slowly changed. As soon as the vibration time corresponds with the mechanical vibration time of the material, the electric amplitude suddenly becomes much greater, and the loudspeaker included in the circuit produces a click or a loud noise.[1]

Piezoelectric crystals are used [2] to convert mechanical vibrations into electrical vibrations, and vice versa: in pick-ups, for the generating of ultrasonic waves (for example, in depth sounding), for keeping radio wavelengths constant, in very accurate clocks, and for measuring the elastic constants of crystals and other materials.

Elasticity

The deformation depends on the stresses. In a mechanically isotropic bar the elongation is proportional to the stress (Hooke's law), but there is always also a transverse contraction about one-third as great as the elongation (Poisson).

In a crystal, each of the nine strain components γ_{pq} depends linearly on all nine stress components σ_{ik}; strain and stress are thus connected here by a IV-tensor (s = elastic constants; Voigt and Wooster call them elastic moduli):

$$\gamma_{pq} = s_{ikpq}\sigma_{ik}$$

As an example we can write:

$$\gamma_{33} = s_{1133}\sigma_{11} + s_{2133}\sigma_{21} + s_{3133}\sigma_{31} +$$
$$+ s_{1233}\sigma_{12} + s_{2233}\sigma_{22} + s_{3233}\sigma_{32} +$$
$$+ s_{1333}\sigma_{13} + s_{2333}\sigma_{23} + s_{3333}\sigma_{33}$$

[1] A. Schleede & E. Schneider, *Röntgenspektroskopie und Kristallstrukturanalyse*, II (1929), p. 261.

[2] L. Bergmann, *Schwingende Kristalle* (1953).

The relation may be written in reverse order $(c =$ elastic moduli):

$$\sigma_{pq} = c_{ikpq}\gamma_{ik}$$

In each mechanically isotropic body the principal components of strain fall in the same directions as the principal components of stress. A crystal shows a more intricate behavior. There are eighty-one tensor components, and in transformations they all have to be considered separately. Many, even for asymmetric crystals, are equal:

$$s_{ikpq} = s_{kipq} = s_{ikqp} = s_{kiqp} = s_{pqik} = s_{qpik} = s_{pqki} = s_{qpki}$$

Often an abridged way of writing is used, and 11 is noted as 1, 21 as 6, etc., thus:

11	22	33	23 and 32	31 and 13	12 and 21	(tensor notation)
1	2	3	4	5	6	(matrix notation)

The above example is accordingly noted as

$$\gamma_3 = s_{13}\sigma_1 + s_{63}\sigma_6 + s_{53}\sigma_5 +$$
$$+ s_{63}\sigma_6 + s_{23}\sigma_2 + s_{43}\sigma_4 +$$
$$+ s_{53}\sigma_5 + s_{43}\sigma_4 + s_{33}\sigma_3$$

or as

$$\gamma_3 = s_{13}\sigma_1 + s_{23}\sigma_2 + s_{33}\sigma_3 + 2\,s_{43}\sigma_4 + 2\,s_{55}\sigma_3 + 2\,s_{63}\sigma_6$$

So, also, γ_{23} and γ_{32}, added together, become

$$2\,\gamma_4 = 2\,s_{14}\sigma_1 + 2\,s_{24}\sigma_2 + 2\,s_{34}\sigma_3 + 4\,s_{44}\sigma_4 + 4\,s_{54}\sigma_5 + 4\,s_{64}\sigma_6$$

There are then six components γ and thirty-six components s, and $s_{ik} = s_{ki}$, so that there are finally twenty-one different s_{ik} (and also c_{ik}).

For symmetrical crystals many s_{ik} are mutually equal or are zero — for example, for quartz (class 32):

(γ_1)	s_{11}	s_{12}	s_{13}	$2s_{14}$	0	0
(γ_2)	s_{12}	s_{11}	s_{13}	$-2s_{14}$	0	0
(γ_3)	s_{13}	s_{13}	s_{33}	0	0	0
$(2\gamma_4)$	$2s_{14}$	$-2s_{14}$	0	$4s_{44}$	0	0
$(2\gamma_5)$	0	0	0	0	$4s_{44}$	$4s_{14}$
$(2\gamma_6)$	0	0	0	0	$4s_{14}$	$2(s_{11} - s_{12})$

For cubic crystals:

(γ_1)	s_{11}	s_{12}	s_{12}	0	0	0
(γ_2)	s_{12}	s_{11}	s_{12}	0	0	0
(γ_3)	s_{12}	s_{12}	s_{11}	0	0	0
$(2\gamma_4)$	0	0	0	$4s_{44}$	0	0
$(2\gamma_5)$	0	0	0	0	$4s_{44}$	0
$(2\gamma_6)$	0	0	0	0	9	$4s_{44}$

For a cubic crystal there are thus three constants. For a mechanically isotropic body, moreover, $2s_{44} = s_{11} - s_{12}$; here, therefore, are two constants, which generally are indicated as E and m:

$$s_{11} = \frac{1}{E}; \quad s_{12} = -\frac{1}{mE}; \quad 4s_{44} = \frac{1}{G}$$

In the last expression

$$G = \frac{mE}{2(m+1)}$$

In the tensor notation

$$\gamma_{11} = \frac{1}{E}\left[\sigma_{11} - \frac{1}{m}(\sigma_{22} + \sigma_{33})\right], \text{ etc.}$$

$$2\gamma_{12} = \frac{1}{G}\sigma_{12}, \text{ etc.}$$

For a bar-shaped crystal stretched lengthwise along the direction X'_3

$$\gamma'_3 = s'_{33}\sigma'_3$$

$$\sigma'_3 = \frac{1}{s'_{33}}\gamma'_3$$

Therefore $\dfrac{1}{s'_{33}}$ corresponds to Young's modulus E. We use s and not c because application of tension 1 is practically possible and strain 1 is not.

If $\dfrac{1}{s'_{33}}$ is marked off along the radius vectors, we obtain the so-called elasticity figures (Fig. 191).

A few values of s are given in Table 33.[1]

| a | b |

FIG. 191. Elasticity figures of (a) fluorite (CaF$_2$, cubic) and (b) barite (BaSO$_4$, orthorhombic).

TABLE 33 **(The unit is 10^{-13} cm^2/dyne.)**

	s_{11}	s_{12}	s_{13}	$2s_{14}$	s_{33}	$4s_{44}$
halite	24	−5				78
quartz	12.98	−1.66	−1.52	−4.31	9.90	20.04
(steel)	5	−1.3				12.6

[1] Further data will be found in E. Schmid & W. Boas, *Kristallplastizität* (1935), pp. 200, 266.

The compressibility constant κ indicates the proportion of decrease in volume to increase in hydrostatic pressure:

$$-\frac{dV}{V} = \kappa dP$$

If we examine a cube of a cubic crystal with edges of 1 cm along the axes, the decrease in length along the X_1 axis is γ_1, and the decrease in volume is, therefore, γ_1.

$$\gamma_1 = s_{11}\sigma_1 + s_{12}\sigma_2 + s_{12}\sigma_3$$

In this expression

$$\sigma_1 = \sigma_2 = \sigma_3 = dP$$

The total decrease in volume is $3\gamma_1$. Hence

$$-\frac{3\gamma_1}{1} = 3(s_{11} + 2s_{12})\, dP$$

$$\kappa = 3(s_{11} + 2s_{12})$$

A mechanically isotropic bar transmits a longitudinal wave with a velocity v (ρ = density):

$$v = \sqrt{E\,\frac{1}{\rho}}$$

If the bar is clamped at the center, the wavelength of the fundamental vibration is two times the length L of the bar (ν = frequency):

$$v = \nu\lambda = \nu \times 2L$$

A small bar 1 cm long, cut out of a quartz crystal in the direction X_1 and therefore parallel to a twofold axis, may vibrate in the same way:

$$v = 2\nu = \sqrt{\frac{1}{s_{11}}\,\frac{1}{\rho}}$$

$$2\nu = \sqrt{\frac{1}{12.98 \times 10^{-13}} \times \frac{1}{2.66}}$$

$$\nu = 268,000$$

This value is not entirely correct, for the vibration phenomenon is not completely isothermal but rather adiabatic.

B. Explanatory Part [1]

The crystal is, in principle, considered a homogeneous discontinuum, a strictly ordered entity of atoms, a structure complying with Groth's definition (*ideal crystal*).

Many properties, however (especially the so-called structure-sensitive ones: gliding, diffusion, ionic and electronic conductivity, and, to a lesser degree, tensile strength and hardness), depend on the usually numerous but restricted imperfections of the structure (*real crystal*). These imperfections are the cause of the often apparently capricious behavior of solid matter, and they give a crystal a certain individuality.

Imperfections of the Structure [2]

1. *Heat* movement of the particles. The average amplitude of the ions in an NaCl structure at room temperature is 0.245 A for the Na ions and 0.235 A for the Cl ions; at 900° K it is approximately 0.58 A. These movements can be described as the cooperation of a number of harmonic waves [3] (p. 250).

2. Rotating parts. In some crystals, as a rule, at a temperature not far below the melting point, radicals (p. 167) or molecules (p. 177) *rotate*, often causing an increase in symmetry, anomalies in the specific heat, etc.[4]

3. The *surface* of a structure is never ideal. In an NaCl crystal the outer ions are drawn to the inside by about 5% of the layer distance, but only with very small crystals ($< 0.1\mu$) is the influence of the surface perceptible through the entire structure (p. 255).

4. Particles may occur in an *excited state:* one or more of the valence electrons of such a particle are brought into a higher energy state by addition of energy, but they remain within the electron cloud of their own atom (*exciton*); this state moves through the structure. The excited state may be generated by — for example — ultraviolet radiation, and its disappearance may be accompanied by emanation of light.[5]

---

[1] C. Kittel, *Introduction to Solid State Physics* (1953); C. Zwikker, *Physical Properties of Solid Materials* (1954); G. V. Raynor, *An Introduction to the Electron Theory of Metals* (1949).

[2] F. Seitz in *Imperfections in Nearly Perfect Crystals* (1952); A. L. G. Rees, *Chemistry of the Defect Solid State* (1954).

[3] F. Seitz, *loc. cit.*, p. 87 (*phonons*).

[4] R. C. Evans, *Introduction to Crystal Chemistry* (1948), p. 267.

[5] S. G. Curran, *Luminescence and the Scintillation Counter* (1953); "Luminescence," British J. Applied Physics, Suppl. 4 (1955).

5. There may be *free electrons* and *free holes*. In a metallic crystalm any valence electrons move freely through the structure.

A special case of paragraph 4 is found in semi-conductors. An electron may become temporarily free and move through the structure. The ionized atom constitutes a (positive) hole. If an electron from a neighboring atom moves to the hole, the result is the same as if the hole moved; we can therefore speak of free holes moving through the structure in the same way as free electrons but in opposite direction (p. 248).

6. The structure is either a *defect* structure or a *crowded* structure. In the defect structures some sites (1 in 10,000, for example, or, with AgCl, even 1 in 100) are not occupied by a particle, but are sometimes occupied by an electron.

We distinguish between Frenkel defects and Schottky defects. With the former the missing particles are still present interstitially, and the structure is therefore locally crowded; with the latter this is not so (p. 245). Sometimes the site of a negative ion is occupied by an electron (cf. *F* center, p. 247). In an ionic structure the sum of the positive charges equals the sum of the negative, and in this respect the composition is fixed; in an atomic or metallic structure (FeS, for example; see p. 154), since the number of empty sites of one kind of atom may often vary greatly, the composition is not entirely fixed and stoichiometric.[1]

7. The structure contains *foreign particles*, which may replace particles on structural sites (forming mixed crystals) or may be present interstitially (forming a solid solution; see p. 161). A slight "contamination" may have a great influence: replacement of 0.01% of the germanium by arsenic makes a germanium crystal suitable for use as a transistor (p. 249), and the same percentage of bismuth in copper makes the copper brittle (p. 161).

Photons (light quanta), α- and β-particles, and neutrons may be regarded as transient foreign particles, and they often possess enough energy to bring structural particles into an excited state or even to ionize them.

8. The two parts of a crystal at both sides of a lattice plane in the Bravais lattice have a periodic nature, and a movement of one part along this plane over one or more periodicity distances leads to a crystal with an unchanged structure. Many crystals, indeed, show the possibility of movement along certain planes in certain directions (*gliding*, p. 238).

---

[1] W. E. Garner, *Chemistry of the Solid State* (London, 1955), p. 44.

A *dislocation* [1] may be described as generated by the gliding of a limited section of one part of the crystal along a limited area of a lattice plane (which may or may not also be known macroscopically as a glide plane). This area is enclosed or bounded by the *dislocation line* — enclosed when the line falls entirely within the crystal, bounded when the line terminates on the crystal surface or within the crystal (for example, on a second dislocation). The dislocation line is a physical line; it might be better to speak of a dislocation torus or cylinder. In the interior of the torus or cylinder the particles are dislocated, but outside they occupy virtually normal sites (Figs. 192, 193, 194). Disloca-

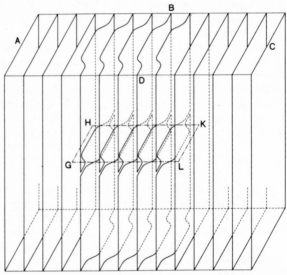

FIG. 192.   Schematic representation of a dislocation. Gliding of the upper part of the lattice to the left and of the lower part to the right causes dislocation of a few cells along the dislocation line *GHKL*. Lines *GH* and *KL* are edge-dislocation lines, lines *HK* and *GL* screw-dislocation lines.

tions cause stresses. Macroscopically, two kinds of stress are distinguished: normal stress (compressive or tensile) and shear stress, also called volume stress and deformation stress. The stresses caused by dislocations are also of these two kinds. A closed dislocation line shows alternate parts along which pressure (or strain) stresses and shear stresses appear; at the transitions mixed stresses may appear.

[1] W. T. Read, *Dislocations in Crystals* (1953); A. H. Cottrell, *Dislocations and Plastic Flow in Crystals* (1953); W. Shockley & others, *Imperfections in Nearly Perfect Crystals* (1952); J. S. Koehler & others, *Dislocations in Metals* (1954); J. C. Fisher & others, *Dislocations and Mechanical Properties of Crystals* (New York, 1957).

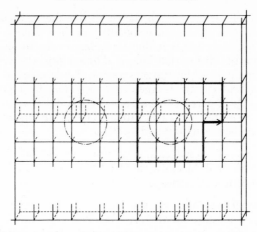

FIG. 193. Vertical section AC, in which the edge-dislocation lines of Fig. 192 are indicated as sections of cylinders; for the sake of clearness the layers outside the cylinders are indicated as displaced too, but one has to imagine that the displacement (and the tension) outside the cylinders has gradually vanished. The Burgers vector **B**, *perpendicular* to the dislocation line, has been indicated for the right cylinder.

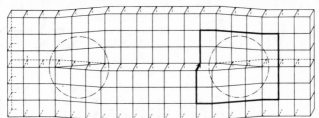

FIG. 194. Vertical section BD, in which the screw-dislocation lines of Fig. 192 are indicated as sections of cylinders. The Burgers vector **B**, *parallel* to the dislocation line, has been indicated for the right cylinder.

We speak of *edge dislocations* if the stress is of the first kind, of *screw dislocations* if it is of the second. From Fig. 193 it follows that an edge dislocation may be described as generated by interpolation (or omission) of one or a few partial extra planes of cells.

The "gliding" may be represented by a vector, the *Burgers vector*. This is situated in the glide plane and is perpendicular to the edge-dislocation parts, and parallel to the screw-dislocation parts, of the dislocation line; its length is an integral multiple of the periodicity distance.[1] We may find this vector by comparing the structure with an ideal structure. If we draw in the latter a closed line through a number of

[1] This is not true for the so-called Shockley dislocations, which may occur in cubic close-packed structures.

cells (for example, three cells to the right, five down, then three to the left, and finally five up), the corresponding line in the deformed structure will also be a closed line if it does not enclose the dislocation line. If it does enclose the dislocation line, it shows a *gap;* the vector between the ends of the gap is the Burgers vector. The number of dislocations in a good natural crystal is about 10^8 per cm^2; in a good synthetic crystal it is 10^9; in a cold-worked metallic crystal it is 10^{12} and therefore about 1 per area of 1,000 atoms. The mean distance in a good crystal may be between 10^{-3} and 10^{-4} cm.

9. The apparently homogeneous crystal shows *mosaic texture:* that is, it is divided into small blocks with edge lengths of about 10^{-5} cm, which are somewhat differently oriented, but not over more than a few minutes.

10. If the *deformation* of the structure by external forces is homogeneous, the state of stress can be derived by means of a powder photograph. If the deformation is not homogeneous, the structure is bent; on account of the different orientation of the various parts, a Laue photograph shows not sharp spots but streaks (*asterism*). On heating, the streaks break up into dots — a change which indicates that the bent parts of the structure have been *polygonized;* that is, bent lines have become broken lines, and numerous, small, undeformed crystals, separated by well-defined dislocations, have been generated (Fig. 195).

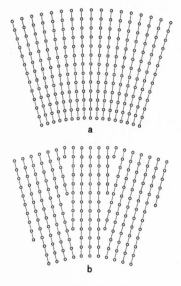

FIG. 195.   (*a*) Deformed structure under tension; (*b*) polygonization, proceeding with abolition of the tension.

11. Other imperfectly ordered structures may be mentioned: (a) stackings of (hexagonal) layers (p. 158, note), (b) fibrous materials (p. 178), (c) stretched rubber (p. 182), (d) tubular crystals,[1] (e) micelles,[2] (f) liquid crystals,[3] (g) vitreous materials (Zachariasen).[4]

[1] "Chrysotile," etc., Acta Cryst. 7 (1954), 827 et seq.

[2] C. Zwikker, *Physical Properties of Solid Materials* (1954), p. 40; C. Schuur, Diss. Delft (1955), "Some Aspects of the Crystallization of High Polymers."

[3] Zeitschrift für Kristallographie A 79 (1931), 1–347.

[4] J. M. Stevels, *Progress in the Theory of the Physical Properties of Glass* (1948).

Structure Energy of an Ideal Crystal [1]

The structure energy U_0 is the potential energy of all the ions in a mole of an infinitely large structure if no external forces are applied.

If all the ions of the mole are infinitely far removed from one another, their potential is taken as zero, and the structure energy is therefore negative. That energy is the work gained in transferring the ions from infinity to their positions in the structure.

If two spherical charges $+e$ and $-e$ (e.s.u.) are at a distance r cm, their potential energy u is

$$u = - \frac{e^2}{r} \text{ ergs}$$

As the equilibrium distance between two oppositely charged ions is apparently not zero, a repulsive force exists between them, and we therefore write (Mie, 1903)

$$u = - \frac{e^2}{r} + \frac{b}{r^n}$$

For many ionic structures, $n \sim 9$. A mole contains N pairs of ions (Avogadro). If the mutual influence of these pairs of ions in the structure is not taken into account, their potential energy U is (Born, 1918)

$$U = - \frac{Ne^2}{r} + \frac{Nb}{r^9}$$

If this influence is taken into account, the potential energy depends on the type of structure:

$$U = - MN \frac{e^2}{r} + \frac{B}{r^9}$$

In this expression M is *Madelung's constant* (Table 34).

TABLE 34

type of structure	M
NaCl	1.748
CsCl	1.763
α-ZnS (sphalerite)	1.639
β-ZnS (wurtzite)	1.64
CaF$_2$	5.039

[1] For considerations of the structure of metallic crystals see G. V. Raynor, *An Introduction to the Electron Theory of Metals* (1949), p. 87.

If the structure is in equilibrium, the potential is a minimum; hence

$$\left(\frac{\partial U}{\partial r}\right)_{r=r_0} = MN\frac{e^2}{r_0^2} - 9\frac{B}{r_0^{10}} = 0$$

from which it follows that

$$B = \frac{1}{9} M N e^2 r_0^8$$

and the structure energy is

$$U_0 = -\frac{8}{9} M N \frac{e^2}{r_0}$$

r_0 being the smallest separation of oppositely charged ions.

The value of n, and thus the factor 8/9, is derived from the compressibility constant κ (p. 225). For the halite structure this may be calculated as follows.

In a cube with edges along which x ions are placed, the length of the edges is xr and the volume $x^3 r^3 \equiv V$. In this cube there are $2N$ ions; so $x^3 = 2N$ and

$$V = 2N r^3$$

$$r = \sqrt[3]{\frac{V}{2N}}$$

When we insert this value and take P as the hydrostatic pressure

$$P = -\frac{\partial U}{\partial V}$$

we obtain, after having put $r = r_0$,

$$-V\frac{\partial P}{\partial V} = \kappa = \frac{4}{9} M \frac{e^2}{r_0^4}$$

The structure energy is determined indirectly by means of the Born-Haber cycle.

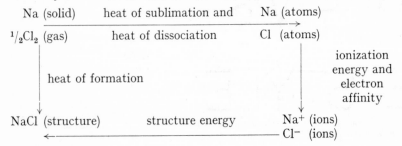

Na (solid)   heat of sublimation and   Na (atoms)

$^1/_2Cl_2$ (gas)   heat of dissociation   Cl (atoms)

heat of formation   ionization energy and electron affinity

NaCl (structure)   structure energy   Na⁺ (ions)
Cl⁻ (ions)

If the five energies are known, the structure energy can be derived from them. If the structure energy is calculated by means of Madelung's constant, a good estimate of the heat of formation can be made, even for hypothetical compounds. We reach the conclusion that the following structures, for example, would be strongly endothermal and therefore probably do not occur.[1]

NeF	$< - 241$ cal	NaCl type
NaF_2	$< - 156$ cal	TiO_2 type
MgF_3	$< - 111$ cal	AlF_3 type
AlF_4	$< - 700$ cal	molecular structure (BF_3)

Among compounds of the type AX, the constant M is largest for the CsCl type. Not all AX crystallize according to this type, however, because of the influence of other factors: the radius ratio of the ions and their polarizability (p. 139). The latter has very little or no influence in a coordination structure, but it is present in a layer or molecular structure (Fig. 196).

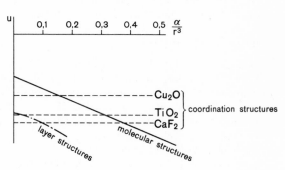

FIG. 196.   Relation between polarizability of the ions and structure energy for some types of AX_2. Strongly polarizable ions preferably give rise to layer and molecular structures.

Surface and Surface Energy

Surface particles are drawn somewhat into the interior, in the case of NaCl about 5% of the distances between the layers.[2] Also the surface tends to contract, and small "shrinkage cracks" of atomic dimensions may occur (Buerger).

It is assumed that polishing produces a shallow amorphous layer (Beilby), but the electron-diffraction picture is the same for all metals and probably originates from a rubbed-in hydrocarbon.[3]

[1] H. G. Grimm and K. F. Herzfeld, Zeitschrift für Physik 19 (1923), 141.

[2] J. E. Lennard-Jones and B. M. Dent, Transactions of the Faraday Society 24 (1928), 92.

[3] Journal of Applied Physics 23 (1952), 1412.

Sintering may be the result of a superficial melting or of diffusion (p. 243).[1]

The surface energy [2] of an ideal crystal is the work per square centimeter of surface that is newly formed when one part of the structure is separated from the other and removed into infinity.

Yamada derives the surface energy of any crystal face from that of a certain face. He finds that for NaCl the energy of (100) is the least, and he believes that this may be related to the cleavability.

Compared with the structure energy, the surface energy is important only for very small particles. If a mole of an NaCl crystal is divided into cubes with an edge length of 1 μ, the total surface energy is 0.0057 kcal, whereas the structure energy amounts to 180 kcal. One may verify the value 0.0057 approximately by dissolving very small cubes; the heat of solution is somewhat smaller than that for a large cube.

Tensile Strength

If we calculate [3] the (electrostatic) force perpendicular to (100) between two parts of an NaCl crystal, we arrive at about 200 kg/mm², whereas observation results in 0.5 kg/mm². The difference is mainly ascribed to the effect of cracks. If the surface shows a small crevice normal to the direction of strain, the tension at the end of the crevice is very large; elongation occurs very soon, and the crevice extends itself over the entire diameter.

If we avoid the crevices by keeping the crystal in an unsaturated solution during the application of the strain, a tensile strength as great as 160 kg/mm² may be observed (*Joffé effect*).[4] In this test, however, the influence of the mantle of water molecules round the NaCl structure is neglected.

Planes exhibiting little cohesion between them often occur as *cleavage planes*. These are always crystallonomic planes, often with very simple symbols. The cleavage is caused by strain, pressure, or a blow. If, for instance, one taps on a needle whose point is placed on and normal to a sheet of muscovite, the result is a star whose three rays are the passages of vertical cleavage planes (percussion figure, Fig. 197). [5]

[1] J. A. Hedvall, *Einführung in die Festkörperchemie* (1952), pp. 125, 240.

[2] F. Seitz, *The Modern Theory of Solids* (1940), p. 96, with literature survey and mention of G. Wulff's construction of the crystal boundary, derived from the surface energy, Zeitschrift für Kristallographie 34 (1901), 449.

[3] M. D. Shappell, Am. Min. 21 (1936), 75.

[4] A. F. Joffé, *The Physics of Crystals* (1928), p. 56.

[5] But cf. H. Tertsch, *Die Festigkeitserscheinungen der Kristalle* (1949), p. 257 (pressure figure).

In many structures (for example, NaCl, graphite) the cleavage planes are smooth planes with close packing and therefore with large spacing. In others (pyroxenes and amphiboles, Figs. 198 and 199) the cleavage planes zigzag between the Si-O chains.

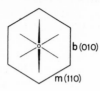

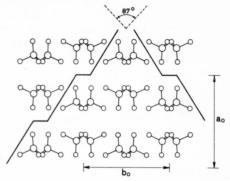

FIG. 197.   Percussion figure in a muscovite sheet.

FIG. 198.   Projection along the C axis of a pyroxene, only the $[SiO_3]$ chains being indicated; these chains remain intact on cleavage.

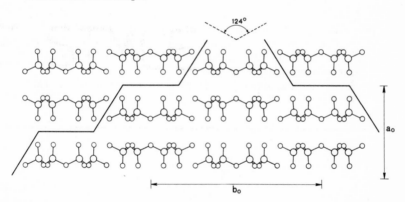

FIG. 199.   Projection along the C axis of an amphibole, only the $[Si_4O_{11}]$ chains being indicated; the chains remain intact on cleavage.

Nora Wooster [1] has given a number of rules for the relation of structure and cleavage planes: cleavage does not break radicals, nor does it attack the chains and layers present in pyroxenes, amphiboles, and micas; chain structures, indeed, often cleave into fibers, and layer structures into layers, but in framework structures, such as feldspars, the three-dimensional "radical" is readily broken.

[1] Science Progress 103 (1932), 462.

Hardness [1]

Hardness, a rather vague idea, is the resistance to the loosening of crystal particles with mostly arbitrary boundaries. The removal of a small part of a structure from its surface requires another — and a much worse defined — kind of work than pulling a structure into two parts along a certain plane. There is obviously only a slight functional relation between hardness and tensile strength.

The shape and therefore also the bond of the loosened particles depend on the manner in which the hardness test is carried out. The results thus depend on the method of examination. We distinguish three kinds of hardness:

1. *Scratching hardness.* Harder material scratches softer material. In mineralogy the Mohs *hardness scale* (1812) is often used, in more accurate work the sclerometer, which draws a hard point over the surface under a constant pressure (Seebeck, 1833).
2. *Grinding hardness.* The material is ground away with standard powders (Rosiwal, 1896).
3. *Indentation hardness.* A given pressure is exerted by a steel ball or point, in contact with the crystal, and the permanent depth of the impression it makes determines the hardness. This method is used especially in metallurgical technics (Brinell, Vickers) and is now used on a micro scale in the study of minerals.

The results for the minerals of Mohs' scale are indicated in Table 35.

TABLE 35

Mohs' scale	sclerometer	grinding method	pressure method
1. talc		0.03	5
2. gypsum.	0.04	1.25	14
3. calcite	0.26	4.5	96
4. fluorite.	0.75	5	106
5. apatite.	1.23	6.5	237
6. orthoclase.	25	37	253
7. quartz	40	120	270 (900 [2])
8. topaz.	152	175	525 (1,300 [2])
9. corundum.	1,000	1,000	1,150 (2,100 [2])
10. diamond		140,000	2,500

[1] A. E. H. Tutton, *Crystallography and Practical Crystal Measurement* (1922), p. 534; D. Tabor, "Hardness of Solids," Endeavour 13 (1954), 27; H. Tertsch, *Die Festigkeitserscheinungen der Kristalle* (1949), p. 171.

[2] Vickers hardness, Metalen 10 (1955), 412.

If the values of the hardness are marked off along all radii, the surface of the end points, even for regular crystals, is a complicated figure, which complies, however, with the symmetry of the class [1] (Fig. 200).

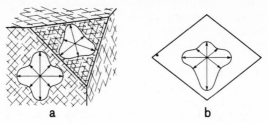

a   b

FIG. 200.   Curve of hardness on the faces of (a) fluorite (CaF_2) and (b) a cleavage rhombohedron of calcite ($CaCO_3$).

V. M. Goldschmidt [2] shows that hardness depends but little on the type of structure but increases with a rise in the charge of the ions and with a decrease of their distances (Table 36).

TABLE 36

	LiCl	SrO	MgO	CaO	SrO	BaO
charge	e	$2e$				
distance	2.57 A	2.57	2.12	2.40	2.57	2.77
hardness (Mohs)	3	3.5	6.5	4.5	4.5	3—3.5

Friederich [3] gives, for the hardness H of ionic structures, formulas which are summarized as follows by Goldschmidt:

$$H = s \, \frac{e_A e_X}{r_0^m}$$

In this expression s is a constant for a structure type; for the halite type m is 4—6, and for other types it is larger, especially when the bond is mainly homopolar; e_A and e_X are the charges of the ions.

---

[1] F. Exner, *Untersuchungen über die Härte an Kristallflächen*, Preisschrift Akademie Wien (1873).

[2] Geochemische Verteilungsgesetze VIII (1927), 102. Detailed discussion of the relation of hardness and structure.

[3] Fortschritte der Chemie, Physik und Physikalische Chemie 18 (1926), 717.

Gliding

Primary Gliding

Many crystals have crystallonomic planes along which the two parts may move in certain crystallonomic directions without losing their cohesion or changing the structure (Table 37). Pure metallic crystals, especially, show glide planes; the crystals themselves and also their polycrystalline aggregates owe their ductility to gliding. If a shear stress is applied to a crystal, a number of parallel glide planes, separated by glide bands, is observed. These bands are from 10^{-3} to 10^{-4} cm thick, and each, on accurate examination, appears to consist of still finer bands about 200 A thick. The length of slip along such a small band may be as great as 2,000 A.

TABLE 37 [1]

	glide plane T	direction of glide t	gliding stress kg/mm^2
Cu	(111)	$[1\bar{1}0]$	0.10
W	(112)	$[11\bar{1}]$	
Zn	(0001)	$[11\bar{2}0]$	0.094
Cd	(0001)	$[11\bar{2}0]$	0.058
NaCl	(110)	$[1\bar{1}0]$	0.1
ice	(0001)		
soap crystals (monoclinic)	(001)	$[010]$ and others	

If a bar-shaped crystal of Cd or Zn, the principal axis of which does not coincide with the axis of the bar, is stretched, slip-bands move along the glide planes; the bar becomes flat but does not constrict further and does not break until it has been stretched by several hundred percent (Fig. 201).

The gliding of two parts of the NaCl structure may easily be understood because during the movement the distance between differently charged ions becomes virtually no greater and that between equally charged ions no smaller; the two parts, therefore, do not repel each other, and the cohesion is maintained (Fig. 202).

The movement of glacier ice is chiefly explained by the easy gliding along (0001) in ice crystals. Fig. 203 shows the behavior of differently oriented plates cut from an ice crystal.

[1] H. Tertsch, *Die Festigkeitserscheinungen der Kristalle* (1949), p. 56; E. Schmid & W. Boas, *Kristallplastizität* (1935), p. 239.

The minimum shear stress that will cause gliding in a structure of the NaCl type decreases with increasing polarizability of the ions, the stress along (100) more quickly than that along (110).[1] This stress, which

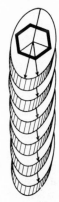

FIG. 201. Bar-shaped crystal of zinc, in which the glide plane (basal pinacoid), the prism $\{10\bar{1}0\}$, and the direction of gliding $[11\bar{2}0]$ are indicated; the long arrow indicates the direction of the major axis of the ellipses which become visible with the gliding process.

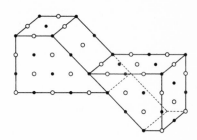

FIG. 202. Gliding in an NaCl crystal on (011) in the direction $[01\bar{1}]$.

is approximately 0.1 kg/mm², is many times smaller than the calculated stress,[2] at least when the crystals are not too small and the glide planes are "smooth." Foreign particles of different size in the structure considerably hamper the gliding.

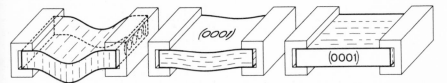

FIG. 203. Sagging and bending of an ice crystal.

It is remarkable that, with very small crystals, such as the so-called *whiskers* (length a few mm, thickness a few μ) formed, for example, at the surface of melts, gliding does not occur, and the observed tensile strength corresponds more or less with the calculated one.[3]

In an attempt to explain the discrepancy in stress between observation and calculation, the *dislocation theory* has been developed: the local stresses caused by a dislocation, together with the external force, may be large enough to give rise to local gliding. On account of this gliding new local stresses occur in the direction of the movement;

[1] M. J. Buerger, Am. Min. 15 (1930), 174, 226.
[2] H. Müller, Am. Min. 16 (1931), 237.
[3] R. H. Doremus and others, *Growth and Perfection of Crystals* (1958), pp. 1–287.

so, as a result of subsequent local glidings, there is a gliding along the entire plane (Fig. 204) — but over only one periodicity distance. For after the displacement one layer has moved to the boundary, and thus

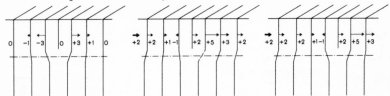

FIG. 204. An extra layer facilitates gliding. If it is assumed, for example, that a stress of five units on a layer causes it to glide, and that an extra layer imposes on the neighboring layers stresses of three units and on the following layers stresses of one unit, the increase of stress produced by an external stress of two units causes a large number of layers to glide.

no extra layer now occurs within the crystal. However, since the experiment shows that a glide plane remains active much longer, a mechanism that maintains the dislocation must be at work. If an extra layer which displaces itself encounters an obstacle in the glide plane (for example, a foreign particle or a second dislocation intersecting the plane), it can form itself there again and again (*Frank-Read source*). Fig. 205 shows this schematically; the dots represent the particles

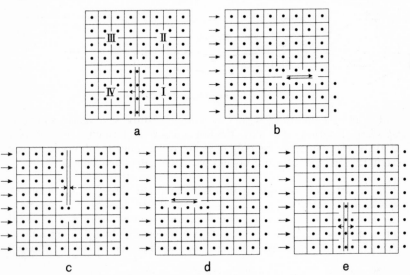

FIG. 205. Schematic representation of the action of a Frank-Read source. The double lines are parts of the dislocation lines.

of the moving layer next to the glide plane. If a force is applied to the right, the row at the right of the extra layer will be the first to move (but not the hampered part), and situation *b* exists. Then, at the boundary I—II, a screw dislocation occurs, and the forces exerted by it on the particles of II, together with the external force, become sufficient to cause gliding of II, and therewith situation *c* exists, with a negative edge dislocation at the boundary II—III. The elastic forces exerted thereby on III, together with the external force, bring situation *d* and finally, in the same way, *e* into being. If we assume that afterwards the hampered particle also moves, the entire plane will have finally moved over one periodicity distance, but an extra layer will still be present on the original site.

The smoothness of a glide plane diminishes after gliding, but we do not know exactly how. The crystal does undergo a *work hardening;* its stiffness becomes greater. This phenomenon occurs generally when metals are cold-worked — for example, when wire is drawn through too small an opening and when metal plates are rolled. During these operations the crystal parts glide along the most favorably situated glide planes and orient themselves gradually, a rolled plate finally being more or less one crystal (Table 38, Fig. 206).

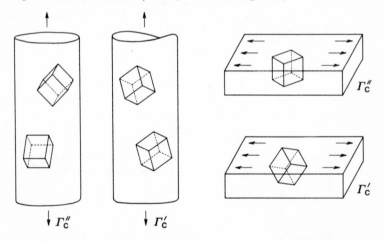

FIG. 206.   Orientations of the crystals in a drawn wire and a rolled sheet.

One can overcome hardening and orientation by *annealing* — that is, by holding the metal piece for some time at a higher temperature (p. 265).

If the gliding of a crystal takes place along equidistant planes $// X_1 X_2$

TABLE 38

| | lattice | drawn wire | rolled plate | |
		in the direction of the wire axis	in the plane of rolling	in the direction of rolling
Fe Mo W	cubic I (Γ'')	[110]	(100)	[110]
Al Cu Ag Au	cubic F (Γ')	[111], also [100]	(110)	[112], also [100]

in the direction X_2, the deformation of the crystal is homogeneous (p. 193):

$$u_1 = 0$$
$$u_2 = \gamma_{32}x_3$$
$$u_3 = 0$$

A sphere changes into an ellipsoid, and a round cylinder with axis $// X_1$ changes into a cylinder with elliptical section (Fig. 207). One can bring about this gliding by subjecting two faces of a cube to pressure and two others to strain.

Secondary Gliding

In secondary gliding, which also occurs along definite crystallonomic planes and directions, all net planes are displaced by an equal distance in relation to the neighboring planes, and the structure comes into a reflected position with respect to the glide plane; in this way the two crystal parts form a twin (*secondary twin*).

Calcite is a well-known example. If we

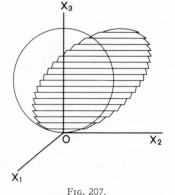

FIG. 207.

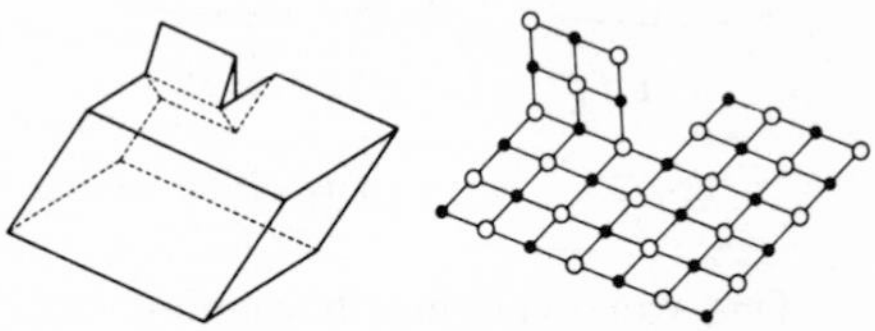

FIG. 208.   Gliding in a calcite crystal ($CaCO_3$), a secondary twin being the result.

press a knife normally on the obtuse edge of a cleavage rhombohedron $\{10\bar{1}1\}$, the net planes parallel to the glide plane $(01\bar{1}2)$ glide successively until they are in twin position, the re-entrant angle being approximately 38°. Unless the crystal breaks, this angle is always produced, and the relation of the two parts is a twinned one (Fig. 208). Metallic crystals also show this twin gliding.[1]

Creep [2]
This is the endless — or, at least, long-continued — plastic deformation of a (polycrystalline) piece of metal under the influence of stresses. The rate of deformation by creep is indiscernible for small loads, but the deformation may sometimes become dangerous and lead to fracture. Creep is favored by high temperature. The phenomenon is ascribed chiefly to slip along the boundaries of the crystallites, but gliding and recrystallization (p. 265) may also play a role.

Thermal Expansion

Not much is known about the relation between thermal expansion and structure; in a layer structure the expansion coefficient γ is, as a rule, largest normal to the layers. For a number of cubic coordination structures with ions, the expression [3]

$$\gamma q^2 \infty 10^{-6}$$

in which $q = \dfrac{\text{charge of ion}}{\text{coordination number}}$, is valid.

Diffusion [4]

In a pure solid compound, poly- or mono-crystalline, the atoms (ions) do not remain constantly at the same site; there is always some interchange (*self-diffusion*). This is demonstrated by the migration of radioactive isotopes. Foreign atoms, too, participate in the diffusion process and may be incorporated in the structure or segregated off. Chemical reactions between the particles of pressed powders (p. 186) may occur without a gas or liquid intermediary.

From a crystallographic viewpoint, diffusion in a single crystal is

---

[1] E. Schmid & W. Boas, *Kristallplastizität* (1935), p. 100; H. Tertsch, *Die Festigkeitserscheinungen der Kristalle* (1949), p. 61.

[2] E. Orowan, *The Creep of Metals* (1947).

[3] H. D. Megaw, Dissertation, Cambridge (1935).

[4] R. F. Mehl, Journ. Applied Ph. 8 (1937), 174; W. Jost, *Diffusion in Solids, Liquids, Gases* (1952); J. A. Hedvall, *Einführung in die Festkörperchemie* (1952), pp. 55, 84.

of most interest, but experimental data in this field are few. Since most measurements of diffusion velocity have been achieved with polycrystalline materials, the results bear upon diffusion both within the crystallites and along the boundaries of the crystallites. The latter is certainly not less important!

In general, Fick's law (1855) is valid:

$$J = -D \text{ gradient } n$$

J is the number of atoms diffusing through 1 cm² per second, D the diffusion constant, and n the number of atoms per cm³. The value of D for solids is often between 10^{-5} and 10^{-6} cm²/sec and may be taken at a first approximation as independent of temperature and concentration; on closer consideration, however, the dependence may not be neglected. For the self-diffusion of Ag, for example, it is found that

$$D = 0.3e^{-\frac{44,700}{RT}}$$

if R = gas constant = 1.986 cal/degree and T = absolute temperature. From this formula it follows that $D_{700°C} \backsim 10^{-10}$ and that $D_{1,000°C} \backsim 10^{-8}$.

Since the diffusion velocity is a small quantity, it is perceptible, in general, only at high temperatures. In order to give an impression of the phenomenon, Fig. 209 shows the concentration of Ni and Cu in a bar

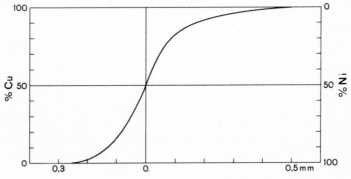

FIG. 209.   Diffusion of Ni into Cu and of Cu into Ni.

of Ni on which Cu has been electrodeposited. The bar has been held at 1,025° C for five days, and it appears that Ni diffuses faster into Cu than Cu into Ni; both D's are approximately 10^{-10}.

The diffusion velocity increases with the number of imperfections, and in a nearly perfect crystal it is very small; for the diffusion of Rn, for example, through a good crystal, $D \backsim 10^{-22}$. The velocity is considerable when the structure becomes unstable (just below the melting point) or when a change in modification occurs (α-$Ag_2SO_4 \rightleftarrows \beta$-$Ag_2SO_4$).

Diffusion is also large in severely deformed crystals, as in the separation of Cu from the strongly deformed, unstable alloy of 96% Al and 4% Cu. Here the diffusion runs from low concentration to high, and the sign in Fick's relation is positive. The diffusion is a thousand times as fast as in the undeformed alloy, and on the glide planes small Cu crystals are formed.[1]

The granitization theory contends that some massive granites, frequently regarded as igneous rocks, might rather be metamorphosed sedimentary formations. The necessary transport of large quantities of Na and Ca and smaller quantities of Al was achieved by diffusion (during geological time).[2]

Ionic Conduction [3]

Transparent crystals, including those with ionic structure, are insulators; that is, their specific resistance is larger than about 10^{10}. As a rule, however, they show some ionic conduction, for which Faraday's laws of electrolysis are valid.[4] Measurement is difficult; many polarization phenomena occur at the electrodes, and dendritic, conducting secretion products are formed along small cracks in the crystal.[5]

Two cases may be distinguished:

1. The structure has communicating canals, through which foreign ions can move from one electrode to the other. Quartz conducts Li and Na ions in the direction of the principal axis, but not K and Cu ions, which are apparently too large. Li ions, but not Na ions, pass normally to the principal axis (Joffé).

2. The structure shows (local) defects:
   a. Frenkel defects (Fig. 210). Some ions have left their sites and are in the interstitial spaces; the specific gravity of the crystal is unchanged. In AgCl, for example, as many as 1% of the ions may have left their sites.

[1] Philips' Technisch Tijdschrift 15 (1953), 307.

[2] H. Williams, F. J. Turner, & C. M. Gilbert, *Petrography* (San Francisco, 1954); P. Baertschi, Nature 166 (1950), 112; H. H. Read, *The Granite Controversy* (1956).

[3] N. F. Mott & R. W. Gurney, *Electronic Processes in Ionic Crystals* (1948), p. 26; F. Seitz, *The Modern Theory of Solids* (1940), p. 547; W. E. Garner, *Chemistry of the Solid State* (1955), p. 29.

[4] C. Tubandt & S. Eggert, Zeitschrift für anorganische Chemie 110 (1920), 196; A. F. Joffé, *The Physics of Crystals* (1928), p. 90.

[5] J. A. Hedvall, *Reaktionsfähigkeit fester Stoffe* (1938), p. 108.

  b. Schottky defects (Fig. 210). The ions which are not in their sites enlarge the crystal; the specific gravity has diminished — in the alkali halides, for example, by 0.01 percent. Structures such as that of γ-Al_2O_3 (p. 158) may be considered a special case of this.

  c. Defects caused by replaced ions.

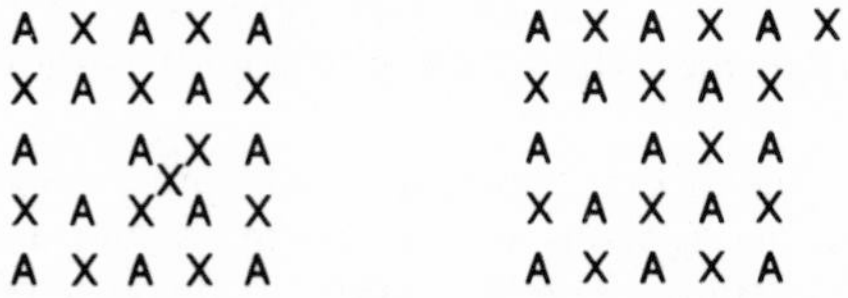

```
A X A X A           A X A X A X
X A X A X           X A X A X
A   A X A           A   A X A
X A X A X           X A X A X
A X A X A           A X A X A
```

FIG. 210. Frenkel defect (left) and Schottky defect (right).

The interstitial ions and the cavities move spontaneously and irregularly by self-diffusion; an applied voltage gives a direction to the displacement and causes the transport of ions and cavities and therefore also of material.

We have had to come to the theory of defects because calculation shows that in a perfect structure about 1 volt per ion is needed to displace the ions — that is, about 10^8 volts per cm. This value is in agreement with the observations made on plates thinner than 5 μ. In thicker plates a kind of chain process in an electric field occurs: the structure disintegrates when the electric potential gradient is smaller.[1] The observed gradient is insufficient to cause ionic displacement in a non-defect structure.

In KCl, at higher temperature, both ions move, in AgCl only the Ag ion; AgI above 140° shows an abnormally high conduction; Ag_2HgI_4 between 50° and 140° possesses a thousandfold stronger ionic conduction than any other crystal. Small contaminations often play an important role; a few parts per thousand of $PbCl_2$ or $CdCl_2$ in AgCl increase the conduction considerably.

Electronic Conduction

  It is not our purpose to explain fully the theory of this conduction, but we mention the great importance of the theory of Brillouin zones.[2]

  The difference in electronic conduction between conductors, semiconductors, and insulators is probably only a difference of degree,

---

[1] A. F. Joffé, *The Physics of Crystals* (1928), p. 162.

[2] G. V. Raynor, *Introduction to the Electron Theory of Metals* (1949); N. F. Mott & R. W. Gurney, *Electronic Processes in Ionic Crystals* (1948).

and even in purely ionic structures there are some "free" electrons.[1] A remarkable fact is the relatively great photoconductivity of ionic crystals such as halite, fluorite, and the silver halides, in which F-centers (Farbzentren, color centers), between 10^{15} and 10^{19} per cm^3 in number, are generated. Such centers are generated on radiation with X-rays or on diffusion of Na vapor. In the latter case the Na atom, on penetrating, loses an electron, which diffuses into a vacant Cl site and forms there an F-center, while the Na ion occupies a vacant Na ion site or remains present interstitially. On cooling down, the sodium segregates and causes a blue coloration, the crystals then showing a strong absorption band in the visible range. On radiation with visible light, the electronic conductivity is considerable (*photoconductivity*).[2]

In the good conductors, such as the metal crystals, all or some of the valence electrons can move freely and can be considered common to all the metal ions. The conductivity depends on the number of free electrons and the heat movement of the "atoms"; higher temperature causes the atoms to hamper the electrons in an increasing measure and, therefore, reduces the conductivity. The rigorous examination of electronic conduction (Brillouin zones) leads to the following results: the number of free electrons is determined by the (periodic) field of the atoms and the energy of the electrons; in the scheme of energy values, according to the quantum theory, values are possible only in bands. These bands overlap partly in good conductors.

In semi-conductors, a number of valence electrons may acquire so much additional energy, from heat or radiation, that they become free electrons; a characteristic of semi-conductors, therefore, is the increase in conductivity that accompanies a rise of temperature. We use this property in *NTC* (negative temperature coefficient) *resistances*. Since replacement by foreign ions considerably increases the possibility of freeing electrons, contamination often strongly decreases the resistance.

Five classes of semi-conductors may be distinguished:
1. Intrinsic ones. In the pure crystal, electrons are released by a relatively small addition of energy.
2. Extrinsic ones. The releasing is connected with the presence of foreign particles (contamination).
3. Non-stoichiometric ones (p. 227). The cavities cause irregularities in the internal field, promoting releasing of the electrons.
4. With ambivalent ions. For example, in Fe_3O_4 a valence electron can change from one iron ion to another; we can write Fe_3O_4

---

[1] E. J. W. Verwey, "Electronic Semi-conductors," Ned. Tijdschrift voor Natuurkunde 14 (1948), 205.
[2] F. Seitz, *The Modern Theory of Solids* (1940), pp. 459, 563.

as $Fe^{2+}Fe_2^{3+}O_4$. Other examples are NiO with contamination Li, written — for example — as $Li_{0.1}Ni_{0.8}^{2+}Ni_{0.1}^{3+}O$.

5. Others (TiN, CuS, etc.). The conduction is still insufficiently understood.

An important application of semi-conductors is found in the crystal rectifier and the transistor.[1] If we replace about one of the ten million quadrivalent Ge atoms in a pure (p. 265) germanium crystal (diamond structure) by a quinquevalent atom (Sb, for example), or a tervalent one (Al, for example), the crystal becomes a semi-conductor. In the first case the fifth valence electron of Sb splits off easily (*n-germanium*). In the second case the Al atom attracts a valence electron from a neighboring Ge atom. The positive site left by this electron moves because it attracts an electron from a neighboring Ge atom, etc., and then we have free positive electron defects, or *holes* (*p-germanium*). Holes move as electrons do, but in opposite directions.

Rectifier (Crystal Detector)

A *p*-domain and an *n*-domain (Fig. 211-a) are created artificially in a Ge crystal. In the *p*-domain there are p_1 free holes and n_1 free electrons

$(p_1 \gg n_1)$, in the *n*-domain n_2 free electrons and p_2 free holes $(n_2 \gg p_2)$; for convenience we may assume that $p_1 = n_2$ and $p_2 = n_1$.

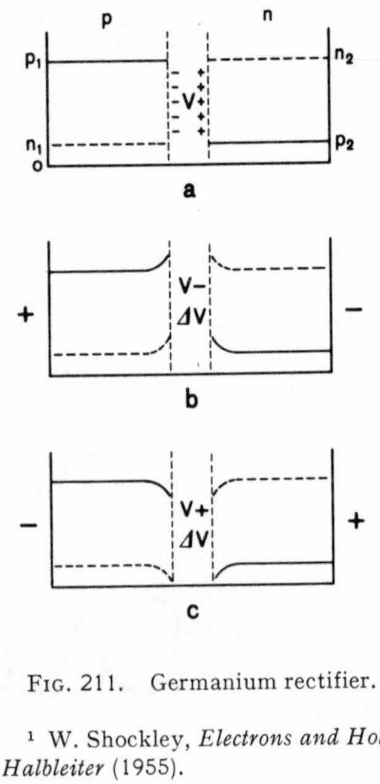

Outside the narrow transition zone no free electric charges can exist; this means (*c* is a constant) that

$$p_1 - n_1 = c$$
$$n_2 - p_2 = c$$

At equilibrium (*K* is a constant, analogue: law of mass action)

$$p_1 n_1 = p_2 n_2 = K$$

Some of the abundant free holes diffuse into the *n*-domain, and some of the abundant free electrons diffuse into the *p*-domain, causing in the transition zone an electric double layer in which the voltage *V* is determined by

$$\frac{p_1}{p_2} = \frac{n_2}{n_1} = e^{qV}$$

FIG. 211.   Germanium rectifier.

[1] W. Shockley, *Electrons and Holes in Semi-conductors* (1951); E. Spenke, *Elektronische Halbleiter* (1955).

in which q is a constant depending inversely on the temperature.

Application of an external voltage as in Fig. 211-b (forward direction) has two consequences: (1) weakening of the double layer; (2) in the p-domain repulsion of the holes from the positive electrode and in the n-domain repulsion of the electrons from the negative electrode. Hence near the transition zone we find an increase of p_1 and n_2. Note that the quantities $p_1 - n_1$ and $n_2 - p_2$ remain equal and constant. These consequences require an increase of the diffusion through the transition zone, and we observe an electric current flowing through the crystal.

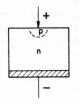

Application of an external voltage as in Fig. 211-c (backward direction) causes the double layer to become strengthened and p_1 and n_2 to decrease. Hence there will be a decrease of the diffusion, and the observed electric current will be small.

FIG. 212. Crystal detector. A p-domain in the crystal has been formed by a strong electric pulse.

It can be seen from this rather schematic picture that a p-n junction acts as a rectifier and as a crystal detector (Fig. 212).

Transistor

With a Ge crystal in which the three parts indicated in Fig. 213 have been artificially formed by diffusion, it is possible for a small energy (*emitter circuit*) to influence a larger one (*collector circuit*) — that is, to produce the same effect as a triode.

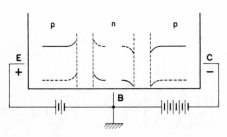

FIG. 213. A type of transistor.

If a small positive voltage is applied to the emitter E and a rather high negative one to the collector C, the situation is as indicated.

If the distance between the two transition zones is small enough (50 μ), the increased numbers of holes (and electrons) in the left zone diffuse partway up to the right one; there they increase the concentration and create more or less the conditions shown in Fig. 211-b (forward direction). In this way it is possible to influence a high energy in the collector circuit by a low energy in the emitter circuit.

Vibrations of the Structure

A crystal may conduct elastic (acoustic) progressive waves and support standing waves, the propagation velocities depending on the direction (p. 225). The ions (atoms) behave as if they were bound quasi-elastically; they perform single or compound harmonic vibrations, the frequencies of which form, with progressive waves, a continuous spectrum, but depend, with standing waves, on the dimensions of the crystal.

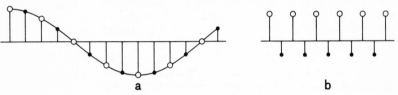

FIG. 214.   Waves: (a) acoustic; (b) optical.

The irregular thermal movement of the ions may be imagined as composed of a large number of standing acoustic waves having frequencies up to about 10^{13}. These waves explain certain weak X-ray interference maxima (*diffuse spots* or figures on diagrams) which are about a thousand times weaker than the adjacent spots caused by the principal maxima (see p. 109); and, contrariwise, we can derive from these diffuse spots the elastic constants of the crystal.[1] The average amplitude of the Na ions in an NaCl structure at room temperature is 0.245 A, and that of the Cl ions is 0.235 A; at 900° K they are both approximately 0.58 A.[2]

A special very important case of resonance occurs with certain "optical" wavelengths: the positive part of the lattice vibrates in opposite phase to the negative part (Fig. 214). This frequency, about 10^{13} per second (infrared light),[3] is independent of the dimensions of the crystal. If infrared light of this frequency falls on the crystal, the structure vibrates with a large amplitude; much of the light is reflected, and the refracted light is strongly absorbed (metallic reflection). Rays of this frequency are called *residual rays* (Reststrahlen).

If there are p ions in a primitive cell, there are, for triclinic, monoclinic, and orthorhombic crystals, $3(p-1)$ residual-ray frequencies; for those with a principal axis, $2(p-1)$; and for cubic crystals, $p-1$; for NaCl, therefore, 1.

---

[1] K. Lonsdale, *Crystals and X-rays* (1948), p. 152.

[2] Values for other crystals will be found in K. Lonsdale, Acta Cryst. 1 (1948), 142.

[3] K. Schaefer & F. Matossi, *Das ultrarote Spektrum* (1930).

Two groups of residual rays may be distinguished:

1. $\lambda = 30 - 150 \, \mu$. If radicals are present, the ions of a radical vibrate in the same phase. Examination is carried out with a bolometer or with a thermoelectric couple (Rubens). The wavelengths of the residual rays of mixed crystals vary linearly with the composition.

2. $\lambda = 10 - 20 \, \mu$. In radical structures the positive ions of a radical vibrate in opposite phase to the negative ones. Examination is carried out by optical means.[1] Since the frequencies of H_2O and OH are both approximately $3 \, \mu$, only a very accurate examination is able to demonstrate in which form water is present in a crystal. — The difference in restoring force on O^{2-} in and normal to the plane of the radical CO_3 is clear (Fig. 215).

The frequencies of residual rays can be measured spectroscopically with great accuracy by means of the *Raman effect.* If monochromatic light falls on a crystal, even an entirely transparent crystal scatters part of it. Most of this scattered light

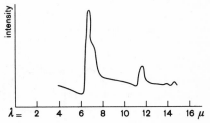

FIG. 215.   Difference in intensity between the residual rays (Reststrahlen) $\lambda = 7\mu$ (vibration plane $\perp$ to principal axis) and $\lambda = 11.4 \, \mu$ (vibration plane $//$ to principal axis) for a calcite crystal $(CaCO_3)$.

has the same frequency as the incident light (Tyndall effect), but a small part has another frequency (Raman effect); that is,

$$\nu_{Raman} = \nu_{Tyndall} \pm \nu_{residual\,rays}$$

Whereas infrared rays are able to make quasi-elastically bound ions vibrate, visible light rays make the much lighter valence electrons vibrate. The structure may then be regarded as an ordered collection of dipoles, of which only the negative parts take part in the vibration. If an electromagnetic light wave passes through such a structure, each dipole will emit an elementary (secondary) wavelet whose frequency is the same as that of the original wave; the composition of the wavelets of the dipoles situated in one plane is such that its phase is retarded by 90°. The effect of this is as if the original wave were retarded (Ewald). A large amplitude of the scattered wavelets corresponds to a strong retardation. This amplitude depends on the bond strength; hence the retardation depends on the direction in which the light vibrates (birefringence).

We may also look at this problem in another way. If we assume that

[1] L. Schaefer & F. Matossi, *Das ultrarote Spektrum* (1930).

the influence of the field of the environing dipoles may be neglected, in an electromagnetic field $\mathbf{E}$ the moment $\mathbf{p}$ of an atom (ion) is (p. 139)

$$\mathbf{p} = \alpha\mathbf{E}$$

This gives, for each cubic centimeter in which N' atoms are present, a moment $\mathbf{P}$:

$$\mathbf{P} = N'\mathbf{p} = \alpha N'\mathbf{E}$$

Now (p. 197)

$$\mathbf{D} = \mathbf{E} + 4\pi\mathbf{P} = \varepsilon\mathbf{E}$$

$$\varepsilon = 1 + 4\pi\alpha N'$$

and (n = refractive index)

$$n^2 = 1 + 4\pi\alpha N'$$

In a crystal, however, the influence of adjacent dipoles is not negligible; $\mathbf{E}$ changes locally. For a regular crystal the change is the same in all directions, and here we find (Lorentz-Lorenz) that

$$\frac{n^2 - 1}{n^2 + 2} = {}^1/_3 \times 4\pi\alpha N'$$

If one mole of a compound A_pB_q... weighs M grams, the number of molecules therein being N and the density of the crystal ρ, the number of atoms A is equal to Np. For this atom we find N' from the expression

$$N' : Np = \rho : M$$

$$\frac{M}{\rho} \frac{n^2 - 1}{n^2 + 2} = {}^4/_3\pi N(p\alpha_A + q\alpha_B + \ldots) = pR_A + qR_B + \ldots$$

For each kind of atom R is a constant, the *atomic (ionic) refraction* (Table 39).

TABLE 39

	R		R
Li+	0.15	F−	2.20
Na+	0.74	Cl−	8.45
K+	2.85	O²− (in radicals)	3.5
Ca++	1.99		

The R and therefore also the n of a compound are calculated by addition of the R's of the elements. In this way we find for NaCl that $R = 9.19$ and $n = 1.59$, which agrees well with the observation that $R = 8.52$ and $n = 1.54$.

If the electrical vector and so the induced dipoles are parallel to the line joining two atoms, the polarizability is enhanced. If the electrical vector is normal to that line, the polarizability, compared with that of an isolated atom, is diminished. So we find that, for a flat radical with a central ion, such as CO_3^{2-} or NO_3^-, n is large for a light ray whose electrical vector vibrates in the plane of the radical and small for a light ray whose electrical vector vibrates normally to the plane.

Bragg [1] showed that the principal refractive indices of calcite can be calculated satisfactorily with simple suppositions.

In molecular structures the velocity of light propagation depends both on the properties of the molecules and on their arrangement. In general, the following two situations may be considered:

1. If long molecules lie parallel to one another, n is larger in that direction than in the direction normal to it, and the birefringence is positive. If the molecules are parallel to one plane but are otherwise arbitrarily distributed, the birefringence is negative.

2. If flat molecules are parallel only to a plane, their directions being, for the rest, arbitrarily distributed, the birefringence is negative. If the molecules are parallel to a line, the birefringence is positive (Fig. 216). [2]

In structures with a screw-like arrangement the effect of the secondary light wavelets emitted by the dipoles may be such that the vibration

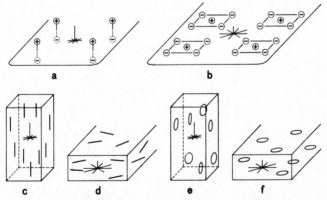

FIG. 216. Birefringence caused (a) by the parallel arrangement of dipoles (+); (b) by parallel flat radicals (—); (c-f) by long or flat molecules.

[1] W. L. Bragg, *Atomic Structure of Minerals* (1937), p. 120.

[2] W. A. Wooster, *A Textbook on Crystal Physics* (1949), p. 175; A. F. Wells, *Structural Inorganic Chemistry* (1945), p. 229; C. W. Correns, *Einführung in die Mineralogie* (1949), p. 122.

plane of a polarized light ray is rotated. This *optical activity* may occur in many crystals belonging to certain classes without a center of symmetry. [1] The rotation angle is proportional to the length of the path traversed (p. 213).

Some ultraviolet frequencies also are strongly absorbed in ionic structures.[2] Haber indicates that the ratio of the wavelengths is approximately

$$\frac{\lambda_{\text{infrared}}}{\lambda_{\text{ultraviolet}}} = 42.8\sqrt{M}$$

M being the molecular weight.

For NaCl $\lambda_{i.r.} = 52\,\mu$ and $\lambda_{u.v.} = 0.158\,\mu$.

The measurement is carried out with spectrometers, the lenses and prisms of which are cut out of fluorite or a similar compound.

Genesis of Crystals [3]

Sub-microscopic crystals — those with a diameter smaller than 0.1 μ — are called crystal nuclei, crystallites, or colloidal particles. They occur spontaneously in supersaturated solutions, supercooled melts, supersaturated vapors, and deformed aggregates (metals).

The number of nuclei formed in 1 cm³ per second is called the *nucleus number*.[4] The nucleus number depends on the temperature, and its maximum lies in the temperature domain of the supercooled melt (Fig. 217).

Nuclei may grow in two ways: by assimilation of not yet crystallized material and by growing together. The latter process may occur especially with very small nuclei, whose relatively large surface, being very active, causes the nuclei to orient themselves and thus form a normal structure or perhaps a twin.

The average size of the nuclei can be derived by X-ray methods from the

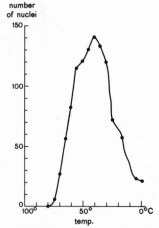

FIG. 217. Dependence of the number of nuclei on the temperature in a supercooled piperine melt (melting point 129° C).

[1] W. A. Wooster, *Crystal Physics* (1949), p. 156.

[2] The theory will be found in Nederlandsch Tijdschrift voor Natuurkunde 14 (1948), 219.

[3] M. Volmer, *Kinetik der Phasenbildung* (1939).

[4] G. Tammann, *Kristallisieren und Schmelzen* (1903).

breadth of the lines on a powder photograph. When the particles become very small, the lines broaden and finally become bands; these bands often appear also in the photographs of the vitreous state of the material in question.

For small cubic crystals the "integral" breadth B of the line caused by reflection from the planes parallel to the cube faces is

$$B = \frac{\lambda}{\Lambda \cos \theta} \text{ radians}$$

λ being the wavelength of the X-rays and Λ being given by the average dimension of the particles normal to the reflecting planes.[1] The broadening is perceptible if $\Lambda < 0.1 \ \mu$.

Crystal Growth [2]

Not much is known about the mechanism of the growth of nuclei in a deformed crystal or aggregate.[3]

If a crystal is allowed to grow undisturbed in a solution or vapor, the atoms (ions) collide with its surface, move along it, and fix themselves on the sites where the strongest attractive force is exercised, which are, first of all, the micro-pits of the surface. [4] In this way a o-ion at f (Fig. 218) is strongly attracted; it will stay there and fill up the pit. The attraction is somewhat less at a and b and least strong at e; so a new layer is begun only after complete occupation of the old one. In this way the occurrence of flat faces and the absence of re-entrant angles are explained.

If the attraction at d is stronger than at c, there is a great chance that an ion moving over the cube face will fall over the edge and become a particle of the rhombic dodecahedron face. This means that (100) moves forward less rapidly than (110).

That the atoms (ions) move along the surface and may fall over the edge has been established for a mercury crystal growing from the vapor. If we calculate the number of atoms colliding with the surface, it appears that fewer atoms fix themselves than collide on the basal pinacoid, and that more atoms fix themselves than collide on the faces of the hexagonal prism; it has to be concluded, therefore, that a number of those colliding on the basal pinacoid fall over the edge.

[1] For further details and non-cubic crystals see I. Waller, R. Soc. Uppsala IV, 11, No. 7 (1939); J. Bouman and P. M. de Wolff, Physica 9 (1949), 833.

[2] H. E. Buckley, *Crystal Growth* (1951); O. Knacke & I. N. Stranski, "Die Theorie des Kristallwachstums," Ergebnisse der exakten Naturwissenschaften 26 (1952), 383.

[3] W. G. Burgers, "L'Etat solide," 9e Conseil de Physique (1952), 88 (nucleation).

[4] A. E. van Arkel & J. H. de Boer, *Chemische binding als electrostatisch verschijnsel* (1930), p. 248.

Whether a particle on a flat face will reach the edge depends on the velocity of the crystallization, the size of the face, the viscosity of the surrounding medium, and the strength of the heat movement. From this it follows that the *assemblage of forms* (German *Tracht*) and the *habit* (p. 259) of the crystal will depend on these factors, provided that the

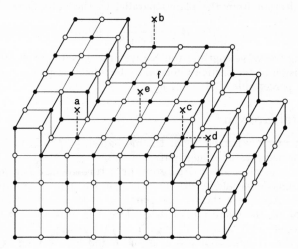

FIG. 218.   Structure of the NaCl type.

differences in growth are not influenced by flowing of the liquid along the faces, by boundary or surface tension, or by the diffusion velocity of the solution.[1]

Absorption of foreign particles by the faces lessens the mobility of the colliding particles. Perhaps this fact explains why urea in a solution of NaCl causes the crystals to develop octahedrally and not cubically (Romé de Lisle, 1783) and why lead nitrate crystallizes from a solution containing methylene blue in cubes and not, as from the pure solution, in octahedra. Quartz grows from a viscous melt without prism faces; on crystallization from a solution, these faces are often strongly developed.

Dislocations appear to play an important role in growth. Sometimes it is even maintained that the faces of an ideal crystal can grow only when there is strong supersaturation or supercooling.

---

[1] B. J. Mason, "Snow Crystals," Endeavour 10 (1951), 212.

Growth in a *spiral* as a result of a screw dislocation (Frank, 1949) [1] has been noted. The face (Fig. 219) always shows sites *a* and *d* (Fig.

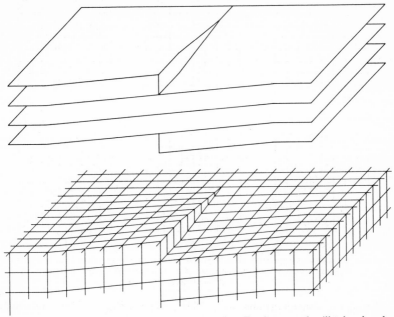

FIG. 219. Surface of a crystal with screw dislocation. Further growth will take place by spiral steps.

218), where new particles are bound, and thus the formation of a new layer is avoided; all newly added material forms one surface, being built up round the screw axis like a spiral staircase (Fig. 220).

This way of building gives an excellent explanation of the fact that in a number of layer structures the absolute axial length entirely or nearly normal to the layers is extraordinarily large — in other words, that only after many layers does repetition occur (p. 159). The repetition distance (the axial length) is the pitch of the spiral.

If two faces of different crystals show sufficient resemblance in atomic structure (difference in periodicity distance being not more than about 15%), the crystal of one compound can grow on one of the

---

[1] W. Dekeyzer & S. Amelinckx, *Les dislocations et la croissance des cristaux* (1955); A. R. Verma, *Crystal Growth and Dislocations* (1953); R. L. Fullman, "The Growth of Crystals," Scientific American 192 (1955), 74. The pitch of a spiral is measured by a light-interference method which can measure less than 100 A: S. Tolansky, *Multiple-beam Interferometry of Surfaces and Films* (1948).

faces of the other in an oriented way (*epitaxis*) — for example, NaNO₃ on a cleavage plane of $CaCO_3$, staurolite on disthene, ice on AgI at $-6°$ C.[1]

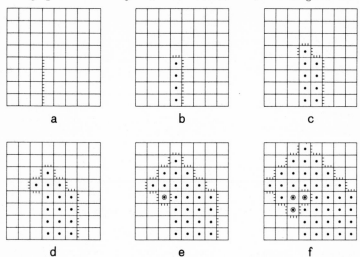

FIG. 220. Schematic representation of spiral growth in the presence of a screw dislocation. The steep border where growth takes place is indicated at each turn; ● first layer, ○ next layer.

From the considerations on p. 255 it follows that particles fall over the edge from a closely packed face to less closely packed faces because on the former the spacing and therefore also the distance from the new particles to the face are greater. For this reason the closest-packed faces move forward less quickly when growing and spread in the width; so, in the end, those that are openly packed are driven out, or, more exactly, if S and T (Fig. 221) intersect, b, after some time, is driven out. For a cubic crystal this phenomenon can be expressed by a formula.[2]

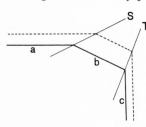

FIG. 221. The faces a, b, and c, when growing, move with unequal velocities.

[1] J. H. van der Merwe, "Crystal Growth," A General Discussion of the Faraday Society 5 (1949), 201; G. A. Deicha, Nature 164 (1949), 68; E. Bauer, Zeitschr. f. Krist. 107, (1956), 263.

[2] P. Niggli, *Lehrbuch der Mineralogie und Kristallchemie* (1941), p. 375. The extension of Bravais' hypothesis by Donnay & Harker discusses the face development of more complex structures; see the footnote on p. 99.

Table 40 gives values for the growth velocity of some faces of an alum crystal.

TABLE 40

face	(111)	(110)	(100)	(221)	(211)	(210)
growth velocity	1	4.8	5.3	9.5	11	27

It has not yet been explained why *vicinal faces* (p. 8) are often developed. Supersaturation of a solution may be great when crystals having only faces with small indices are present — for NaCl 0.045%. In the presence of vicinal faces supersaturation is practically impossible.

If, on account of incomplete development, the crystal faces are not entirely flat and if excrescences project, foreign particles are strongly attracted by the unsaturated bonds of the excrescences, the surface absorbs strongly, and the attracted particles, which in this way are brought close to one another, react easily (H. S. Taylor's explanation of catalytic activity).[1]

Investigations of growth are often carried out with spheres cut out of a crystal, a method that avoids favoring any of the crystal faces in advance.[2]

Genesis of Twins

The colliding particle will possess on the smooth surface a minimum of energy as soon as it has reached the spot where it extends the normal structure. However, if there is a site with a somewhat weaker minimum, the particle may, under certain conditions, fix itself there, and the newly formed layer is then the first of a part of the crystal that is in twin position with regard to the original. Perhaps a transition layer (Fig. 222) is formed first (W. L. Bragg).[3]

Morphology [4]

The *assemblage of forms* of a crystal indicates which combinations of forms are present; the *habit* depends on the sizes of the faces (the habit may be fibrous, flat, etc.).

[1] J. A. Hedvall, *Reaktionsfähigkeit fester Stoffe* (1938), p. 54. On adsorption see J. H. de Boer, *Electron Emission and Adsorption Phenomena* (1935); C. L. Mantell, *Adsorption* (1951).

[2] P. Niggli, *Lehrbuch der Mineralogie und Kristallchemie* (1941), pp. 371, 401.

[3] W. L. Bragg, *The Crystalline State*, I (1933), p. 176.

[4] Data on the largest natural crystals will be found in C. Frondel, Am. Min. 20 (1935), 469; C. Palache, Am. Min. 17 (1932), 362.

About the morphology (science of assemblage of forms and habit) of minerals much statistical material has been collected,[1] and attempts have also been made to bring morphology into relation with the structure [2] and the environment in which the crystal grows (vapor, solution).[3]

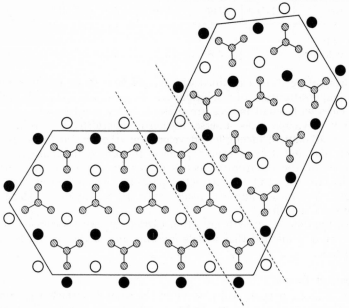

FIG. 222.   Projection along the C axis of a twin of aragonite (orthorhombic CaCO₃), with twin plane (110), and showing a transition layer (W. L. Bragg); the large circles are Ca ions, the others CO₃ radicals.

Often the crystals with flat primitive cells or molecules are stretched in the direction of the small dimension of the cell (needles of rutile), and crystals with long cells or molecules normal to the length are flat (muscovite).

Solution

The dissolving of crystals is approximately the reverse of their growth. Rounded-off forms appear, as a rule, and only in extremely slow dissolu-

[1] V. M. Goldschmidt, *Atlas der Kristallformen*, 18 vol. (1913–23).

[2] P. Niggli, *Lehrbuch der Mineralogie und Kristallchemie* (1941), pp. 450, 535; P. Hartman & W. G. Perdok, Acta Cryst. 8 (1955), 49, 521, 525.

[3] R. Kern, Bulletin de la Société de Minéralogie et Cristallographie 78 (1955), 461, 497.

tion do the faces remain flat. If a sphere of NaCl cut out of a crystal is slowly dissolved, a body like that shown in Fig. 223 develops.[1]

FIG. 223.   Successive stages in the slow solution of a sphere cut from an NaCl crystal.

Of importance is the beginning of solution or, what is analogous in this respect, the slight chemical effect known as *etching* (Daniell, 1816). Small pits develop in the faces [2] and become bounded by new crystal faces, often vicinal ones. Since the situation and form of the small pits are in accordance with the crystal symmetry, we often use etching to determine the symmetry (Fig. 224).[3] A very sensitive method of observing etched figures is to look at a candle flame through the etched crystal plate, held close to the eye; we then observe the so-called light figure (Fig. 225).[4] In this way we may examine the twinning of quartz

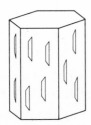

FIG. 224.   Apatite crystal (phosphate) with prism and basal pinacoid, etched with dilute HCl; the form of the etch pits indicates that the crystal belongs, not to the dihexagonal-bipyramidal class, but to the hexagonal-bipyramidal class.

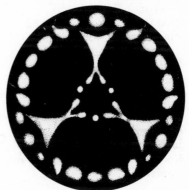

FIG. 225.   Light figure of tourmaline.

[1] W. Kossel in *Zur Struktur und Materie der Festkörper* (1952), p. 56.

[2] See symmetry of the faces on p. 12.

[3] H. Baumhauer, *Die Resultate der Aetzmethode* (1894); A. P. Honess, *The Nature, Origin and Interpretation of Etch Figures on Crystals* (1927).

[4] F. Rinne, *Kristallographische Formenlehre* (1922), p. 77.

crystals in order to judge their usefulness for radiotechnical purposes (p. 220).

Solution of a concave spherical surface causes flat faces to come into being (*negative crystal*, Fig. 226).

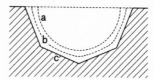

FIG. 226. Successive stages in the solution of a crystal having a semi-spherical cavity.

Melting and Evaporation [1]

The heat of sublimation of an ionic structure can be calculated approximately (p. 231).

The melting points of ionic structures, in general, rise as the ionic distances become smaller or as the charges become larger (Table 41).

TABLE 41

	NaF	NaCl	NaBr	NaI	NaF	CaO
ionic separation in A	2.31	2.82	2.98	3.23	2.31	2.40
melting point	988°	801°	740°	660°	988°	2,570°

Preparation [2]

A number of methods have been developed for making a seed crystal grow. Often much patience is required if good results are to be obtained.

1. The saturated solution is allowed to cool very slowly and quietly after the seed crystal is introduced or to evaporate at a constant temperature.[3] In this way one may obtain, for example, very good crystals of Rochelle salt, which can be made to grow flat between two parallel glass plates.

[1] O. Knacke & others, "Die Verdampfung von Kristallen" in *Zur Struktur und Materie der Festkörper* (1952), p. 34.

[2] H. E. Buckley, *Crystal Growth* (1951); "Crystal Growth" in Discussions of the Faraday Society 5 (1949). A. Neuhaus, "Moderne Einkristallzüchtung," Chemie-Ingenieur-Technik 28 (1956), 155, 350, with references. A very large crystal, 72 pounds of NaI (+Tl), has been mentioned in Nucleonic News 5 (1956), No. 4.

[3] W. Eitel, "Kristallzüchtung" in *Handbuch der Arbeitsmethoden der anorganischen Chemie* IV (1926), pp. 448–73; W. G. Cady, *Piezoelectricity* (1946), p. 522.

2. The crystals developed in a solution by electrolysis are oriented on the electrodes; for Ni crystals [100] lies in the direction of the current, for Cr [112], etc.[1]

3. As the melt is kept a little above the melting point, the cooled seed crystal is dipped into it and slowly raised. If a cool metal bar is immersed, many small crystals are formed at first on its point; but, when the bar is raised, only one of these crystals finally grows, its orientation depending on chance. It is quite easy, in this way, to form long monocrystals of Zn or Cd;[2] NaCl crystals and others may also be formed.[3]

A variation of this method consists in melting the material in a glass tube and moving this slowly out of the oven. Stöber[4] lets the material melt from the top downwards in a hemispherical vessel and cool from the bottom upwards so that no convection currents occur in melts which expand on heating. In this way he obtains, in a week's time, a hemispherical NaNO$_3$ crystal weighing several kilograms (Fig. 227).[5] According to this method, melts which shrink on heating have to be cooled from the top downwards, as water slowly freezes in nature: large hex-

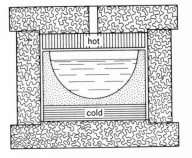

FIG. 227.

agonal ice crystals, sometimes a few square meters in area, may be formed, the principal axis being vertical because the heat conduction of the crystal is greatest in that direction.

4. If supercooled liquid drops of Al$_2$O$_3$ are sprayed, at a suitable temperature (about 2,000° C), on a crystal of corundum, this continues to grow as a single crystal (Verneuil's method for the preparation of synthetic sapphire and ruby). In this way one may also prepare sizable rutile crystals, which, though not colorless at first, become nearly colorless after heating in an oxygen atmosphere, and then

[1] H. Fischer, *Elektrolytische Abscheidung und Elektrokristallisation von Metallen* (1954); R. Glocker, *Materialprüfung mit Röntgenstrahlen* (1958), p. 408.

[2] E. Billig & others, Acta Cryst. 8 (1955), 353 (growth of long Ge crystals).

[3] S. Kyropoulos, Zeitschrift für allgemeine und anorganische Chemie 154 (1926), 308.

[4] Zeitschrift für Kristallographie 61 (1925), 312.

[5] Under D. S. Stockbarger's patents melting takes place in a cylindrical platinum crucible, which ends at the bottom in a cone; on cooling, crystallization begins at the apex.

show even more fire than diamond owing to the much higher dispersion of the refractive indices.

5. When a thread-shaped crystal of W, obtained by the Pintsch process (p. 265), is heated electrically in an atmosphere of WCl_6 up to 1,000° C, the WCl_6 decomposes, and the thread grows to a crystal some millimeters in thickness. The Cl_2 formed reacts with W powder at 400° C and again forms WCl_6 (Fig. 228).[1]

One can also obtain quartz crystals by growing them out of a mixture of SiO_2 and a 10% solution of Na_2CO_3 in H_2O, whether or not above the critical point of water. At first many difficulties occurred in this procedure, but these have been overcome (Fig. 229).[2]

Growing Zn or Cd crystals in metal vapor is less difficult.

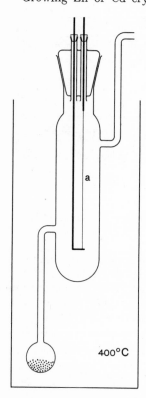

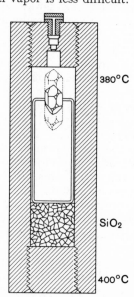

FIG. 229. The bomb, partially filled with particles of SiO_2 and a 10% soda solution, is heated to 380—400° C, the pressure becoming about 1,000 atm; the growth of the seed crystal is about 0.1 mm in twenty-four hours (Nacken's method).

FIG. 228. The tube at the right is connected to a vacuum pump; tungsten powder is at the bottom of the left bulb; a is a Pintsch wire of tungsten.

[1] A. E. van Arkel, Physica 3 (1923), 76.

[2] Bell Telephone System, Tech. Pub. Monograph B 1683 (1949); Industrial and Engineering Chemistry 42 (1950), 1369; Nature 167 (1951), 940.

6. Since small crystals have greater surface energy than large ones, there is always a tendency for the larger ones to grow at the expense of the smaller ones (*aggression*, "Sammelkristallisation"). If, for example, anhydrite powder is heated and subjected at the same time to a pressure of 10,000 atmospheres, a single crystal results.[1]

If, with the use of some adhesive material, we make some W powder, mixed with 2% ThO_2 as a catalyst, into a thin thread, and if we heat this thread to 2,600° C, all the small crystals are taken up into the larger ones, and crystals some meters in length are often produced (Pintsch process).[2] We heat the thread, which is about 0.4 mm thick, electrically by leading it over two small cylinders between which a voltage is maintained.

A method of making large Cd crystals is based on the same principle: a polycrystalline bar is heated at one place by means of a glowing spiral until the melting point is nearly reached; then the bar is pulled slowly through the spiral (Fig. 230). In this way crystals (metal crystals, Ge for transistors) may also be purified to a very high degree.[3]

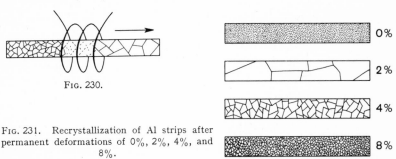

FIG. 230.

FIG. 231. Recrystallization of Al strips after permanent deformations of 0%, 2%, 4%, and 8%.

0%

2%

4%

8%

7. If the small crystals in a metal are given higher energy by a permanent deformation (for example, a 2% elongation), *recrystallization* [4] takes place quickly at a suitable temperature. The newly formed crystals are free from stress and, if the elongation was not too large and therefore did not produce too many nuclei, are much larger than the original ones (Fig. 231). Thus, by recrystallization, a cold-worked metal becomes stress-free, and the orientation of the crystals (p. 241) is lost.[5]

[1] E. Washken, Am. Min. 31 (1946), 512.
[2] Zeitschrift für Elektrochemie 23 (1917), 121.
[3] Endeavour 14 (1955), 200; W. G. Pfann, *Zone Melting* (1958).
[4] W. G. Burgers in *L'Etat solide* (1952).
[5] E. Schmid & W. Boas, *Kristallplastizität* (1935), with citations of the literature.

Index of Names

Index of Subjects

271